D1572129

Corrosion and its Control
An Introduction to the Subject

H. Van Droffelaar and J.T.N. Atkinson

NACE International

Library of Congress Catalog Card Number: 95-087424
ISBN 1-877914-71-1

NACE International Book Publications:

Director of Publications – *J. Littleton*
Senior Editor, Books – *A. Pierce*
Book Editor – *C. Wynne*
Graphics Support – *K. Martinez*

NACE International, 1440 South Creek Drive, Houston, TX 77084

In memory of my friend, Dr. Jim A. Atkinson

Contents

Preface

The second edition of *Corrosion and Its Control* has been marred by the untimely passing of my friend and co-author, Dr. Jim Atkinson, on April 15, 1991. Jim is sadly missed by his many friends, colleagues, and his family.

This book developed from the notes used by the authors for more than two decades in their course, "The Corrosion and Protection of Metals" taught to junior and senior students in various branches of engineering at Queen's University, Kingston, Ontario, Canada. The students have good backgrounds in basic science and engineering. The reader will find some background in chemistry, material science, and strength of materials of construction helpful.

The intention of the authors has been to emphasize the engineering aspects of corrosion and its control in ways that will be helpful to the practicing engineer. Therefore, chapters are included on corrosion economics, detecting and monitoring corrosion, regulations, specifications, safety, and a major section on the selection and use of materials of construction with special emphasis on the use and corrosion of stainless steels.

To the second edition we have added more than 100 pages of text distributed over the 17 chapters. We have placed particular emphasis on updating chapters on corrosion monitoring, corrosion fundamentals, and materials of construction, including plastics and failure analysis. We also have introduced a new chapter 18 dealing with an introduction of "The Use of the Computer in the Practice of Corrosion." We trust the reader will find the introduction to computers and a description of the "corrosion expert system" helpful and stimulating.

No attempt has been made to provide extensive coverage of corrosion data that can readily be found elsewhere, trusting the text will provide the engineer with the information to make critical use of such data.

In a book that developed in the fashion described, there have been numerous helpful discussions with the authors' colleagues at Queen's University; DuPont Canada, Inc.; Atomic Energy of Canada, Ltd. (AECL); and with members of the corrosion community in general. Specific mention of R.D. Watson of AECL for information on stretch oxidation and to T.R.B. Watson of Corrosion Services, Ltd. for permission to extract from his work on economics. Furthermore, we wish to express our appreciation to Dr. W. Thompson, Royal Military College, for providing data on computerized Pourbaix diagrams and to J.J. Lamoureux of L. Ecole Polytechnique, Montreal, for information on his "Corrosion Expert System." A special thanks to DuPont Canada, Inc. for their encouragement of the authors and their contribution of data and illustrations used in this book. And last, but not least, to Mrs. Shirley Donnelly of Queen's University for her assistance with the preparation of the book and to Cicely Wynne of NACE for her expedient and competent completion of the book manuscript.

Prof. H. Van Droffelaar,
Queen's University,
Kingston, Ontario, Canada K7L 3N6

Introduction

Corrosion and its control is an important, but often neglected, element in the practice of engineering. Of necessity, it is a pragmatic subject since the proper solution to any corrosion problem is the most economical one, provided safety is assured. This solution is not always the most aesthetic; rust has to be tolerated whenever it is the least costly alternative. Of course, all cost elements, both direct and indirect, have to be considered. The proper solution to a corrosion situation often involves the use of low-cost, low-performance materials, such as carbon steel, with regular replacement as necessary.

Corrosion engineering seeks to minimize corrosion costs for a particular owner or operator. Because of the distorting influence of taxation on these costs, it does not necessarily minimize total corrosion costs for society as a whole. Nor does it necessarily minimize the energy requirement that results from the various anticorrosion strategies. Such considerations are outside the scope of this work.

Selection of a material for use in a corrosion situation must be based on sound economics. Both the cost of the material and the ongoing cost of preventive measures must be included. Sound judgment about materials must include the recognition that the relative corrosion resistance of materials and the cost of supplementary protective measures can change significantly from one corrosive medium to another. For example, weathering steels have much better corrosion resistance than carbon steels in an unpolluted atmosphere. However, where chlorides are found, much of this advantage is lost; for immersion in chloride contaminated waters, weathering steels show no corrosion advantage at all.

The interrelationships in material selection are shown in Figure 1. Factors that influence material selection are distinguished from those that interact in a more complex fashion. For example, ease of fabrication influences selection because weldability, workability, etc. will define whether a the material can be used for the intended application. On the other hand, mechanical properties are not uniquely defined for all environments. If the material is to be used at low temperatures (e.g., in the Arctic), embrittlement can be a serious problem. At high ambient pressure on the deep ocean floor, brittle behavior related to tensile

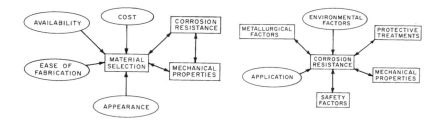

Figure 1 *Factors affecting material selection:* ⬭ *direct influences;* ▭ *interactive factors.*

Figure 2 *Factors affecting corrosion resistance of a material:* ⬭ *direct inflences;* ▭ *interactive factors.*

stresses is much less of a problem. The endurance limit for corrosion fatigue can vary dramatically from one corrosive environment to another. Corrosion resistance is even more complicated, as indicated in Figure 2.

The interactions between metallurgical factors and corrosion resistance are straightforward. Less obvious are the interactions with the application. For example, a system to contain drinking water or a pharmaceutical product, where contamination is stringently limited, can call for a more resistant material than would be specified on economic grounds alone. Protective treatments are viewed as a means of extending the use of a particular material; they carry an inevitable associated cost.

The performance level of the typical engineer in fighting corrosion has been seriously deficient. Enough surveys have been conducted to show that every developed country is spending about 4% of its gross national product on metallic corrosion, with close to 25% of this total being preventable by the application of appropriate known technology (Chapter 11). There also are serious cost and safety hazards associated with deterioration of nonmetallic structures. Creep and ultraviolet degradation are the prime culprits for plastics. A nonproductive expenditure of the magnitude indicated is more than the various national economies should have to bear. Strong action is needed.

The purpose of this text is to help equip the engineer with the knowledge to make appropriate choices in the struggle against corrosion through recognition and evaluation of all relevant factors. The public certainly is entitled to better protection than it has been getting.

1

Electrochemical Background of Corrosion

Virtually all known instances of metallic corrosion are electro-chemical in nature, including high-temperature oxidation reactions. For this reason, a solid background in electrochemistry is essential with emphasis on the potential to current relationships when there is a departure from equilibrium. Most older texts are inadequate in this area; one of the best modern texts for self-study by a nonexpert is Bockris and Reddy's *Modern Electrochemistry*.[1] Those who start with a better background in electrochemistry may prefer the more compact treatment in Bockris and Drazic's *Electrochemical Science*.[2]

Suppose a clean and pure electrode of each common metal is immersed in a 1N solution of one of its salts. Under these conditions, each metal will eventually assume its own unique potential. This potential cannot be measured directly because the available measuring devices can measure only a difference in potential. To overcome this limitation, we add a standard hydrogen electrode (SHE) to the system by means of a suitable salt bridge. The difference between the SHE and the electrode of the metal of interest can now be measured. Since the potential of the SHE is (by arbitrary definition) zero, the difference in potential between the SHE and the metal electrode gives the potential of the latter on the hydrogen scale thus defined.

Choice of a sign convention for whether the differences are plus or minus is arbitrary. However, it is convenient to assign positive potentials to metals such as copper and gold that are cathodic with respect to hydrogen, and negative potentials to metals such as iron and zinc that are anodic with respect to hydrogen. The collected values of these potentials are termed the electromotive series (Table 1.01). Additional data referring to redox potentials are given in Table 1.02.

Data from Table 1.01 permit the determination of the potential differences between any set of two metals, each immersed in a 1N solution of one of its own salts, with the electrolytic path completed by a salt bridge.

For example, the Daniell cell potential is correctly predicted as

1

TABLE 1.01

The Electromotive Series

Electrode	Cell Reaction	$E°$ (volts)
Li^+ ½ Li	½ $H_2 + Li^+ = Li + H^+$	-3.025
K^+ ½ K	½ $H_2 + K^+ = K + H^+$	-2.925
Ca^{2+} ½ Ca	½ $H_2 + ½ Ca^2 = ½ Ca + H^+$	-2.870
Na^+ ½ Na	½ $H_2 + Na^+ = Na + H^+$	-2.714
Mg^{2+} ½ Mg	½ $H_2 + ½ Mg^{2+} = ½ Mg + H^+$	-2.370
Al^{3+} ½ Al	½ $H_2 + 1/3 Al^{3+} = 1/3 Al + H^+$	-1.660
Zn^{2+} ½ Zn	½ $H_2 + ½ Zn^{2+} = ½ Zn + H^+$	-0.763
Fe^{2+} ½ Fe	½ $H_2 + ½ Fe^{2+} = ½ Fe + H^+$	-0.440
Cd^{2+} ½ Cd	½ $H_2 + ½ Cd^{2+} = ½ Cd + H^+$	-0.402
Ni^{2+} ½ Ni	½ $H_2 + ½ Ni^{2+} = ½ Ni + H^+$	-0.250
Sn^{2+} ½ Sn	½ $H_2 + ½ Sn^{2+} = ½ Sn + H^+$	-0.136
Pb^{2+} ½ Pb	½ $H_2 + ½ Pb^{2+} = ½ Pb + H^+$	-0.126
H^+ ½ H_2, Pt	½ $H_2 = H^+ + e$	0.000
Cu^{2+} ½ Cu	½ $H_2 + ½ Cu^{2+} = ½ Cu + H^+$	+0.337
Ag^+ ½ Ag	½ $H_2 + Ag^+ = Ag + H^+$	+0.799
Au^+ ½ Au	½ $H_2 + Au^+ = Au + H^+$	+1.680

In general: ½ H_2 + (Oxidized State) = H^+ + (Reduced State).

TABLE 1.02

Selected Standard Redox Potentials

Reaction	E_O (volts)
$Fe + S^{2-} = FeS + 2e$	-1.000
$Ni + S^{2-} = NiS (\alpha) + 2e$	-0.860
$Cu + 2CN^- = Cu(CN)_2^- + e$	-0.780
$Cu + S^{2-} = CuS + 2e$	-0.760
$Pb + SO_4^{2-} = PbSO_4 + 2e$	-0.560
$Ag + 2CN^- = Ag(CN)_2^- + e$	-0.290
$Cu + 4NH_3 = Cu(NH_3)_4^{2+} + 2e$	-0.050
$Fe^{2+} = Fe^{3+} + e$	+0.771
$PbSO_4 + 2H_2O = PbO_2 + SO_4^{2-} + 2e$	+1.685

the copper potential minus the zinc potential (+0.337 minus -0.763 volts) for an overall potential difference of 1.1 volts. The classic form of the Daniell cell is a copper electrode in a copper sulfate solution, contained in a porous pot sitting in a larger container of zinc sulfate solution that contains a zinc electrode.

From Table 1.02, it is possible to draw further inferences. The presence of Fe^{3+} at the cathode of a corrosion cell where it can be reduced to Fe^{2+} can give a potent cathodic reaction.

The 0.771v associated with this reaction adds algebraically to the voltages corresponding to whatever other reactions are occurring. It is no surprise then that the presence of an ion in solution that can be in more than one valence state can have a powerful effect on corrosion reactions.

If we now consider the standard electrode potential for copper, i.e., +0.337v, as shown in Table 1.01, we see that copper does not replace hydrogen in a standard acid solution. The corrosion of copper can only proceed if there is a concurrent reaction with Cu^{2+} or H_2 to force the reaction to continue by providing more energy than is represented by the 0.337v barrier noted above.

Example 1.01 Determine the standard potential for the dissolution of copper in cyanide solution.

> **Solution:** The basic data is given by entries in Tables 1.01 and 1.02, i.e.,
>
> **½ H$_2$ = H$^+$ + e   E = 0.00v**
>
> **and, Cu + 2CN$^-$ = Cu(CN)$_2^-$ + e   E = - 0.780v**
>
> Reversing the first of these and adding, we have:
>
> **Answer: Cu + H$^+$ + 2CN$^-$ = Cu(CN)$_2^-$ + ½ H$_2$**
> **E = -0.780v.**

We can see the strong tendency for copper to pass spontaneously into solution with the evolution of hydrogen. In addition to being soluble in hydrocyanic acid, copper also is soluble in solutions of cyanide salts, such as NaCN or KCN.

In addition to using a complexant for copper as a facilitator for

3

dissolving copper in acids, anything that has an energetic reaction with hydrogen will have the same effect. Atmospheric oxygen or an oxidizing agent such as nitric acid qualify in this sense.

In general then we would say that copper, despite being noble to hydrogen, can be expected to corrode in solutions containing complexants and/or oxidizing agents. Silver and gold behave somewhat similarly. For example, gold can be dissolved in a dilute solution of sodium cyanide that also contains dissolved oxygen from the air. Such generalizations are helpful in understanding corrosion phenomena.

So far, the SHE has been considered the reference electrode of choice. In the practice of corrosion, other electrodes often are more convenient. A number of such reference electrodes and their voltage relation to the SHE are shown in Table 1.03.

TABLE 1.03

Common Reference Electrodes

Designation	Composition	Electrode Reaction	Potential Relative to SHE (volts)	Temp. Coefficient (mV/C°)
Saturated Calomel Electrode (SCE)	$Hg, Hg_2Cl_2(s)/$ KCl (saturated)	$Hg_2Cl_2 + 2e^-$ $= 2Hg + 2Cl^-$	+ 0.2446	- 0.76
0.1 M Calomel Electrode	$Hg, Hg_2Cl_2(s)/$ KCl (0.1 M)	$Hg_2Cl_2 + 2e^-$ $= 2Hg + 2Cl^-$	+ 0.3338	- 0.07
0.1 M Silver Chloride Electrode	$Ag, AgCl(s)/$ KCl (0.1 M)	$AgCl + e^-$ $= Ag + Cl^-$	+ 0.2881	- 0.65
1 M Mercury Sulfate Electrode	$Hg, Hg_2SO_4(s)/$ K_2SO_4 (1 M)	$Hg_2SO_2 + 2e^-$ $= 2Hg + SO^-$	+ 0.6600	- 0.80
Saturated Copper Sulfate Electrode	$Cu/CuSO_4$ (saturated solution)	$Cu^+ + 2e^- = Cu$	+ 0.3200	

4

Concentration Cells

If two different portions of a piece of metal are exposed to two different concentrations of a solution of one of its salts, a current will tend to flow in the direction that will decrease the concentration difference. The metal exposed to the low concentration will become the anode and corrode, and there will be a plating out on the cathode from the solution of higher concentration [Equation (1.01)].

$$-\Delta G = nFE = RT \ln \frac{c_1}{c_2} \qquad (1.01)$$

Where ΔG is the change in Gibbs Free Energy associated with the reaction:

$$Mc_1 \rightarrow Mc_2 \qquad (1.02)$$

where: n is the valence of the metallic ion in solution; F is Faraday's constant (96,500 joules/volt equivalent); E is the potential difference associated with the reaction; R is the gas constant (8.3125 joules/ degree); T is the absolute temperature; C_1 is the concentration (or activity) of metallic ion in solution in the more concentrated solution; and C_2 is the concentration (or activity) of metallic ion in solution in the less-concentrated solution.

The corrosion cells that occur in practice often can be regarded as a combination of the two metals in question from Table 1.01 modified by concentration cell terms, as calculated by Equation (1.01). A different form of concentration cell also is significant in some types of corrosion—the oxygen concentration cell. In the cell, the anode reaction is:

$$M^\circ - 2e \rightarrow M++ \qquad (1.03a)$$

While the cathode reaction is:

$$4H^+ + 4e + O_2 \rightarrow 2H_2O \qquad (1.03b)$$

or some similar reaction-consuming oxygen.

Note that the location where the oxygen concentration is high becomes the cathode while the anodic corrosion occurs at the oxygen-depleted site. The potential of the oxygen concentration cell is given in Equation (1.04), a modified form of Equation (1.01).

$$nFE = RT\ell n \ \frac{PO_2}{P'O_2} \tag{1.04}$$

where: PO_2 is the vapor pressure of oxygen at the cathode; and $P'O_2$ is the vapor pressure of oxygen at the anode.

This type of corrosion cell is characteristic of pitting, crevice corrosion, and pipelines passing from aerated to nonaerated soil (e.g., clay). In this case, O_2 is consumed at the cathode, and the O_2-starved area suffers anodic corrosion.

A Closer Look at Electrode Processes

When a clean and pure metal is immersed in a solution of one of its salts, it reaches a state of dynamic equilibrium in which the rates of reactions are equal. Equation (1.05) will correspond to an anodic current flow, and Equation (1.06) will correspond to a cathodic current flow.

$$M° - 2e \rightarrow M^{++} \tag{1.05}$$

$$M^{++} + 2e \rightarrow M° \tag{1.06}$$

The electrical circuit is completed by the electrolytic conductivity of the salt solution and the electronic conductivity of the metal. Each equal current flowing both ways at equilibrium is called the exchange current, and the potential of the system is the equilibrium potential associated with the system under study. Unfortunately, it is not possible to measure this equilibrium potential directly. As before, a reference electrode, such as the SHE, is needed.

At equilibrium, Equations (1.05) and (1.06) will occur at local anodes and cathodes, respectively. With the exchange current flowing, there will be a vanishingly small potential difference between the two types of site. The oxidation or corrosion reaction at the anode will be exactly balanced by a reduction reaction (in this case, plating out) at the cathode. If there is a small disturbance from the equilibrium potential, currents (i_{an} and i_{cath}) corresponding to Equations (1.05) and (1.06) will no longer be equal, and the net current will follow the applied disturbance in potential.

If the exchange current is designated as i_{ex}, the situation at equilibrium will be:

$$i_{ex} = i_{an} = i_{cath} \tag{1.07}$$

If there is a shift in potential in the cathode direction, the net current flowing, i, will be given by:

$$i = i_{cath} - i_{an} \tag{1.08}$$

And if the shift in potential is in the anode direction:

$$i = i_{an} - i_{cath} \tag{1.09}$$

The net current is directly measurable.

If the value of the exchange current is large, there will be a large change in i for a given change in potential. In practice, this means the electrode for which the exchange current is high will exhibit a potential that is stable and difficult to disturb significantly. The electrode with the highest exchange current known in aqueous solution is the platinized platinum electrode at which hydrogen is the reacting species. Such an electrode, in which the gaseous hydrogen is at a pressure of (strictly fugacity) and hydrogen ion is in 1N concentration (strictly activity), is known as the SHE and is the primary reference electrode. It is assigned the arbitrary potential of exactly zero at 298 K.

On the other hand, if the exchange current is small, large differences in potential from equilibrium can lead only to small net restoring currents, and the electrode is said to be readily polarized. The difference between the equilibrium potential and the actual potential is referred to as the overvoltage or overpotential of the electrode. The relationship between net current and overvoltage is of prime importance in the study of corrosion. A reasonable model of the current to overvoltage relationship leads to the Butler-Volmer Equation (Equation 1.10). Traditionally, the interest in electrochemistry has focused on equilibrium processes, particularly since these are amenable to accurate measurement and interpretation. However, for the study of electrochemical processes that occur at significant rates, including corrosion, there has to be more emphasis on the actual rate of particular reactions, though the data may be somewhat imprecise.

Equilibrium and Nonequilibrium Aspects
of Electrochemistry

Thus far, only the equilibrium case has been considered. The potential is a guide for showing which way a reaction tends to go, but can offer no conclusion as to whether the reaction will be significantly rapid and cause significant corrosion. Therefore, the rates of corrosion must be examined, as measured by the corrosion current flowing and changes in potential associated with current flow. Polarization is the term used to denote the change in voltage that results from the passage of current. This is the difference between the equilibrium potential, as studied earlier, and the actual case of the working corrosion cell.

There are various kinds of polarization, ranging from the inevitable resistive iR drop (because a current i flows through a resistance R) to specific effects at anode and cathode. The terms "overvoltage" and "overpotential" refer to polarization effects at a specific electrode.

One of the most significant types of polarization is activation polarization. When this controls the rate of an electrochemical reaction, the activation energy of the reaction is the "bottleneck" limiting the rate of reaction. A theoretical model of the current/overvoltage reaction can be drawn up in the form of the Butler-Volmer Equation 1.10 (Figure 1.01).

$$i = i_{ex}\{\exp[(1 - \beta)F\eta/RT] - \exp(-\beta F\eta/RT)\} \quad (1.10)$$

This can be related to absolute reaction rate theory. For example, in Glasstone, Laidler, and Eyring, where i_{ex} is the exchange current as before β is the symmetry factor (usually 0.5), and η is the overpotential.[3]

There are two important limiting cases of the Butler-Volmer Equation. When η is large (> 50 mv), the second term in the equation becomes small and may be neglected. The equation then becomes:

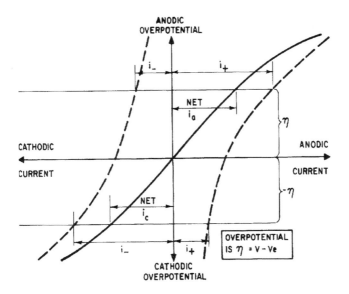

FIGURE 1.01 *The voltage to current diagram for an electrode reaction (after Bockris and Reddy[1]).*

$$i = i_{ex}\exp[1 - \beta)F\eta \ /RT] \qquad (1.11)$$

for positive values of η, or:

$$i = i_{ex}\exp(- \beta \ F\eta/RT) \qquad (1.12)$$

for large negative values of η. Equation 1.11 may be rewritten as:

$$\ell ni = \ell ni_{ex} + \ \frac{(1 - \beta)F\eta}{RT} \qquad (1.13)$$

or as:

$$\eta = - \ \frac{RT}{(1 - \beta)F} \ \ell ni_{ex} + \ \frac{RT}{(1 - \beta) \ F \ I} \ \ell ni \qquad (1.14)$$

9

Since only η and i are variables for a given electrode system, this reduces to:

$$\eta = a + b\ell ni \qquad\qquad (1.15)$$

where a and b are constants.

This is the so-called Tafel Equation, in which the linear relationship between overvoltage and logarithm of current was established on an empirical basis and applies where the reaction is under activation control.

The other limiting case of the Butler-Volmer Equation occurs at low values of $\setminus \eta \setminus$ (< 5 mv). In this case, the exponential terms in the equation may be replaced by the first two terms in the McLaurin series expansion of e^x, and the Butler-Volmer Equation (1.10) becomes:

$$i = 1_{ex}\left[1 + \frac{(1 - \beta)F\eta}{RT} - 1 + \frac{\beta F\eta}{RT} \right] \qquad\qquad (1.16)$$

where:

$$i = \frac{i_{ex}}{RT} F\eta \qquad\qquad (1.17)$$

And:

$$\eta = \frac{RT}{i_{ex}F} i \qquad\qquad (1.18)$$

These relationships are shown graphically in Figures 1.02 and 1.03.

The value of this approach is that low overvoltage laboratory studies of reactions under activation control can be made with adequate experimental control and can allow calculation of i_{ex}.

Tafel constants derived from this serve as the basis for predicted behavior under the more practical condition of high overvoltage. This constitutes the so-called linear polarization method for study of corrosion processes.

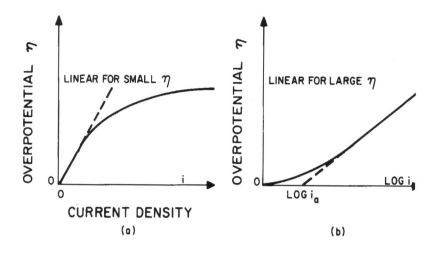

FIGURE 1.02 *Current density to overpotential relationships: (a) for small overpotentials; and (b) for large overpotentials (after Bockris and Reddy[1]).*

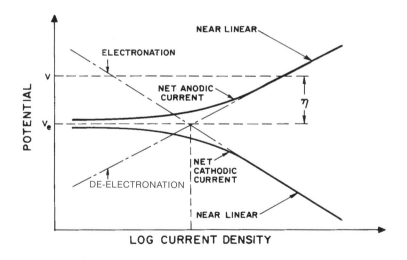

FIGURE 1.03 *Log current to potential relationships (after Bockris and Reddy[1]).*

11

Polarization

Any electrode in which a net current is passing must, of necessity, be polarized. A variety of types of polarization is possible.

The simplest type of polarization is resistance polarization. Since the electric circuit involved has finite resistance, there must be an iR voltage drop. If the current is interrupted, this voltage drop disappears immediately.

Concentration polarization is another type. During an electrode process, a species depletes as it escapes or reacts at each electrode, and a buildup of reaction product or noninvolved species occurs. This results in a back electromotive force (EMF), as given by Equation (1.01). When the current is interrupted, this concentration polarization decays with a half-life characteristic of a diffusional process, indicating an activation energy of only a few Kcal/mol.

Where polarization is the result of building up activation energy for a chemical reaction, the activation term would be several tens of Kcal/mol, and the decay of this potential would be a good deal slower. This is the case considered earlier in the Butler-Volmer Equation.

In the typical case, the process occurring after a sudden interruption of the electrochemical current will be an immediate loss of the iR drop followed by the more gradual decline of the components of polarization operating as the sum of a number of exponential decay curves. This usually can be analyzed to expose the individual decay components, hence, indicating what sort of electrode processes are occurring since particular ranges of activation energy are characteristic of particular polarization reactions. A detailed account of polarization is found in Vetter's monograph.[4]

Limiting Corrosion Current Density

In many cases, an upper limit for the possible corrosion rate may be set by the availability of a reactant such as oxygen. For example, as long as oxygen can diffuse up to the cathode and the corrosion products can diffuse away from the anode, corrosion can continue to increase until the limiting current density is reached. Here, the primary diffusion is just sufficient to maintain the original corrosion reaction. The system then polarizes in response to a further potential increase to the extent a new reaction can add on to the original one. On an overall basis, the mixed reaction can continue. Examples of this will be considered later.

Hydrogen Overpotential

One possible cathodic reaction is the generation of hydrogen. This occurs in the acid corrosion of many metals and in the codeposition of hydrogen and another metal in electroplating or related operations. In either case, the hydrogen reactions involved will be:

$$H^+ + e \rightarrow H_{(ads)} \tag{1.19}$$

$$H_{(ads)} \rightarrow H_{(sol)} \tag{1.20}$$

$$2H_{(ads)} \rightarrow H_2 \, (g) \tag{1.21}$$

$$H^+ + H_{(ads)} + e \rightarrow H_2 \, (g) \tag{1.22}$$

For most metals, the first of these, Equation (1.19), is the rate-determining step. However, for platinum and palladium, the third, Equation (1.21), controls the rate. The second, Equation (1.20), also comes into play where hydrogen can pass into solution in the metallic electrode; hydrogen damage of various kinds can result.

The values for the exchange current densities for the hydrogen reaction on a number of metals are given in Table 1.04.

TABLE 1.04

Exchange Current Densities for the Hydrogen Reaction[5]

Metal	Exchange Current Density (amp/cm2 at 25°C)
Pb, Hg	10^{-13}
Zn	10^{-11}
Sn, Al, Be	10^{-10}
Ni, Ag, Cu, Cd	10^{-7}
Fe, Au, Mo	10^{-6}
W, Co, Ta	10^{-5}
Pd, Rh	10^{-4}
Pt	10^{-2}

This table summarizes the collation of data presented in Chapter 4 of Bockris' and Conway's *Modern Aspects of Electrochemistry*.[6] (Used with permission of Van Nostrand Reinhold.)

In cases such as mercury, lead, and zinc, where the exchange current is small, a given change in current at the electrode must lead to a large change in potential. Platinum electrodes, on the other hand, can tolerate the same change in current with a trivial voltage response. In other words, any current on Hg, Pb, Zn, etc., corresponding to a hydrogen reaction at a technically significant rate must lead to a high value of hydrogen overpotential. On the other hand, the hydrogen overpotential on the Pt group metals is low. Numerical values are given in Table 1.05.

If metals are subjected to corrosive attack by a nonoxidizing acid

---

TABLE 1.05

Hydrogen Overvoltage in Volts on Various Materials and at Different Current Densities

	Hydrogen Overvoltage		
	10^{-3} A/cm^2 (volts)	10^{-2} A/cm^2 (volts)	10^{-1} A/cm^2 (volts)
Platinized Pt	0.015	0.030	0.04
Bright Pt	0.025	0.070	0.29
Ni_3S_2	—	0.100	0.20
NiS	0.120	0.300	0.40
Fe_3C	0.050	0.800	—
Au	0.240	0.390	0.59
Coke	0.270	0.340	0.41
Mo	0.300	0.440	0.57
Ni	0.330	0.420	0.51
Fe	0.400	0.530	0.64
Ag	0.440	0.660	0.76
Graphite	0.470	0.760	0.99
Cu	0.600	0.750	0.82
Zn	0.720	0.750	1.06
Sn	0.850	0.980	0.99
Cd	0.910	1.200	1.25
Pb	0.910	1.240	1.26
Hg	1.040	1.150	1.21

that is free of dissolved oxygen, two factors determine the corrosion rate. First, the equilibrium potential difference as detailed in Table 1.01 established whether corrosion can occur at all and sets a maximum value the hydrogen overvoltage can assume. The current that corresponds to this can be found from Table 1.05; this is the maximum attainable corrosion current, assuming the anode does not polarize to a significant extent. The second factor is the hydrogen overpotential that determines the actual rate of reaction to be associated with that potential difference. Zinc is an interesting case in that its corrosion rate in acid is slower than would be expected on the basis of its equilibrium potential with respect to hydrogen because of its high hydrogen overpotential. The corrosion rate also could be sensitive to the presence of surface impurities for which the exchange current densities for hydrogen differ strongly from those of zinc.

Thus, corrosion rates in practical cases are affected by both the difference in equilibrium potential and the polarization associated with specific anodic and cathodic reactions at the electrodes of interest. An electrode reaction that is easily polarized has a low exchange current for a given overvoltage and seems a promising candidate for allowing effective control of a corrosion process.

The relationship between the weight of metal put into solution or converted to oxide, etc., by a given anodic current to that current is given by Faraday's Law. According to the law, the passage of 96,500 coulombs will cause dissolution of a gram equivalent weight of the metal concerned. This allows calculation of uniform corrosion wastage corresponding to a known corrosion concept.

A Closer Look at a Wetted Interface

When a metal is immersed in an electrolyte, its potential can be designated only with respect to an arbitrary reference electrode. It is desirable to determine the potential with respect to a suitable ion (normally a cation) of its own species in solution. This is the potential difference that should be used in assessing the electrochemical behavior of the electrode. In a typical corrosion situation, an atom in the metallic state has a certain number of metal-to-metal bonds broken; later it forms some number of additional metal-to-ligand bonds if it forms an oxide film. The net result of these changes will be a potential difference between the metal in the metallic lattice and in the corrosion product or solution.

Unfortunately, this particular potential difference is not measurable. However, some factors that contribute to it can be identified. Adsorption of charged particles, such as ions or other accumulation of charge in the vicinity of the interface, clearly would be significant, and when currents are flowing there are overpotential terms to consider. This creates an electrified interface. The properties of electrified interfaces, and how these interact with ions—particularly in aqueous systems—need to be studied in somewhat more detail.

If the immersed metal is negatively charged it will attract an excess of positive ions to its vicinity, but if positively charged, there will be an excess of negative ions. The latter corresponds to the conditions at the anode, where the loss of metal by corrosion occurs.

The ions themselves typically will be highly hydrated and surrounded with water dipoles, as can be seen in Figures 1.04 and 1.05. It is helpful to think of these dipoles as roughly triangular in shape with the O atom its apex and the two H atoms its base. The term dipole is appropriate because the former is negatively charged and the latter is positively charged. This means the dipoles surrounding a positive ion will be apex inward, which is more efficient spatially and, hence, more energetically favorable than the apex-outward configuration around negative ions.

Hydration sheaths around positive ions are more stable and need more energy for their removal than sheaths around positive ions. Thus, it is easier for negative ions to lose all or part of their hydration sheath, approach closer to a metallic electrode, and become more energetically adsorbed there. For very large ions, however, the differences are much less important because in neither case does the hydration sheath cover the entire surface of the ion and adsorption can occur with relatively minor disturbance of the sheath.

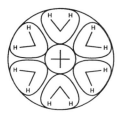

FIGURE 1.04 *Representation of a positive ion surrounded by a sheath of apex inward water dipoles (after Bockris and Reddy[1]). (Used with the permission of Plenum Publishing.)*

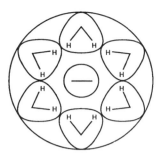

FIGURE 1.05 *Representation of a negative surrounded by a sheath of apex outward water dipoles (after Bockris and Reddy[1]). (Used with the permission of Plenum Publishing.)*

In many ways the structure of the metal-electrolyte interface resembles that of an oversized ion. This structure is shown in Figure 1.06. Both water dipoles and negative ions can come to the inner Helmholtz plane (IHP), whereas positive ions cannot come this close to the surface (Figure 1.07).

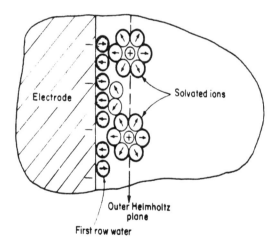

FIGURE 1.06 *A layer of hydrated positive ions whose hydration sheath cannot be stripped, on the layer of first row water. The locus of the centers of these ions defines the OHP (after Bockris and Reddy[1]). (Used with the permission of Plenum Publishing.)*

17

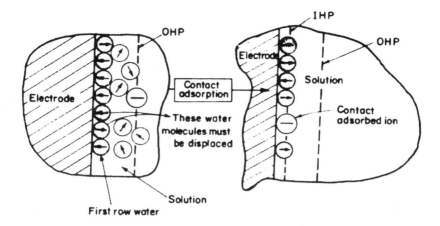

FIGURE 1.07 *The process of contact adsorption in which a negative ion can lose its hydration and displace first row water. The locus of the centers of the ions defines the IHP. (After Bockris and Reddy[1]) (Used with the permission of Plenum Publishing.)*

Detailed consideration of these matters is beyond the scope of this book, but the interested reader is referred to Bockris and Reddy.[1]

Adsorption of negative ions, particularly chloride ions, is an important phenomenon in corrosion. The small chloride ion can adsorb closely to the metal surface at the inner Helmholtz plane. When adsorbed, it leads to irregularities in adsorbed water dipoles, chemisorbed oxide ions, etc., largely because of the associated high gradients in charge density in its vicinity. It is hard to either maintain or develop protective films when chloride ions are present. The effects of various adsorbed ions are shown in Table 1.06.

However, a related matter is highly significant. When considering scaling phenomena in which scales (for example) of calcium carbonate are deposited on or near a heat exchanger surface, the potential seen by the liquid medium is of great significance in determining whether the deposit will be an adherent scale or a loose sludge that can be flushed off.

In general terms, homogeneous nucleation processes would yield sludges, whereas heterogeneous nucleation would cause a scale to form. If not removed in time, sludges eventually will be consolidated into scales in a secondary manner.

TABLE 1.06

Effect of Adsorbed Anions[7]

F^-, ClO_4^-, SO_4^{2-}, CO_{3-}^{2-}, PO_4^{3-}, CrO_4^{2-}, OH^-

Low Molar Polarizations
Low Adsorbability
High Overpotential
Smooth, Fine Grained Electrodeposits
Low Corrosivity
Weakly Peptizing
Passivating
Weak Electrocapillarity Effect
Weak Hydrogen Embrittlement

Cl^-, NO_3^-, Br^-, HS^-, I^-, SCN^-, S^{2-}

High Molar Polarizations
High Adsorbability
Low Overpotential
Treeing, Coarse Crystalline Electrodeposits
High Corrosivity
Strongly Peptizing
Activating
Strong Electrocapillarity Effect
Strong Hydrogen Embrittlement

Representation of Corrosion Equilibria

Consider the reaction:

$$2H_2O = O_2 + 4H^+ + 4e \qquad (1.23)$$

In the usual notation:

$$\Delta G = \Delta G° - RT \ln PO_2 [H^+]^4 \qquad (1.24)$$

Similarly:

$$E = E° + \frac{0.059}{4} \ log \ PO_2 \ [H^+]^4 \qquad\qquad (1.25)$$

Whence:

$$E = 1.228 - 0.059 \ pH \qquad\qquad (1.26)$$

In a similar manner, the reaction:

$$H_2 = 2H^+ + 2e \qquad\qquad (1.27)$$

yields the result:

$$E = 0.000 - 0.059 \ pH \qquad\qquad (1.28)$$

Plotting these two results on an E vs pH diagram yields Figure 1.08.

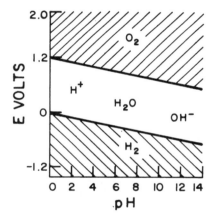

FIGURE 1.08 *Simplified Pourbaix diagram for water at 25°C.*

Figure 1.08 is somewhat akin to the familiar phase diagram. In this case, the upper part defines the potential pH range in which oxygen evolution is expected, the central part of the diagram shows the water is stable, and the lower part of the diagram shows that hydrogen is stable. This is the Pourbaix diagram for water first proposed by Marcel Pourbaix.

To characterize the corrosion behavior of a metal it is necessary to place additional lines on the diagram representing equilibria between the metal and its various corrosion products and the components of water. Zinc is selected as an example because its chemistry is relatively simple. In the construction of a more complex Pourbaix diagram such as this it is necessary to select an arbitrary concentration of zinc-bearing species in solution. The concentration 10^{-6} M is accepted as indicating that concentration above which corrosion starts to become important. This furnishes the basis for calculating lines on the diagram to separate regions in which zinc and its corrosion products are stable. Results of this calculation are shown in Table 1.07 (Figure 1.09).

TABLE 1.07
Data Concerning Zinc to Water Reaction

Reaction	E vs pH Equation	Shown on Figure 1.09
$Zn^{++} + 2e = Zn^{\circ}$	$E = -0.76 + 0.059/2 \log[Zn^{++}]$	I
$ZnO + 2H^+ + 2e = Zn^{\circ} + H_2O$	$E = -0.44 - 0.059$ pH	II
$ZnO_2^= + 4H^+ + 2e = Zn^{\circ} + 2H_2O$	$E = -0.44 -0.118$ pH $= 0.0295$ $\log[ZnO_2^=]$	III
$Zn^{++} + H_2O = ZnO + 2H^+$	pH $= 8.3$	i
$ZnO + H_2O = ZnO_2^= + 2H^+$	pH $= 11.9$	ii

Diagrams of this nature are useful for predicting the corrosion behavior of an unfamiliar metal, for comparing the corrosion behavior of various metals, and for defining conditions under which soluble species can be leached out from (in this case) zinc-containing solids.

It must be remembered that the Pourbaix diagram, like the more familiar phase diagram, can represent only equilibria. Additional data is required to establish rate of reactions when the diagram indicates a reaction is possible.

In Figure 1.09, corrosion occurs in the two zones with stable and soluble corrosion products (Zn^{++} and $ZnO_2^=$). More examples of Pourbaix diagrams will be considered in Chapter 2.

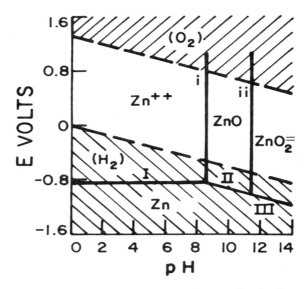

FIGURE 1.09 *Simplied Pourbaix diagram for zinc in water.*

References

1. J. O'M. Bockris, A.K.N. Reddy, *Modern Electrochemistry* (New York, NY: Plenum Press, 1970).
2. J. O'M. Bockris, D. Drazic, *Electrochemical Science* (London, UK: Taylor and Francis, 1972).
3. Glasstone, Laidler, Eyring, *Theory of Rate Processes* (McGraw-Hill, New York, 1941).
4. K.J. Vetter, *Electrochemical Kinetics* (New York, NY: Academic Press, 1967).
5. J.M. West, *Electrodeposition and Corrosion Processes* (New York, NY: Van Nostrand Reinhold, 1965).
6. J. O'M. Bockris, B.E. Conway, *Modern Aspects of Electrochemistry* (London, UK: Butterworths, 1954).
7. G. Wranglen, *An Introduction to Corrosion and Protection of Metals* (London, UK: Chapman and Hall, 1973).

2

Electrochemistry of Corrosion Cells

This discussion begins with the familiar Daniell Cell. The cell was used in the early years to power telegraph lines before other sources of power were generally available. In the Daniell Cell, a zinc electrode is immersed in zinc sulfate solution, a copper electrode is immersed in copper sulfate solution, and a porous pot separates the two solutions. When an external circuit is completed between the two electrodes, the zinc behaves as anode and dissolves while the copper behaves as cathode and is subject to plating out. As the resistance of the external circuit is decreased, a larger current is drawn from the cell. When the cell is short-circuited, both electrodes must have the same potential and there will be an associated limiting corrosion current. This situation is represented schematically in Figure 2.01.

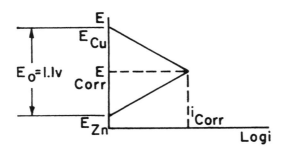

FIGURE 2.01 *Polarization diagram for Daniell cell (schematic).*

The open circuit potential is given by ECu-EZn and is about 1.1 volts, as seen before. When the cell is short-circuited, the entire potential difference is used up in various polarization processes, and both electrodes come to a steady-state mixed-potential E_m, whose particular value is shown as E_{corr} in Figure 2.01 and corresponds to

23

the corrosion current i_{corr} for the system. This current is relatively large because the cell has been designed for low polarization of the electrodes.

The corresponding true corrosion cell, with zinc and copper in electrical contact and exposed to an electrolyte, behaves similarly. The open circuit potential will be only slightly different because the Cu^{++} and Zn^{++} concentrations at the electrode are both lower. Depending on the relative areas of the copper and zinc in contact with the electrolyte, there will be differing slopes of E vs i curves as well as differing values of E_m and i_c. In general, i will be much lower for an accidental corrosion cell than for a device designed as a working battery. The shape of the polarization diagram also will depend on whether current, current density, or the logarithm of one of these is selected for the abscissa. Polarization diagrams of this nature were introduced by U.R. Evans and often are referred to as Evans diagrams. Zinc to copper couples are rarely encountered in practice. The more common case is a coupling of iron or steel to copper or brass. The simple polarization diagram will resemble Figure 2.01 with E_{Fe} in place of E_{Zn}. However, the practical implication deserves further study.

From about 1860 to 1950, the typical ship consisted of a combination of a painted steel hull and an unpainted copper base alloy propeller or propeller and rudder combination. Where the paint on the hull was deficient for any reason, intense corrosion of the exposed steel was inevitable. At sea, repairs of perforations might involve slabs of bacon shored up by timbers. Since the late 1940s, the techniques of cathodic protection have been applied increasingly (Chapter 7), and this problem has been largely overcome.

Two items of marine lore deserve consideration. One is that wrought iron hulls corrode less than steel hulls. This was true because early propulsion units, such as sail, wooden or steel paddle wheels, or cast iron propellers, did not provide cathodic stimulation of the hull corrosion. The other item is the current view of East Coast fishermen that bronze propellers wear well on large ships but not on small ones. Typically, the larger vessels are steel-hulled while the smaller ones are wooden or reinforced plastic. Perhaps the propellers need to be coupled to a sacrificial anode!

An elegant example of the copper-to-steel couple was demonstrated by a pair of steel-to-copper assemblies. One consisted of steel plates joined by copper rivets, and the other consisted of copper plates joined by steel rivets. These were exposed separately to seawater for

24

a few months at Harbor Island, North Carolina. The steel rivets disappeared while the copper rivets merely caused somewhat increased corrosion of the surrounding steel. This underlines the principle that a large cathode to anode area ratio can be disastrous while a small cathode to anode area ratio of a potentially damaging couple can, at times, be tolerated.

Another method of coping with a copper-to-steel couple is by coating the copper alloy with a metal that polarizes more readily. In one practical case, the steel casing surrounding a bronze impeller was coated with tin in a wiping operation, as would be done by a typical plumber. Little alteration in potential of the corrosion couple resulted from this change, but the corrosion current dropped drastically because tin polarizes much more readily than bronze.

Corrosion couples can be demonstrated effectively by the use of a solution of potassium or sodium chloride as corrodent with the addition of potassium ferricyanide and phenolphthalein as indicators; this is gelled with agar. Anodes on steel put ferrous ion in solution and generate an intense blue (Turnbull's Blue) while cathodically generated alkali causes the phenolphthalein to show its characteristic pink color. The reactions would be, for example:

$$Fe^\circ - 2e \rightarrow Fe^{++} \tag{2.01}$$

$$\tfrac{1}{2} O_2 + H_2O + 2e \rightarrow 2OH^- \tag{2.02}$$

As a laboratory demonstration, the agar has to be dissolved in boiling water, the other components added, and the mixed solution allowed to cool and set in petri dishes. Corrosion samples are then pressed into the gel, demonstrating the characteristic colors in a few hours. Anodes on metals other than iron do not give any color reaction.

One of the more insidious copper-to-iron couples is in domestic hot water systems. Most plumbing codes allow steel pipe for hot water in any size over 50 mm, requiring copper for smaller sizes. In once-through systems using more or less hard water, formation of calcium carbonate scale on the steel may allow this system to function. For recirculating systems, particularly with soft water, there will be objectionable rust discoloration of the water. Use of insulating couplings on the piping clearly will be ineffective unless all other metallic connections (such as pipe hangers) also are insulated to prevent corrosion currents from taking a less direct route. Insulation, of course, does not stop deposition of dissolved copper on steel parts of the piping system, which leads to a secondary bimetallic corrosion.

Another galvanic couple that can cause problems is the one between copper tubing, used in water systems, and the lead-based solder used to join the components. This gives a combination of a large copper cathode and a small lead alloy anode, and is particularly troublesome in a new building. Traces of soldering flux containing chlorides serve to depolarize the reaction and increase corrosion.

This can lead to water supplies containing more than the safe lead level. However, the problem may disappear in time, particularly if the piping picks up a coating of scale from hardness salts in the water. To be on the safe side, lead-free solder should be used. One required specification, in place in Scandinavia for decades, calls for a tin-based solder containing a little silver. In existing houses, the problem is only likely to occur when water stands stagnant for many hours. A government laboratory in Ottawa, Canada, which identified this problem, now requires that its drinking fountains be left on 24 hours a day. It is, therefore, prudent as a morning routine to flush the toilet and run the kitchen tap for a while before drawing water for morning coffee.

Stray currents of any kind can mimic damaging corrosion couples. Street railways are the classic example, although welding generators, high-voltage DC transmission lines, telluric currents, and so forth all contribute to the problem. In all instances stray current problems must be countered by insulation of the menace or by provision of an alternative site at which an innocuous anodic reaction may be substituted for a damaging one. Stray AC currents are less dangerous from a corrosion standpoint. They stimulate corrosion to a lesser extent; only in cases where there is a corrosion product film with rectifying properties is there a net overall corrosion current.

Figure 2.02 shows a horrible example of stray current corrosion.

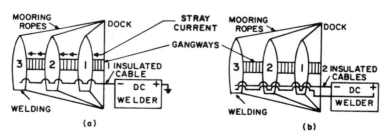

FIGURE 2.02 *Shipboard welding: (a) bad; and (b) good.*

Here, a careless welding operation on the outermost of a set of three ships can cause three separate instances of stray current corrosion. The welding generator should not be grounded on the dock. There should be two cables rather than one to the site of the welding.

Thermodynamics of the Corrosion Process

Two main bodies of thermodynamic data are useful in establishing corrosion tendencies. One is the electromotive series (Table 1.01) supplemented by the galvanic series for particular media. The other is the collection of Pourbaix diagrams. Both are limited since they are equilibrium data and can define only possibilities.

The electromotive series establishes, at least approximately, the potential difference that can result from a particular couple. It shows only that a corrosion process is or is not likely. It has no bearing on whether observed corrosion will be sufficiently rapid to be technically significant. More nonthermodynamic data has to establish this.

The Pourbaix diagram goes a step further. On a pH potential plot, it indicates the range in which various chemical species involving the metal of interest are the stable form. If the compounds are chosen appropriately to correspond to the real corrosion products, the diagram is valuable in determining when the metal is stable and when the various soluble and insoluble species are favored. Again, there is no information on rate.

The stability of an insoluble product may or may not be of technical significance as a corrosion control measure. That has to be determined by experiment in each case where passivity is indicated as a possibility. The case of the immunity is not ambiguous corrosion does not occur there. Where active corrosion is shown, there must be some sort of attack. Its extent is not predictable from the diagram.

Pourbaix diagrams also are of value in leaching operations in hydrometallurgy. They define the areas of pH and potential in which particular minerals may be expected to dissolve. Once again, rates of dissolution have to be determined experimentally.

Pourbaix Diagrams of Various Metals

A reasonably complete set of Pourbaix diagrams is shown in Figure 2.03.[1] These diagrams make it possible to compare known and un-

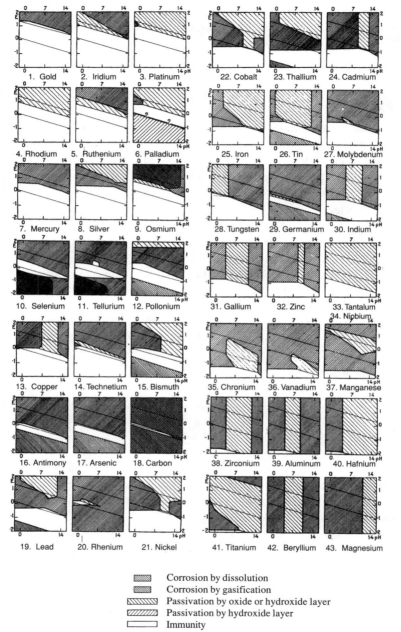

FIGURE 2.03 *Corrosion immunity and passivation domains of metals and metalloid classified in order of nobility due to thermodynamic immunity.*

28

known metals and give a synoptic description of each element. More information could be obtained from a series of diagram sets in a variety of anionic milieux. The most important metal from a tonnage point of view is iron. Its Pourbaix diagram is given in Figure 2.04.

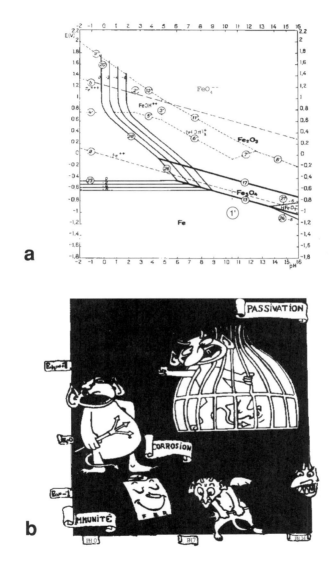

FIGURE 2.04 *Pourbaix artwork: (a) diagram for iron; and (b) animated diagram for iron from a Christmas message from Pourbaix.*

The most important zone of stability on that field is Fe_3O_4, although it is not obvious from the diagram. Empirically, it has long been known that corrosion of carbon steels under conditions obtained in boilers will lead to the formation of magnetite films and that the corrosion rate of magnetite-filmed steel is extremely low. This is a case of technically useful passivity. The corresponding Pourbaix diagram at (for example) 150°C (302°F) will not vary too much from that given for 25°C (77°F).

In this case, the diagram reinforces empirical experience. Acids are to be avoided in boilers, and it would appear that a pH of about 10 should be optimum. Excessive alkali can be damaging, though a pH of approximately 13 is the lower limit. It should be remembered that a local pH of 13 can occur in crevice or other fissures even when the bulk pH is somewhat lower. Oxidants also would move the steel out of the range of Fe_3O_4 stability. Therefore, the prescription of boiler operation is: deaerated water with pH controlled and preferably buffered around 10. Measurement of magnetite solubility under various conditions could help to define the optimum conditions more precisely (Chapter 7).

Note that the Pourbaix approach gives precise, but limited, information. The best regimen for boiler operation is known because of independent information that Fe_3O_4 formation was desirable. The detail of troubles that would result out of the Fe_3O_4 stability zone is not known. That also must be determined independently.

A general conclusion that can be drawn from a study of the various Pourbaix diagrams is that aluminum shows a zone of oxide stability at near neutral pH, regardless of the oxidation potential. Because of the high resistivity of Al_2O_3, this is useful in the prevention of corrosion.

Zinc shows a more restricted zone of passivity from about pH 8 to 12 associated with formation of $Zn(OH)_2$. This does not have as high a resistivity as Al_2O_3, and while it is useful to know the corrosion rate drops in this zone the protection is not as good as that given by aluminum for practical purposes.

Copper has a much more noble potential and shows a wide range of immunity. From the diagram, oxidant-free acids should not be able to corrode copper. On the other hand, acid or strong alkali corrosion should occur in the presence of oxidizing agents. This is in line with the conclusions of example 1.01 of the previous chapter, at least insofar as corrosion of copper by acids is concerned. The

Pourbaix diagram is a compact and convenient method of representing the equilibrium behavior of copper in a wide range of aqueous environments. What is not known from the diagram is the actual rate of corrosion that can be expected in a particular acid saturated with air.

Computer-generated Pourbaix Diagrams

Collections of Pourbaix diagrams were originally restricted to ambient temperature.[2] Their hand calculation was somewhat tedious. More recently, however, computer programs have been developed to prepare the diagrams from stored compilations of thermodynamic data. These use recognized thermodynamic calculations. Two such programs, available on line, are the FACT[3] program developed cooperatively at Royal Military College in Kingston and Ecole Polytechnique in Montreal, and the later and related NACE-NBS program.[4] The FACT program is currently available as an on-line computing service from McGill University in Montreal. A number of other broadly similar programs also have been developed.

Data can be generated to show reactions with solutions at temperatures up to 200 to 250°C (392 to 482°F) without serious complications. Reactions with solids pose no problems. However, the changing properties of water as the critical temperature is approached lead to major irregularities in the specific heats of many ions in solution.[5] This invalidates the extrapolation of specific heat terms and makes the diagrams generated for higher temperatures decidely suspect. In any event, close checking is required.

An interesting extension of Pourbaix Diagram generation is to show the corrosion behavior of alloys. A binary alloy of iron and chromium, with 0.9 activity of iron and 0.1 activity of chromium, will illustrate the process. Since the diagram is notably insensitive to activity in the solid this may be taken as representative of a ferritic stainless steel.

Figure 2.05 shows the diagram constructed with species containing chromium and iron. Note the very large area associated with the spinel (FeO) (Cr_2O_3). The passivity of the system would require an ample supply of oxygen to maintain its orginal passivity. The upper downward sloping dashed line shows the oxygen saturation limit. This gives an insight into the properties of stainless steels generally.

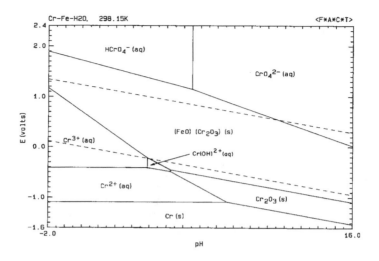

FIGURE 2.05 *Diagram generated by the FACT program for reaction with species containing iron and chromium. Note the large passive area. (FeO) (CR_2O_3) (s).*

Calculations of this sort also could be part of the process for developing new alloy systems with appropriate resistance to particular corrodents. In principle, then, the computer-generated Pourbaix diagrams can help extend fundamental knowledge of the corrosion behavior of known or proposed alloy systems. Corrosion response to dissolved reagents or contaminants, alone or in combination, also can be studied. It must be emphasized that for this process to work the computer's data base must be complete and include all relevant species and their thermodynamic data. Missing data could lead to erroneous diagrams. It is, of course, possible to insert new or estimated data from private sources to override inadequacies in the data bank.

Concentration Cells

The simplest demonstration of a concentration cell is the copper ion concentration cell (Chapter 1). The potential difference is given by:

$$E = \frac{RT}{nF} \ell n \; \frac{a_{Cu}}{a'_{Cu}} \qquad \textbf{(2.03)}$$

32

In practice, any variation in concentration of a species involved in a corrosion reaction can lead to a concentration cell. Cells involving oxygen are the most common cell. The potentials generated by concentration cells are small, being only a few tens of mV for a tenfold change in concentration.

The most obvious common form of oxygen concentration cell found in practice involves underground pipelines. The classic case is a pipeline passing from clay to gravel. The gravel will be aerated, whereas the clay is impermeable and essentially devoid of oxygen. The part of the line in contact with clay must then become the anode and suffer damage. The extent of the damage is determined by soil resistivity and other factors. The reaction would be:

$$Fe° - 2e \rightarrow Fe^{++} \text{ in clay} \qquad (2.04)$$

$$\frac{1}{2} O_2 + H_2O + 2e \rightarrow 2OH^- \text{ in gravel} \quad (2.05)$$

A similar situation obtains wherever a pipeline passes under a paved road or body of water. In addition to the specific effects of road salt and other conditions, oxygen is excluded from these areas so pipe under the crossing (the most difficult to reach if repair is needed) is precisely the site where corrosion is inevitable. The normally exposed pipe serves as cathode. The curve for these problems is cathodic protection (Chapter 7).

Pitting and Related Phenomena

In the laboratory, a related set of problems can be demonstrated in deposit corrosion, crevice corrosion, and pitting. These share a growth mechanism in that there is a restricted oxygen supply under the deposit or in the pit or crevice. These areas become the anode, and, hence, are sites of active corrosion. A secondary mechanism tends to make the progress of pitting autocatalytic. The primary anodic product is hydrolyzed, as in the following reaction:

$$Fe^{++} + 2OH^- \rightarrow Fe(OH)_2 \qquad (2.06)$$

The mechanism of pit propagation is illustrated in Figure 2.06.

The base of the pit is anodic, and metal dissolves there to form ions. These ions will diffuse toward the mouth of the pit and hydrolyze to give a hydroxide deposit. There will be a net increase in acidity within the pit as hydroxyl ions are consumed, although some of them will come from the external region where alkali is being produced. The acid reaction within a pit also can be used to show if a pit

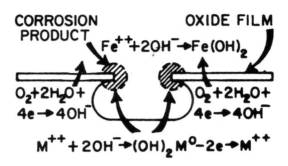

FIGURE 2.06 *Pitting mechanism.*

is active. The normal test uses indicator paper. If this shows an acid reaction, the pit is active. In the example cited, the anodic pit was working against a surrounding cathodic region of filmed metal with free access to oxygen. Any other cathode, such as an electroplated coating of a more cathodic metal, also would be effective

Pits can be of varying shapes. In cases where intergranular material is anodic to the surrounding grains, the form of attack will tend to follow the grain boundaries. Intergranular attack is related closely to pitting, though it may be convenient to distinguish between the two when cataloging cases of corrosion.

The propagation of pitting is well-understood, although its initiation is not. Both aspects are important in the practical case. Pitting initiation is certainly a statistically determined process; this means that the sample(s) chosen must have sufficient total area to have a high probability that some of the potential pit sites will develop pits.

Small samples are not appropriate for pitting studies.

Potential pit sites on many metals appear to be related to structural imperfections at the metal-to-air formed oxide film boundary. On immersion in an aggressive medium, some sites progress to true pits

34

while others do not. It seems much easier to suppress pit initiation than pit propagation. Even gentle flow conditions can prevent the transition from potential site to actual pit for metals such as aluminum or stainless steel, etc. This appears to be effective because it prevents local development of acid and alkaline areas at incipient anodes and cathodes, respectively.

There also is evidence for the requirement of attaining a critical pitting potential for pit development in some materials (such as stainless steels). Such potentials must be interpreted with caution, but can certainly be used to rank relative pitting tendencies on various materials.

Other ranking procedures can be used for pitting, at least in a general sense. Stainless steels and other materials will pit to some extent in pure water at 300°C (572°F) or above. As the material is changed from 300 series stainless to higher alloy material and to super alloys, the pits will be increasingly needlelike, if they occur at all.

A number of other corrosion phenomena are closely related to pitting. Waterline corrosion is an example that may be found earlier in beakers or in large process vessels. The meniscus area of a solution has readier access to atmospheric oxygen than solution at depth. If attack starts, it can be expected to continue, with the cathode at the meniscus and the anode a little below it.

Filiform attack also is related to pitting. It occurs under a protective film (such as the lacquer on tin cans) and is wormlike in appearance. The attack proceeds on a narrow track. The anode in this case is the head of the track, the blue-green color of which shows the presence of ferrous ion. The sides of the track collect oxygen and serve as the cathode. The final deposit is red $Fe(OH)_3$. The head of the track continues in a straight line until it meets a barrier, which causes it to reflect. It is unable to cross a previously formed track. This form of corrosion is discussed in detail by Fontana and Greene.[6]

Filiform corrosion has been noted on a finer scale on Mg alloy AZ91-T4 in 3% NaCl solution. On metallographically polished specimens, this was found in the temperature range 20-30°C (68-86°F) and over a wider temperature range on electropolished specimens, according to Lunder.[7]

References

1. M. Pourbaix, *Lectures on Electrochemical Corrosion* (New York, NY: Plenum, 1976).
2. M. Pourbaix, *Atlas of Electrochemical Equilibria in Aqueous Solutions*, 2nd edition (Houston, TX: NACE, 1974).
3. C.W. Bale, A.D. Pelton, W.T. Thompson, "Generation of Pourbaix diagrams using the FACT database computing system," *Proc. Electrochem. Soc.* 3(1985) (Comp. Aided Acquis. Anal.Corros. Data): pp. 165-79.
4. E.D. Verink et al., NACE-NBS Corrosion Data Program Workshop Summary, *Materials Performance* 26 4(1987): pp. 55 - 60; and NACE-NBS Corrosion Data Program, G.M. Ugiansky et al., CORROSION/86, paper no. 39 (Houston, TX: NACE, 1986).
5. J.T.N. Atkinson, "The Development of High Temperature Pourbaix Diagrams, *Proc. Electrochem. Soc.* 9(1984) (Equil. Diag. Loc. Corros.), pp. 175-84.
6. M.G. Fontana, N.D. Greene. *Corrosion Engineering*, third edition (New York, NY: McGraw Hill, 1986).
7. O. Lunder et al., presentation at NACE Corrosion Research Symposium, 1989.

3

Metallurgical Aspects of Corrosion and its Control

So far, corrosion processes have been examined from an electrochemical point of view. If corrosion cell conditions are known, this can be related (by Faraday's Law) to a certain mass of metal undergoing a corrosion reaction. Now it is necessary to determine the practical consequences, in an engineering sense, of the reaction of that amount of metal.

A rapid review of some of the elements of material science seems to be in order. Any reader who has not studied this subject before should do so or at least consult one of the many excellent introductory books on the subject before proceeding. Two such books are: (1) *The Principles of Engineering Materials* by C.R. Barrett, W.D. Nix, and A.S. Tetelman; and (2) *An Introduction to Metallurgy* by A.H. Cotrell. The purpose of the review is to remind the reader of those aspects of metals most likely to be of significance to a corrosion practitioner.

Corrosion is seen as an undesirable interaction between a functional metal and its total environment, including mechanical effects. It is necessary to understand the norm of uncorroded metal as a starting reference.

The essential feature that distinguishes metals from other materials is the nature of the metallic bond. It is nondirectional, whereas other bonds are highly directional in nature. The nondirectional nature of the metallic bond means that small scale bending is natural for metallic arrays, whereas the more directional bonds would tend to resist bending to the point of fracture. Provided the right kinds of imperfection are available in the structure, a metallic bond seems to be able to transfer its attachment from one atom to another without loss of mechanical integrity. Typically, metals are ductile. But certain metals, particularly when cast, can be more or less brittle for a variety of other reasons. We do not need to go into that amount of detail.

It follows that the most stable arrangements of metal atoms in the solid state are those in which the atoms are assembled as crystals more or less closely packed. Crystals of most metals exist in one of three crystallographic arrangements: (1) close-packed hexagonal (cph) (e.g., Zn, Mg); (2) face-centered cubic (fcc) (e.g., Al, Cu, γ-Fe); and (3) body-centered cubic (bcc) (e.g., α-Fe, β-Ti). Of these three structures, cph and fcc are both closely packed while bcc is somewhat less so. Solid metals consist of three dimensional arrays of somewhat imperfect crystals; typically, the crystals are more or less equiaxed unless prior processing (such as casting or cold working) has left its own characteristic pattern of crystal shape and orientation. The presence of imperfections in metals is, in practice, inevitable. We do not need to go into details but should recognize that the imperfections are crucial to any process that tends to change the shape of a given piece of metal

Metallographic examination of a metal is a relatively inexpensive procedure that can develop a large amount of data about a given metal sample. A small sample is cut out and flattened by successive abrasion with increasingly finer abrasive papers. The finishing is completed by rotary polishing with two successively finer abrasive slurries. After rinsing and drying, the sample is lightly etched. This can expose such features as grain size and shape, and may give an approximate indication of the chemical composition of the material merely by viewing it under the microscope. The scanning electron microscope also can be used to examine the piece, but in this case a more crudely prepared sample may suffice.

The examination of a corroded sample should establish whether the structure is what is to be expected for that material. This enables one to determine whether the corrosion is normal for that structure or is a consequence of its departure from its expected structure. This is helpful in terms of proposing remedies. The corrosion engineer should, of course, be familiar with the structures of all materials whose corrosion behavior is being assessed.

When a metal is strained beyond its elastic limit, the individual crystals distort by the movement of dislocations along the most closely packed planes of the crystal. These are 110 planes for bcc materials, such as steel, and 111 planes for fcc materials, such as aluminum. In effect, in what is called slipping each atom involved in such movements will move over by one unit of spacing at a time in the crystal. The aggregate of many such movements can be observed readily and will result in distortion and hardening of the crystal in question. Once a particular crystal is heavily worked in this manner, further straining of the metal structure will result in distortion of some other crystal until all crystals have been distorted heavily. All metals in wrought form will have undergone structural changes of this nature. If the metal originally contained small amounts of nonmetallic inclusions, these will now be distributed in a manner consistent with the metal working process, e.g., aligned in the direction of rolling. If the cold-worked metal is annealed now (heated above its recrystallization temperature), three processes occur:

(1) Residual stresses will be relieved;

(2) Grains of the existing metal will recrystallize, beginning with those most severely distorted; and

(3) All new grains or crystals will attempt to grow larger; eventually some of the larger grains will assimilate the smaller ones, and the final structure will be coarse-grained.

The process is still more complex where there is an allotropic transformation or when there is a change in solubility of some constituent, in addition to the effects of annealing.

Figures 3.01 and 3.02 (on following page) show one example of the phenomena, allotropy and solubility change, respectively. In each case, a strategy can be worked out to develop technically useful hardening and strengthening of the materials represented by the phase diagrams.

In the case of steel, there is a typical eutectoid reaction at 0.8 Wt% C and 723°C (1,333°F). For a steel of 0.08% C at a temperature above 723°C (1,333°F), a single phase of austenitic (γ) is present with carbon in solid solution. If this γ solid solution is cooled to below the eutectoid temperature, the stable condition is nearly pure ferrite (α iron) with little dissolved carbon and a second phase of cementite (Fe_3C).

Diffusion is required to effect this separation. Of course, diffusion is relatively slow in solids that are well below their melting point (or solidus temperature). Consequently, moderate rates of cooling will lead to a two-phase structure in which the diffusion distance required to effect the structure is small. This leads to the classically platelike structure of pearlite, which consists of alternating lamellae of ferrite and cementite. The slower the cooling rate, the coarser the pearlitic structure. The coarsest structure obtains when the steel is furnace-cooled. So-called normalized steel results from withdraw-

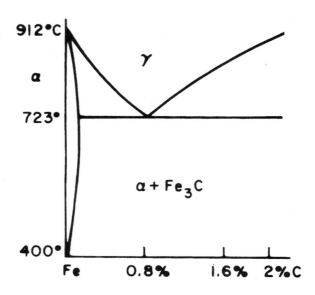

FIGURE 3.01 *A portion of the iron carbide phase diagram.*

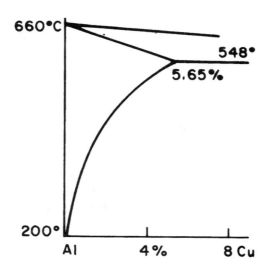

FIGURE 3.02 *A portion of the aluminum copper phase diagram.*

ing the metal from a furnace, the temperature of which is in the austenizing range, and allowing it to cool in still air. The pearlite will be relatively fine; it will require microscopic examination at about 600X or more for convenient visual resolution of its structure. If the cooling rate of the hot austenite is much greater (e.g., by water quenching), there is insufficient time for the formation of even fine pearlite by diffusion. At a much lower temperature, 5,200°C (9,392°F), there is a diffusionless transformation to a distorted tetragonal structure termed martensite. This is extremely hard and brittle, and can be seen under the microscope to be fine needlelike crystals. These crystals can be blunted by heating to slightly higher temperatures (400°C [752°F]). The resulting steel is still relatively hard and strong, but tougher and somewhat more ductile.

In the case of Al-Cu alloys, the hardening treatment can be explained more simply. Typically, an Al 4% Cu alloy is held a little below the eutectic temperature for some time to put all the copper into solid solution. This is then quenched in water to give a supersaturated (hence, metastable) solid solution of Cu in Al at ambient temperature. On aging for a few days at room temperature, or a few hours at (for example) 100°C (210°F), alloys of this general type will increase in hardness, developing maximum hardness and strength because of the precipitation of submicroscopic particles of $CuAl_2$. This process is referred to as age or precipitation hardening. Note that the phase diagrams cannot predict the detail of the hardening and strengthening technology. However, they can identify systems where hardening strategies are likely to be effective.

The thermal and mechanical history of a particular metal or alloy can be inferred to some extent by examining it with an optical or electron microscope. Not only are the clues from the metal itself important, but the amount, extent, and morphology of impurities also are significant. Sulfur impurities in carbon steels are highly damaging if present as FeS, for example.

This compound remains as a low-melting eutectic below the solidus temperature of the steel. This eutectic wets the individual grains and becomes thinly dispersed along the grain boundaries, causing hot shortness and brittleness when cold. Corrosion resistance also suffers. The same amount of sulfur in the form of MnS is much less objectionable. Manganese sulfide has a higher melting point and a nonwetting character. MnS has little effect on corrosion resistance of plain carbon steel.

Metals

The classic research in the field of corrosion of pure annealed single crystals was performed by Gwathmey and coworkers.[1] A single crystal of copper was ground to spherical form and subjected to anodic attack in phosphoric acid. Under these conditions, it was found that the corrosion rate perpendicular to cube faces was only 70% of that perpendicular to the octahedral faces, and the sphere eventually became an octahedron as corrosion progressed. Only the close-packed octahedral faces were developed by the corrosion process.

Another way of expressing the result is that the close-packed planes become slightly anodic to all other faces. The net result is that corrosion of single crystal samples will lead to development of close-packed faces or facets, and that irregularly oriented material will tend to disappear early in the corrosion process.

Commercially pure materials will show impurities, grain boundaries, dislocations, and other crystal imperfections, and often residual or applied stresses to the corrodent. These will add to the effects of orientation in leading to the formation of local anodes and cathodes. Thus, the corrosion pattern of such a commercially pure material is quite complex. As corrosion proceeds, the originally anodic material may corrode out locally, and some other anode will take over. This could lead to more or less uniform overall corrosion.

On the other hand, if the original anode stays anodic, there will be some sort of localized corrosion. This can happen, for example, if the grain boundary or a small zone adjacent to the grain boundary is anodic to the grains. The result, in this case, will be intergranular corrosion. A similar situation obtains in pitting once the pits have developed, and pitting can be expected to continue (Chapter 2).

Single Phase Alloys

Alloy corrosion is more complicated. If the alloy itself has a single-phase structure, it will behave more or less as a pure metal in its corrosion pattern. A single-phase brass (70% Cu 30% Zn) is an interesting case. The free energy of formation of the solid solution is about 4 kcal/mole so the alloy is somewhat more reluctant to dissolve than would be expected from a mixture of zinc and copper. The first stage of reaction is dissolution of the entire alloy. Once there is both copper and zinc in solution the secondary copper deposition reaction can occur at the cathode, and corrosion proceeds on this basis. The previous alternative cathode reactions polarize quite strongly.

The net effect is layer-type dezincification, in which the redeposited copper mimics the physical form of the original brass anode. The redeposited copper is spongy and devoid of mechanical strength. The cure for this phenomenon is to add a little arsenic to the original brass (other group 5 elements also will do). This inhibits cathodic redeposition of copper, and the brass will not suffer dezincification. Plug type dezincification is an alternative form of attack. In this case, the process is concentrated in discrete areas (plugs) under the corrosion product.

Dezincification is more of a problem with modern brasses than with many of the early ones. An example is shown in Figure 15.02. Older refining techniques sometimes left the refined metals with sufficient group 5 impurities to avoid the problem of dezincification. Based on current knowledge, brasses should never be used in water service unless they are inhibited. Brass hardware on boats or in plumbing service are examples where the omission of group 5 inhibition can lead to early loss of function in service.

Many other single-phase alloys with one fairly reactive component can also be subject to demetallification reactions. Such attack is usually restricted to a particular environment. For example, nickel can be leached out from monel only in a combination of chlorides and sulfides. Chlorides alone will not lead to this attack.

Multiphase Alloys

Another case of selective corrosion is the graphitization of grey cast iron. Here, the carbon flakes act as cathode, and the iron phase corrodes out. The physical form of the casting is maintained, but again it has no mechanical strength once the iron has been eaten away. This can occur in cast iron water pipe and similar structures over a long period of exposure. This form of attack is more severe in soils contaminated with particular bacterial species.

Multiphase alloys of all kinds have obvious built-in anodes and cathodes. Of course, impurities may also act in this sense. Once the anode is determined, that part of the alloy will corrode as expected. Normal corrosion rules, as for a separated anode and cathode in the same environment, can be expected to apply.

From a corrosion point of view, carbon steel is an interesting and highly complex material. The two phases observed in non-heat treated structures are αFe and Fe_3C. The former is usually referred to as ferrite. Pearlite is an eutectoid structure consisting of alternating plates of Fe and Fe_3C. Even without impurities, there is automatic availability of local anodes and cathodes. More significant to the corrosion process is the presence of discrete impurities that are both cathodic and semiconducting in nature. Millscale, often found as a surface layer on hot rolled steel, is the most common such offender. It should always be removed. FeS is one impurity that generally leads to poor corrosion performance, though MnS is much less damaging. Sulfides in general are both cathodic and semiconducting. Any corrosion product containing sulfides is, therefore, unlikely to be protective. On the other hand, impurities that are insulators, such as silicates, are reasonably innocuous. Heat-treated steel has a complex structure including at least martensite. Normally, martensite is extremely fine-grained and difficult to resolve under the microscope.

Polishing the surface of a test piece does little to influence the corrosion rate of a specimen. However, it may to some extent delay the onset of corrosion or formation of scales such as $CaCO_3$.

There may be a critical size below which cathodes are ineffective. In the case of age-hardened aluminum alloys, such as Al-4% Cu, properly aged materials show much finer precipitates than overaged alloys of the same composition. The overaged materials will have much poorer corrosion resistance to attack by chloride containing solutions.

Grain boundaries often can show electrochemical differences from surrounding grains, particularly in the presence of the many dislocations that result from working operations. Exfoliation corrosion, following the direction of extrusion, can be found in a number of strong aluminum alloys. Somewhat akin to this is end-face corrosion of some stainless steels in which inclusions aligned in the fabrication direction allow rapid ingress of aggressive corrodents (Figure 6, Appendix B).

Stainless Steel

Austenitic stainless steels deserve special mention. Their corrosion resistance stems from the phenomenon of passivity, as will be discussed in Chapter 16. One way to risk loss of passivity is to sensitize the stainless steels. This can happen if the material is given a

44

stress relief anneal or if it is welded. In this case, there will be a region of sensitized material formed in the heat-affected zone near the weld. This topic will be considered later. Sensitized stainless steels should never be used; if sensitized stainless can survive an environment, a cheaper material would have sufficed. The topic of stainless steel will be covered in detail in Chapter 16.

Materials Selection

Materials selection is a subject that requires consummate care. It will be considered in detail in Chapter 15.

Reference

1. A.T. Gwathmey et al., *Trans. Electrochem. Soc.* 211 (1940): pp. 77; and 1947, pp. 91, 99.

4

The Corrosion Product as a Factor in Corrosion Control

When formed at the site of corrosion, corrosion product films often reduce the corrosion rate. Factors that influence the size of this effect are:

- Solubility of the corrosion product,
- Its adhesion to and fit with the underlying metal,
- Its permeability to various chemical species,
- Its electrical resistivity, and
- Mechanical integrity.

Soluble corrosion products can yield films other than at the site of corrosion. Such films are unlikely to be protective.

The concept of the protective nature of oxide films originated with Pilling and Bedworth.[1] They emphasized the relative sizes of the metal and the oxide formed. Where the corrosion product is close to the same size as the underlying metal it has the highest chance of being protective. In addition, for best bonding film and metal should crystallize in a compatible crystal structure. In most cases, a cubic oxide or other corrosion product is the most desirable since most metals crystallize in the cubic system.

Where the oxide lattice parameter is much smaller than that of the parent metal, the metal develops voids and cannot be protective. Where the lattice parameter of the oxide is much larger, Pilling and Bedworth predicted the oxide would eventually tend to crack and spall off.[1] Strictly speaking, this applies only to films that grow by inward diffusion of oxide ion. But even here there is an exception, as noted in Chapter 5. If the underlying metal is thin enough and is above its creep temperature, the metal may stretch and allow the oxide to remain protective. Where the oxide grows by outward diffusion of metal ion, there can be no volume constraint on a growing oxide. Provided it can deform plastically in response to the compressive stress, it may remain protective.

It is a matter of experimentation to find out how protective a given film can be. Outstanding films, such as Al_2O_3, Fe_3O_4, or other spinels, are logical target films. Data is needed on film properties, as outlined in the first paragraph of this section. Resistance of the film to erosion also is important as is a reasonable match between the coefficients of thermal expansion of the film and substrate.

Tailoring of films is important in developing erosion resistance of the film on cupro-nickels and aluminum bronzes. It has been found that these films resist erosion best when they contain some iron. Therefore, small additions of iron to the original cupro-nickel alloys are appropriate. The same effect can result from iron introduced upstream (Chapter 6).

The formation of magnetite in boilers is a fortunate example of a film with a cubic structure that fits the underlying metal well, coupled with low solubility and electrical resistivity. Magnetite is the simplest example of a spinel type oxide, the general form of which is given by RO, R'_2O_3. In magnetite, both R and R' happen to be iron. Other spinels could have R consisting of iron, nickel, cobalt, etc., while R' could be aluminum or chromium as well as ferric iron.

The corrosion product film on chromium stainless steels has R as Fe^{++} and R' as Cr^{+++}. For chrome nickel stainless steels, such as the 300 series, RO would be a solid solution of FeO and NiO, with R' being Cr^{+++}. Many superalloys show R as some combination of Fe, Co, and Ni with R' being Cr^{+++}, as before. An Fe-Al alloy (approximately Fe-Al 18%) has a highly protective oxide film with R being Fe^{++} and R' being Al^{+++}. Unfortunately, this material is intolerant of interstitials and is difficult to work, besides having a relatively low strength at high temperature.

Single oxides also can show good properties; Al_2O_3 is the best known example, and BeO is excellent, too. Protective films of Fe_2O_3 also can be formed on steels in aqueous media in the presence of a number of inhibitors and inhibitor combinations. Useful corrosion resistance can result from small additions of aluminum to copper, silver, etc. For example, in the case of silver, an alloy results that can have a compact, protective aluminum oxide film formed on exposure to steam in an autoclave. This gives a close approach to the desired goal of a stainless silver that does not need to be polished.

One of the larger applications of protective corrosion product films is in the weathering steels. In this case, low alloy steels are exposed to atmospheric attack and form a reasonably protective and attractive oxide. This takes over a year to come to a stable and pleasing color.

Atmospheric Corrosion

The atmospheric corrosion of metals is the result of an important application of the typical metal. The normal corrodents consist of oxygen and water as vapor or as an adsorbed film on the surface, together with particulate debris and contaminants, such as sulfur dioxide, salt particles, etc. Normally, the washing action of rain is, to some extent, beneficial.

The rate of development of atmospheric corrosion product film is dependent on the conditions of exposure, and, in particular, on the initial conditions of exposure. If a metallic structure or test piece is first exposed at the beginning of a long spell of good weather — with low humidity — the initial film growth tends to be more protective than if the weather starts off with a poorer initial spell. This makes comparison of corrosion in the short term particularly difficult.

The strong tendency of chloride ions to adsorb on a metal surface was mentioned in Chapter 1. If this occurs at an early stage in atmospheric corrosion, the local high gradients in charge density preclude the formation of a film with optimum protective properties. There will be weaknesses in the oxide film associated with the chloride contamination, and pitting and other damage is more probable.

Airborne acid oxides, salts, and soots are the most objectionable contaminants in atmospheric corrosion situations. Surfaces exposed to direct impingement of rain can be less sensitive to contaminants than sheltered surfaces because impurities do not have the chance to accumulate. The presence of sulfur dioxide from the combustion of fuels and so forth, and the presence of salt spray from the ocean or from deicing salts are the most common contaminants. Both sulfur dioxide and soots are becoming less evident locally in industrial environments as more care is being taken to protect the environment, although acid rain is ubiquitous. The trend with salt is less predictable, and in any event, highly seasonal.

From an aesthetic point of view, metals may be expected either to remain bright or to assume a desirable patination, which limits further attack by the atmosphere. A bright finish is the goal for chromium-plated stainless steel and the like, whereas a deliberate patination is in order for copper or for the weathering steels. Metals whose oxides are not particularly protective or will yield unsightly (though protective) films often are painted.

Considerable data has been collected on the atmospheric corrosion of metals in rural, marine, and industrial areas. Because of the diminution in pollution, definitive industrial sites are no longer available. The increasing use of road salt also makes it more difficult to find a site without some marine features, and acid rain complicates the picture. Nevertheless, long-term data on atmospheric corrosion traditionally has involved the use of large sample racks, which in turn must be protected from enterprising small boys. An interesting and less costly approach is Alcan's spool test, which merely needs an inconspicuous wire wound spool on a utility pole.[2] The low cost and high survival rate of such samples makes them an attractive test method. Samples must be in the form of wire. The effect of contact with disparate materials can be evaluated easily.

In some cases, the difficulty in using a metal will relate to its joining to other structural materials. Aluminum alloys generally show good atmospheric corrosion resistance, though some will discolor. Aluminum joints to steel, wood, concrete, and so forth call for careful design. Some examples are given in Chapter 9.

Unsuspected environmental factors may be present, too. The ventilation system for a new university gymnasium was constructed of stainless steel, but failed by perforation in less than 10 years. Chloride contamination from perspiration in the ducting from the shower areas caused the stainless steel to pit to an objectionable extent. The replacement material was reinforced plastic.

Weathering Steels

The atmospheric corrosion rate of steels is generally too high for their successful use unless they are painted. However, it was long known that certain alloy additions, such as Cu and Ni, would give a low alloy steel whose corrosion product film would be more protective and reasonably pleasing in appearance. This approach has led to the production of a number of alloy steels for outdoor use without painting. The color of the oxide film is dark brown with a blue tinge.

In use, steels of this type take a couple of years to attain an oxide film of optimum appearance. During this time in particular the rust may bleed somewhat and discolor the adjacent material. Careful architectural treatment is in order. If chlorides in significant amounts are present, the fully protective film may not be achieved. Buildings or other structures using weathering steel should dry out reasonably promptly. If the steel, or part of it, remains wet or is in contact with wet concrete, its corrosion resistance to such immersed corrosion is no better than any other class of steel. Such surfaces should be painted.

Weathering steels have another advantage for remote structures, where the cost of delivery of the steel can be a highly significant contribution to total cost. Their higher strength allows the use of a lighter structure, thus reducing shipping costs. Power transmission lines in remote locations are an excellent example. Another advantage: The brittle to ductile transition temperature of weathering steels as a class is usually lower than that for the plain carbon steels. The maintenance-free properties of weathering steels in remote areas is optimum because of the freedom from contaminants, such as chloride.

Prediction of the service life of steels in atmospheric exposure is important. A paper by Legault and Preban proposed the use of the relationship:[3]

$$\Delta W = Kt^N \qquad\qquad (4.01)$$

for relating the penetration ΔW (in mils) to the exposure time t (in years), where K and N are constants. For parabolic kinetics, $N = 0.5$, etc. Values of K and N can be determined for relatively short exposures and used to predict penetrations by corrosion at much longer times. It should be noted that the relative ranking of steels at one-year exposure is not necessarily the same as their ranking at 10 years. However, by this technique, data for 10+ years behavior can be predicted from two sets of tests lasting up to only about two years. While this approach is essentially empirical, it does provide a good practical tool for predicting longer-term corrosion behavior from shorter-term tests.

Predictions of the values of the constants K and N in Equation (4.01) also can be made from the chemical analysis of the steel, at least for the Chicago site used in the study. This enables the specific effect of particular alloying elements to be rationalized to some extent.

A more complete treatment of oxidation rates has to consider movements of charged species through a solid electrolyte, the oxide film. This is regarded as an ideal solution of the imperfections that render the transport possible. The treatment is given in an appendix by Hurling in *Evans' Second Supplementary Volume*.[4] The net rate of transport, v, is given by:

$$v = \lambda C \; \frac{kT}{h} \; e\text{-}\Delta G^*/RT \; [e \; \text{-}\alpha\lambda Fd\phi/RTdx \; -$$

$$(1 + \lambda \frac{d\,\ell nC}{dx}) \; e \; (1 - \alpha) \; \lambda zFd\phi/RTdx] \qquad (4.02)$$

Where:
λ = distance between equilibrium positions for migrating species
C = concentration species being transported
k = Boltzmann's constant
h = Planck's constant
ΔG^* = activation energy
R = gas constant
T = absolute temperature
ϕ = inner potential
x = distance in direction of transport
α = symmetry factor.

This is obviously similar in form to the Butler-Volmer equation. The evaluation of this equation can be made by a series expansion of the exponential terms, together with simplifying assumptions.

This approach leads to the parabolic equation $y^2 = kt$ for thick, yet coherent, films at high temperature; the inverse logarithmic equation:

$$\frac{1}{y} = A - B \log t \qquad (4.03)$$

at low temperatures and small film thickness, and to the cubic equation:

$$y^3 = k_c t + \text{constant}$$

Where:

$$\pm \lambda z\Delta G^*/1.72RT \; > y \; > \pm \lambda\Delta G^*/2.32RT \qquad (4.04)$$

These three kinetic forms represent particular limiting cases of the general equation and do not call for any particular assumptions regarding the nature of the film or the species responsible for transport within it. It also permits an interpretation of the constants in these rate equations, in terms of fundamental parameters.

Corrosion by Water and Steam

The next most common environment after the atmosphere will be water and steam. The extreme aqueous environment is seawater and various brines followed by brackish water, fresh water and distilled water. Extremely pure water can be very aggressive, at least until a trace of the corroding metal can build up. Steam tends to be less variable, except where zero solids practice has allowed volatile amines or ammonia to build up and pose a threat to copper alloys.

The corrosion product formed by reaction with water or steam is typically quite similar to that produced by reaction with air. This is in line with the presence of an adsorbed moisture layer whenever air with a relative humidity of 40% or greater is in contact with a typical solid.

Corrosion of steel in waters is much less dependant on the composition of the particular steel than one would expect from atmospheric corrosion data. It is not possible to enhance the corrosion resistance of steel in waters, at least in the composition range that includes carbon and low alloy steels. Extra protection would have to come from protective coatings or inhibitors, where appropriate, or by going to different materials, such as stainless steel.

An example of corrosion by water or steam is found in low pressure boilers where the environment would be deaerated water or the steam produced from it. Standard industrial practice involves close control of water chemistry, including maintaining a very low oxygen level; consequently, the steam also is controlled. Under these conditions the corrosion product would be magnetite, which would be quite protective.

Corrosion in Space

Deterioration processes can be at work in high vacuum systems or in space. The critical factor is whether the metal has had its normal oxide film stripped or not. In lab systems, this corresponds to about

10^{-10} atm and is, of course, automatic in space. The first effect is that volatile components are drawn off from the metal. Zinc would be lost from brass, for example. Alloy selection for use in space must, of course, avoid volatiles completely.

Loss of volatiles is hindered by the presence of even thin oxide films and does not happen in run of the mill vacuum systems. In space, there also are effects due to metal dislodgement from impact by high speed particles, whether ions, neutrons, dust, or larger particles. It is virtually impossible to test for these effects other than in space.

Similar considerations apply to other materials, especially polymers. The higher dosage of UV radiation also is a potent factor in causing damage.

Passivity

Passivity and inhibition are intimately related as corrosion control measures. Passivity usually refers to materials which readily form insoluble corrosion product films that stifle the anodic reaction and cause a marked polarization of the anode. Inhibition serves to modify the environment by addition of small amounts of so-called inhibitors, which help promote the formation of insoluble films and, hence, stifle the corrosion reaction. Most inhibitors produce films on the anode. Both passivity and inhibition are of interest to corrosion engineers only when their action is reliable and when it reduces the residual corrosion current to a small value.

The classic case of passivity is iron in concentrated nitric acid. If a piece of steel is immersed in the acid and then in copper sulfate solution, there will be no deposit of copper on the steel until its passivity is destroyed. Striking the steel with a glass rod will do this. In this case, the passive film is much too flimsy to serve a technically useful purpose.

Combining steel with chromium or a combination of chromium and nickel in sufficient amounts will lead to the possibility of a much more robust film, as discussed earlier in the chapter. In this case, its structure will be a spinel of the $RO.R'_2O_3$ type, where R' is Cr and R is Fe or a solution of Ni in Fe. Such films are easily formed and maintained if an oxidant or anodic potential is available. In the absence of these, the film may be vulnerable to damage by a species such as chloride ion. The general term for alloy steels of this type is stainless steel. Their corrosion resistance is good in oxidizing environments, although they may be extremely vulnerable to attack by even traces of chlorides under conditions where the film is not self-repairing. In cases where oxygen is excluded, as in some boiler and reactor, etc., applications, there is some doubt that the extra cost of the alloying elements is justified. Under these conditions, cheaper and stronger materials also have low corrosion rates.

The development of passivity can be followed by anodic potential vs logarithmic corrosion current plots, as shown in Figure 4.01 in the Evans diagram form.

Figure 4.01a shows the anodic E vs log i curves where the applied current is gradually increased. Until point a is reached, a more or less normal corrosion situation obtains. For this part of the curve, anodic dissolution occurs, together with some film growth as point a is reached. A discontinuous potential jump occurs from a to b. Figure 4.01b shows the result of controlling potential and monitoring current. When the potential at point a is reached, there is a sudden drop in corrosion current to point c. This current stays essentially constant to point d, where again there is an increase in current as the potential is increased. The c to d region typically involves a protec-

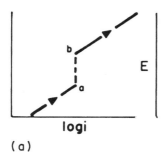

(a)

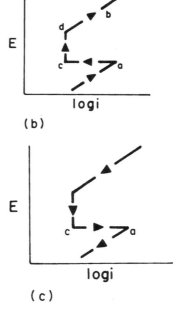

(b)

(c)

FIGURE 4.01

E vs log i plots for passive material (schematic): (a) anodic E vs log i curves where the applied current is gradually increased; (b) result of controlling potential and monitoring current; and (c) reversal of process (may be instability in c to a zone).

tive film 50 to 100 D thick and with definite, but small, electronic conductivity. On reversing the process, both of these curves follow Figure 4.01c, though there may be considerable instability in the c to a zone.

The interpretation of these phenomena is that, as the anodic potential is applied, the corrosion current increases in the normal fashion. When point a is reached, there is sufficient filming of the anode that the corrosion reaction is strongly retarded, and there is either a drastic drop in current at that potential (sometimes called the Flade potential), or a sharp increase in potential if the corresponding current is maintained. At potentials above the Flade potential, a continuous passive oxide film is maintained and the metal stays passive.

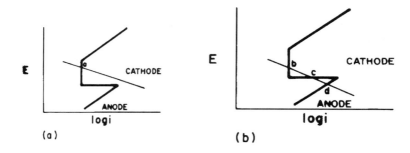

(a)

(b)

FIGURE 4.02 *Role of the cathode in passivity (schematic): (a) combination of the passive anode with a cathode the potential of which is well above the Flade potential; and (b) a less potent cathode. Note the three points of intersection between the anodic and cathodic curves.*

The corrosion implications of the passivity phenomena can be seen in Figure 4.02. Figure 4.02a shows the combination of the passive anode with a cathode the potential of which is well above the Flade potential. In this case, the corrosion current is small. In the case of a less potent cathode, as shown in Figure 4.02b, three points of intersection occur between the anodic and cathodic curve. Point c is of no consequence, as it is electrically unstable and must transfer to either b or d. Point b shows an acceptably low corrosion current and a passive potential, whereas point d shows an active potential and a moderately high corrosion current.

The consequences of the situation shown in Figure 4.02b are of great importance. Since for a given cathode, anode, and environment there can be either acceptable or unacceptable corrosion performance, definite design action has to be taken to ensure that the conditions corresponding to b are maintained and continue to be maintained. This is where the presence of an oxidizing agent, a sufficiently polarized anodic potential, or the presence of a potent cathode is required for satisfactory use of a material (such as stainless steel) the corrosion performance of which results from the passivity. The accidental maintenance of stainless steel at point b is no guarantee the system will not be disturbed to point d on Figure 4.02b. In the absence of repassivating influences, the electrical contacting of a passive material to an active material, or the damaging of the passive film mechanically or otherwise, can lead to major corrosion problems. Successful prior use of stainless steel is not in itself a sufficient criterion for future satisfactory application. It should be noted that the chloride level capable of causing real problems with stainless steel is low, a few ppm or less. The problems encountered often can start from pitting or crevice corrosion. Pitting rates of 5 mm or more per year can be expected on stainless steels under crevice conditions in chloride-containing solutions near neutral pH.

Some theoretical insight into the pitting process can be gained from knowledge of the structure of metal/electrolyte interfaces. Negative ions (such as Cl^-) can adsorb on the interface in the inner Helmholtz plane, particularly during the initial stages of corrosion. The small size of the Cl^- ion leads to a profound disturbance in potential gradient in the oxide film in its vicinity. This enhances the possibility of local electrochemical processes. For further details, refer to Bockris and Reddy.[5]

Pitting in high purity water at above 350°C (662°F) in boilers can be a problem. If pitting is encountered, the pits will be relatively small in diameter, about <1 mm. Progressing from stainless steels to still more resistant alloys (monel, Inconel, etc.), pitting will be of still smaller diameter, if at all. The diameter of the pits gives a crude indication of the resistance to corrosion the metal exhibits.

Inhibition

A corrosion inhibitor is a substance which slows down a corrosion reaction when added in a minor amount to the environment. The action of the inhibitor can be to slow down the anodic or cathodic reaction, or to generate a reasonably thick film and, thus, increase the electrolytic resistance of the circuit. There can be no effect on the metallic part of the circuit. The subject of inhibitors was covered in the monograph by Bregman,[6] which was updated and extended by Nathan[7] a decade later. These two books should be consulted by those who wish to study the subject more deeply.

Inhibitors can be used to retard corrosion by aqueous solutions in general, or to limit corrosion by the moisture film associated with atmospheric corrosion. In the case of pickling operations, where acids are intended to remove oxides, etc. with minimal attack on base metal, inhibitors used often are referred to as pickling restrainers.

An important use of inhibited acids is to clean out corrosion products from various industrial systems during shutdown periods. The acid normally used is inhibited hydrochloric acid, although the more expensive sulfuric and sulfamic acids also find use. Desirable inhibitors must reduce metal corrosion without slowing down solution of corrosion products present. In nuclear plants, an important goal is to remove as much of the radioactive corrosion product or deposit as possible; citric acid may be used, perhaps combined with other chelating agents. In any event, the final step must be careful flushing to remove all traces of acids before returning equipment to service.

The technology of inhibitors is undergoing rapid change. The

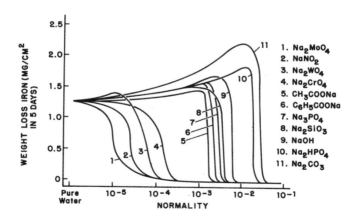

FIGURE 4.03   *Oxidizing and nonoxidizing inhibitors (after Vukasovich and Farr[8]).*

earliest inhibitors were typically discrete inorganic chemicals or mixtures of inorganic chemicals, and of a non-proprietary nature. It seems fitting to consider the inorganic inhibitors first, despite the environmental or other shortcomings of many.

Aqueous systems have two main classes of inhibitors: (1) ones that exhibit oxidizing properties; and (2) ones that rely on dissolved oxygen for their film-forming function. The most obvious oxidizing inhibitors are chromates, although there are others, such as nitrites and possibly molybdates. Whether molybdates also require the presence of an oxidant is not definitively resolved. Molybdates do not inhibit the corrosion of strictly film-free iron in an air-free solution. But there appear to be beneficial effects on naturally filmed iron. In addition, molybdates react synergistically with a wide range of film formers and have not been shown to have undesirable environmental side effects. Non-oxidizing inhibitors include carbonates, silicates, phosphates, and others as shown in Figure 4.03.

As can be seen from the figure, the oxidizing inhibitors are effective at much lower concentrations than those needed for nonoxidizing inhibitors. The films tend to be cubic γ Fe_2O_3, in some cases modified with incorporated anoinic fragments from the inhibitor, often via an initial adsorption process. The films in the presence of inhibitors strongly resemble passive films and are similarly subject to some loss of effectiveness in the presence of chlorides. Larger doses of inhibitors are required when chlorides are present. The choice of inhibitors often is dictated by environmental considerations. Of those listed, chromates are particularly toxic, and phosphates can serve as a nutrient for undesirable growths in the downstream water system. Molybdates may well become an important and relatively nontoxic replacement for chromates, particularly since they have powerful synergistic reactions with a variety of other inhibitors.[9] Additional relevant papers on corrosion inhibitors can be found in the May 1986 issue of *Materials Performance*.

The environmental requirement to eliminate chromates can give rise to a number of other problems. The previous view, that chromate concentration could be drastically reduced by using mixtures of many inhibitors, is no longer acceptable in most jurisdictions. Many inhibitor packages are now based on silicates.[10]

To be effective, high concentrations of silicates inhibitors may be needed, which can lead to precipitation of Ca or Mg salts; therefore, a lower concentration is used and is backed up with other inhibitors, such as molybdates, glassy phosphates, etc. In some cases, as in alkaline cooling waters, the need for on-line analytical methods has led to the development of specialized marker techniques.[11]

Most present technical activity in the inhibitor field relates to organic inhibitors, which must be classified somewhat differently. The earliest examples were soluble oils and benzoates, both of which can adsorb on the metal surface and reduce the area available for reaction. While adsorption is a component of the effectiveness of organic inhibitors generally, it also is convenient to classify their mechanisms of reaction.

The classification proposed by O.L. Riggs in Nathan's book is as follows.[7] He sees the adsorbing species as being either proton acceptors, electron acceptors, or mixed molecules. The last named show both functions in different parts of the same (large) molecule. Proton acceptors will accept hydrogen ions and migrate toward the cathode. The group can be expected to be effective in acid media and includes anilines, quinolines, ureas, and aliphatic amines. Electron acceptors, on the other hand, are generally effective at anodic sites. They are most effective for reactions under anodic control. In addition, passivating inhibitors belong in this group. Examples include organic peroxides, thiols, and selenides. The classification could be regarded as also including organic chromate and nitrites. Mixed molecules will show both functions at different sites, may be a salt of a proton and electron acceptor, or may be effective as a hydrolysis product formed in solution. More complete details can be found in the reference cited.

With organic inhibitors, selective adsorption is an important component of their effectiveness. The adsorption process is dependent on the surface potential of the exposed metal so the effectiveness of these inhibitors will be controlled by the actual surface potential. Given combinations of metals in particular environments will have more or less predictable surface potentials. Consequently, an empirical approach to the selection of inhibitors for particular combinations can give correct results. The concept of surface potential can only be mentioned in a treatment at this level; interested readers should refer to Bockris and Reddy.[7]

Intense competition exists in the development of proprietary organic inhibitors. These tend to be offered for sale on an empirical basis without reference to the underlying adsorption theory. Hydrazine is an example of a passivating inhibitor not always recognized as such (see Chapter 7).

A problem with many inhibitors, as shown in Figure 4.03 is that an inadequate dose is not only ineffective, but can actually increase the overall corrosion.[12] The passivating effect of inhibitors will obviously affect the anode potential and exchange current (or ease of polarization) at the anode. The effect of an inadequate dose of inhibitor is complex; in the worst case, there could be a small anode-large cathode situation, and serious pitting could ensue. This is particularly damaging for cooling systems. Automobile cooling systems merit more detailed consideration.

The need for antifreeze in the automobile cooling water systems is well-established. This application probably will be joined by a variety of roof top solar heating units for domestic hot water heating, etc., which will pose a somewhat similar problem unless air can be excluded permanently. Ethylene glycol water mixtures seem to be the correct technical choice for the automotive application. The corrosion problem stems from hydrolysis of the glycol to organic acids in the hot solution with its inevitable loading of dissolved oxygen. This sets up a need for a reserve of alkaline material to neutralize these acids; this neutralizer has to be replenished regularly on an on-going basis. Experience has shown that borax is a suitable alkali with appropriate buffering characteristics. This controls ferrous corrosion. Zinc, brass, and copper alloys need the addition of a specific inhibitor, such as mercaptobenzothiazole, and the moving parts of the water pump call for soluble oil. Over the past two decades, ways have been found to use the good inhibitive properties of silicates in coolant systems by overcoming the possibility of gel formation. This involves stabilizing the inorganic silicate by copolymerization with a water-soluble organosiloxane polymer.[13] Other coolant inhibitor formulations can be incredibly complex, perhaps with 10 or so special purpose ingredients. It is not wise to mix different brands. The median consumer is well-advised to replace antifreeze on a biannual basis and use equal parts of glycol and water, as this is the most straightforward method of maintaining an effectively inhibited coolant.

The modern trend toward sealed coolant systems for solar collectors and small internal combustion engines might be regarded as lessening the demand for inhibition because of reduced glycol hydrolysis in the absence of air. However, it is hard to eliminate "breathing" of the system entirely, as the temperature (and internal pressure) fluctuate. It is better to regard even sealed systems as subject to the pressure of some oxygen. For solar systems heating potable water, propylene glycol, though more expensive, is preferred to toxic ethylene glycol.

In many applications, the actual cost of the inhibitor is trivial with respect to the potential savings. Under these conditions, the use of any inhibitor is likely to be reasonably economical. Choice may then be based on secondary considerations. Only in those cases involving large volumes of water and large specific flows is the cost of the inhibitor likely to become an important factor. Oil well casings are an example. Here, the choice of inhibitor and technique of application should be based on careful field tests.

The use of inhibitors in oil wells calls for considerable judgment. Continuous injection can be used for open annulus oil or gas wells and for gas lift wells. Both slowly dissolving cartridges and continuous injection pumps can be used. Batch treatment, perhaps at two-week intervals, also can be practiced. A longer term dose of inhibitor can be applied in a squeeze treatment, in which inhibitor is pumped into the well, followed by solvent, and forced into the surrounding formation. This dispersed inhibitor gradually leaches out and may be effective for as long as a year from the time of the original squeeze.

Another segment of the inhibitor field involves the use of additives for the pickling process. Perhaps it is more useful to refer to these compounds as restrainers. These reduce the amount of corrosion associated with the pickling process.

Strongly polar organic molecules, such as aryl sulfonic acids and alkynes, can be effective when they are sufficiently stable to resist degradation in the pickling milieu. Other compounds, some involving arsenic, also can enhance the entry of hydrogen into the work being pickled. For hydrogen-sensitive materials, this can be a problem. In any case, the arsenic compounds involve serious toxicity problems. More alkaline solutions involving complexants may be a safer way to remove oxides. Alternatively, a mild heating operation, such as immersion for some minutes in boiling water, may have to follow to expel hydrogen that otherwise might be retained. Unfortunately, only a portion of the hydrogen can be removed in this fashion.

Anodic Protection

Closely allied to passivity and inhibition is the technique of anodic protection. It can only be applied in those cases where passivity can be achieved and is not a generally applicable method of corrosion control.

In general, when a potential is applied to a corroding anode to intensify the anodic reaction the result is more severe corrosion. However, for those particular anode-environment systems where passivity can occur — and only for those — the anode may be driven into a passive condition. The process is termed "anodic protection" if the residual current is sufficiently low. From the point of view of the E vs log i behavior in Figure 4.02b, this corresponds to starting with a system whose mixed potential and corrosion current are given by point d and polarizing it to point b. This is in the passive range and has a much lower corrosion rate.

One of the simplest techniques for anodic protection is to provide electrical contact to a metal, the potential of which is strongly cathodic. Platinum and palladium are the primary candidates for this technique. Stainless steel, titanium, and so forth, with the addition of a small percentage of either Pt or Pd, will remain passive because of the efficient cathodes brought about by the presence of the noble metal. A more cost-effective use of the noble metal is as a coating, usually electrodeposited or vacuum-evaporated, on the surface of the passivatable material. This coating need not be continuous. A coating with a material cost of a few cents per square foot can be effective.

Platinum or palladium-coated stainless steels are a countermeasure for crevice corrosion, too. The passive film is maintained by the anodic protection applied, and attack cannot be initiated. Similarly, coated tantalum, titanium, or niobium can be used in chloride environments without significant metal loss. Anodes of this type can be used for marine cathodic protection systems or in many industrial electrolytic processes calling for insoluble anodes.

In addition to the anodic protection technique of using noble metal cathodes, it is possible to use impressed current cathodes in which the cathodic current is supplied externally. An example of this is a steel tank for containing sulfuric acid that is either dilute, hot, or both. Steel passivates in cold concentrated acid, but does not passivate in the other media without assistance.

Passivation is achieved by supplying sufficient cathodic current to polarize the tank surface to somewhat above the Flade potential. The power supply must be adequate for this operation; however, once passivation is attained a small cathodic current will be required to maintain passivity. The cathode can be constructed of any suitable inert material. A small current would be required, with the potential being controlled by a potentiostat which senses the potential differences between the tank and a suitable reference electrode.

In many installations where anodic protection is appropriate it is wise to employ fairly sophisticated monitoring systems. Typically, this permits the system to be monitored remotely perhaps by the consultants who designed and installed the system in the first place, in addition to the normal on-site monitoring and alarm system. This provides an extra check. Typically, the cost of computer-transmitted data is very modest.

A possible objection to anodic protection is that the impressed current type is not fail-safe. If the anodic protection failed on a steel tank containing warm dilute sulfuric acid, for example, the entire tank could be destroyed within minutes or hours. It would, therefore, be necessary to provide backup power and/or a suitable sump to receive the entire contents of the tank. More often the result of a failure of the protective current is less catastrophic and can be remedied routinely within a day or two.

Following a power interruption it is, of course, necessary to repassivate the system to its protected potential. Typically, this requires a significantly higher power than would have been needed to maintain passivity in the first place. This may be the determining factor in sizing power units for anodic protection systems.

The definitive text on this subject is *Anodic Protection* by O.L. Riggs and C.E. Locke.[14] This contains a major section on the potentiostat and related electrochemical techniques. It also includes discussion of synergism between anodic protection and inhibitors, and a treatment of sulfuric acid heat exchangers.

References

1. N.B. Pilling, R.E. Bedworth, *J. Inst. Met.* 29 (1923): p. 529.
2. H.P. Godard, *Materials Protection* 2, 6(1963): p. 38.
3. R.A. Legault, A.G. Preban, *Corrosion* 31, 4(1975): pp. 117-122.
4. U.R. Evans, *The Corrosion and Protection of Metals*, second supplementary volume (London, UK: Arnold, 1976).
5. J. O'M. Bockris, A.K.N. Reddy, *Modern Electrochemistry* (New York, NY: Plenum Press, 1970).

6. J.I. Bregman, *Corrosion Inhibitors* (New York, NY: Macmillan, 1963).

7. C.C. Nathan, *Corrosion Inhibitors* (Houston, TX: NACE, 1973).

8. M.S. Vukasovich, J.P.G. Farr, *Materials Protection* 25, 5(1986): pp. 9-18.

9. G.D. Wilcox, D.R. Gabe, M.E. Warwick, *Corrosion Reviews* 6, 4 (1986): pp. 327-65F.

10. A. Marshall, B. Greaves, CORROSION/89, paper no. 439 (Houston, TX: NACE, 1989).

11. B.E. Moriarty, B.E. Hunt, D.R. Malec, CORROSION/89, paper no. 156 (Houston, TX: NACE, 1989).

12. M.J. Pryor, M. Cohen, *J. Electrochem. Soc.* 100 (1953): p. 203.

13. A.N. Pines, et al., US Patent No. 3,341,469 (1967).

14. O.L. Riggs, C.E. Locke, *Anodic Protection* (New York, NY: Plenum, 1981).

5

Oxidation and High Temperature Corrosion

High-temperature corrosion by oxygen of the air or other aggressive gases also is electrochemical in nature, although this is not immediately obvious. The situation is represented in Figure 5.01.

ATMOSPHERE

FIGURE 5.01 *High temperature oxidation.*

The oxide consists of a more or less regular array of M^{++} and $O^{=}$ ions. In the case of oxidation, the former originate at the anode with the reaction:

$$M - 2e = M^{++} \qquad (5.01)$$

while the latter result from a cathodic process such as:

$$\tfrac{1}{2}\, O_2 + 2e = O^{=} \qquad (5.02)$$

At least one ionic species has to migrate through the oxide film. There also must be a flow of electrons between cathode and anode. Once again, the overall process is electrochemical.

Normally, the anodic reaction occurs at the metal/oxide interface. If the oxide film is growing outward, there has to be outward diffusion of metal ion from the anodic site. Outward diffusion of uncharged metal atoms is most unlikely. The balancing cathodic reaction usually occurs at an oxide/atmosphere interface. Even where the film is cracked or porous, there is usually at least a thin adhering oxide. If the oxide film is growing inward, there has to be an inward migration of oxide ions through it.

Again, this is a situation with a separate anode and cathode, and there has to be migration of at least one charged ionic species and an electron flow. In this case, however, the oxide film serves as both ionic and electrolytic conductor. As in the case of the more obviously electrochemical examples of wet corrosion, control can be based on throttling of any one of the four steps of the process. Specific examples will follow later in the chapter. First, the basic requirement for engineering operations at high temperature must be examined.

Energy Conversion and the Need for High Temperature

The oxidation of metals and alloys at high temperature is at the heart of many major problems in current technology. The highest possible efficiency of a power conversion device that derives mechanical energy from chemical energy in any process involving combustion is given by:

$$E = \frac{T_H - T_C}{T_H} \times 100\% \tag{5.03}$$

Where E is the efficiency of conversion of heat to work; T_H is the absolute temperature of the hottest part of the device; and T_C is the absolute temperature of the surroundings which receive waste heat from the process.

Since T_C is usually more or less fixed — typically, the ambient air or water temperature — there is a strong pull to increase T_H. But as T_H increases, so does the associated corrosion problem.

The relationship of conversion efficiency to temperature is immutable. Each and every heat engine or other device for converting heat to work is subject to it. The most typical practical form for conversion of heat to work is a power station with steam turbine-driven generators. The steam is generated in a boiler fueled by either a nuclear reactor or the combustion of fossil fuel. In any event, the search for higher conversion efficiency must use a high temperature, and that can lead to materials problems, including corrosion.

68

The High Temperature Materials Problem

Development of corrosion-resistant alloys for use in gas turbines, superheater tubes in boilers, and the like have been the target of major research efforts for a few decades. Before thinking about this, high-temperature oxidation must be examined from a fundamental point of view.

The ideal solution is a high-temperature oxide that would be as effective a barrier to corrosion as aluminum oxide is on more or less pure aluminum at ambient temperature. What is needed is an insulating oxide that fits the substrate well and can seriously restrict the flow of electricity and/or reactants and products through the film. Unfortunately, the ideal high-temperature oxide has not been found. For realistic fuel purity levels, superheater sections of boilers have ash-contaminated oxidation products that get close to the undesirable liquid oxide regime discussed later in the chapter.

First, it must be determined if a given oxide forms as a result of inward diffusion of oxidant or by outward diffusion of a metallic species. The most direct method of study for this is to decorate the metallic surface with inert markers (e.g., fine platinum wires), and determine if these remain at the surface of the oxide or become buried at a metal/oxide interface. Once the migrating species is identified, ways can be found to hinder that specific migration.

Oxidation of Metals

Generally, oxides are semiconductors. Thus, either a positively or a negatively charged species (not both) is free to migrate through the lattice under an appropriate electric potential. As an example, consider zinc oxide. The structure of zinc oxide is illustrated in Figure 5.02. It consists of a metal excess type oxide in which there are a few extra electrons. These electrons are available for conduction processes as there are adjacent unfilled higher energy levels.

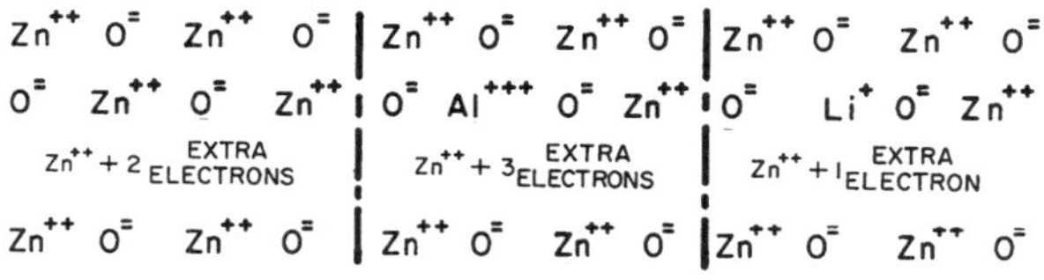

$$
\begin{array}{llll|llll|llll}
Zn^{++} & O^= & Zn^{++} & O^= & Zn^{++} & O^= & Zn^{++} & O^= & Zn^{++} & O^= & Zn^{++} & O^= \\
O^= & Zn^{++} & O^= & Zn^{++} & O^= & Al^{+++} & O^= & Zn^{++} & O^= & Li^+ & O^= & Zn^{++} \\
& Zn^{++} + 2\,\text{EXTRA ELECTRONS} & & & & Zn^{++} + 3\,\text{EXTRA ELECTRONS} & & & & Zn^{++} + 1\,\text{EXTRA ELECTRON} & & \\
Zn^{++} & O^= & Zn^{++} & O^= & Zn^{++} & O^= & Zn^{++} & O^= & Zn^{++} & O^= & Zn^{++} & O^=
\end{array}
$$

FIGURE 5.02 *The arrangement of ions in ZnO.*

If some of the zinc ions are replaced by ions of higher or lower valency, the residual number of available electrons must change. For each Al^{+++} that replaces a Zn^{++} ion, there will be an extra conduction electron. In this case, zinc oxide will become markedly less protective as Al is alloyed with the underlying zinc; conversely, it will become more protective as Li is alloyed with zinc. Because electrons are the current carrying species, ZnO is referred to as an n type semiconductor.

The various characteristic classes of oxides are given in Table 5.01. The meaning of p type semiconduction needs some explanation. For oxides with almost enough electrons to fill available lower energy states, a few "electron holes" remain. It can be shown mathematically by solution of the appropriate Schrodinger equation that the state of affairs that obtains may be represented by postulating that electrons that move about these electron holes have either negative mass or positive charges. Conventionally, positive charge is selected, these oxides being designated as having positive charge carriers, and are thus p type semiconductors.

TABLE 5.01
Characteristics of the Main Classes of Oxides[1]

Semiconductor	Ionic Conduction	Increase in PO_2	Presence of Higher Valency Cations in Oxide	Presence of Lower Valency Cations in Oxide	Example
p Type Metal Deficit Cation Vacancies + Electron Defects	$\tau C \ll 1$ $\tau A = 0$	K_c Increases	K_c Decreases	K_c Increases	CU_2O
n Type Metal Excess Interstitial Cations + Electrons	$\tau C \ll 1$ $\tau A = 0$	K_c Decreases	K_c Increases	K_c Decreases	ZnO
n Type Oxygen Deficit Anion Vacancies + Electrons	$\tau C = 0$ $\tau A \ll 1$	K_c Decreases	K_c Increases	K_c Decreases	Al_2O_3

The influence of stress in the growing oxide and the substrate also is of importance. Stringer has reviewed the origins of such stresses and their effects on the oxide, together with the related topic of oxide adhesion.[2] He shows that a more sophisticated view is needed than the original Pilling Bedworth model, which compares the size of the oxide with that of the metal from which it is formed.[3]

Formation of Scales

High-temperature oxidation normally leads to the formation of thick oxide layers, which are termed scales. These are rarely protective and often complex in nature. Reactants other than oxygen, e.g., sulfur rich gases, can lead to the formation of other than oxide scales.

A convenient system for study is the sulfidation of silver at about 450°C (842°F), as shown in Figure 5.03.

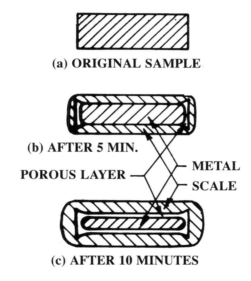

(a) ORIGINAL SAMPLE

(b) AFTER 5 MIN.

POROUS LAYER — METAL — SCALE

(c) AFTER 10 MINUTES

FIGURE 5.03 *Sulfidation of silver at 444°C (831°F).*[5]

Initially, there will be a single layer scale that is compact and adherent. In many cases, it can be shown by markers to grow by outward diffusion of metal. As the reaction proceeds, the outward diffusion of metal is complemented initially by an inward plastic flow of sulfide that is more effective on the flats than at specimen corners. Therefore, porosity develops at the corners where imperfect scale to metal contact obtains.

As the process of scale formation continues, the thicker scale becomes less plastic and loses full contact with the substrate, even at the flats. At this stage, there is a two-layer scale: (1) an inner porous layer with maximum thickness near the corners; and (2) an outer compact layer. Thus, a single-phase structure is no guarantee of a simple scale morphology. Multiphase systems are even more complex.

Consider the oxidation of iron, for example, in a mixture of CO and CO_2 at 1,000°C (1,832°F). The reaction:

$$2CO + O_2 \rightleftharpoons 2CO_2 \qquad\qquad (5.04)$$

has a definite equilibrium constant and defines an oxygen partial pressure corresponding to each particular ratio of CO/CO_2 concentrations in the gas. If the oxygen pressure exceeds the dissociation pressure of FeO, but not that of Fe_3O_4 or Fe_2O_3, a scale is formed consisting of FeO, but with none of the higher oxides. If the oxygen partial pressure exceeds the dissociation pressure of Fe_3O_4, the outer layer of the scale will be Fe_3O_4, but with an intermediate FeO layer between the base metal and the outer magnetite. For still larger oxygen partial pressure, there will be an outer hematite (Fe_2O_3) layer with intermediate magnetite (Fe_3O_4) and wustite (FeO). The relative thickness of the various layers is determined by kinetic considerations; the relative thickness of the components at a given temperature typically is independent of total film thickness, and porosity remains a complicating factor, as is the influence of gravity.

Kinetics of Scale Formation

The complexity of the process of scale formation leads to difficulties in applying parabolic, etc. kinetics to relate weight gain to time in conventional kinetic studies. It is convenient (as demonstrated by Mrowec et al. [4,5]) to correct the simple parabolic equation by introducing a more precise expression for the surface area of the metallic core, rather than by assuming that the sample area remains constant as scaling proceeds.

Oxidation of Alloys

The simplest case is where both components of an alloy are approximately equal in oxidation characteristics. Here, the structure of the oxide will be important, as was the case for more or less pure metals. Oxides of the spinel type $RO.R'_2O_3$ have a cubic structure, fit the underlying metal reasonably well, and tend to be protective. Stainless steel is the outstanding example. Here, R' is Cr, and R is a solid solution of Ni in Fe. Conductivity of such oxides is low. An interesting alloy of about 18% Al with the balance Fe produces a dark red $FeO-Al_2O_3$ with excellent corrosion resistance. This alloy competes with the chromel as a candidate for furnace windings, but has low strength at high temperature. Unfortunately, the Fe Al alloy is difficult to fabricate, is highly sensitive to interstitial elements, and must be hot worked at 1,200°C (2,192°F) before it can be cold-worked successfully. Superalloys usually have higher nickel and cobalt contents. They also are protected by a spinel type oxide. Such oxides show gradual transition from a protective film to a nonprotective scale as the temperature increases.

Corrosion resistance to oxidation in alloys also can be built up by burning out of the less noble element, leaving a surface enriched in the nobler constituent. For example, if the nobler constituent is gold, a substantial resistance to corrosion can exist in the gold layer produced. Precious metal alloys and even some of the nickel alloys can develop reasonably good corrosion resistance in this fashion.

Predicting High Temperature Corrosion Behavior

A recent paper looks into the issue of corrosion in high temperature gases with particular reference to predicting the behavior of commercial alloys in long-term exposure situations, as would occur in many items of commercial equipment.[6] Four steps are involved: 1) to assess the proximity of the environment to equilibrium; 2) to determine the corrosion products that are stable; 3) to predict corrosion rates for the specific exposure conditions; and 4) to assess the accuracy of the predictions and develop correlations with a wide variety of published data. The methodology is incorporated into a computer-based information system for commercial alloys that can be accessed by the public.

Corrosion mechanisms are classified according to the corrosion products formed — sulfidation, sulfidation/oxidation, oxidation, carburization, and dew point corrosion by oxy-acids of sulfur. Exposure to the various corrosion regimes was reported to have a more or less additive effect on long-term behavior. Pre-oxidation, for example, would be able to influence short-term behavior in another environment, but would become less of a factor as the total time of exposure was increased.

Differences have been noted between laboratory tests, under constant conditions, and data obtained in the plant. This is ascribed to the greater variability in the plant, with its inevitable temperature cycling during shutdown, which can have major thermal/mechanical effects on corrosion product, etc.

Breakaway Oxides

Zirconium is known as one metal that exhibits "breakaway" in its oxidation behavior. Below about 500°C (932°F) in air, zirconium will form a greyish black oxide that is adherent and highly protective. Above 500°C (932°F) , the oxide will become creamy white, flake off, and be essentially nonprotective.

A somewhat similar situation obtains when zirconium is exposed to pressurized water or steam. The oxide develops increasing compressive stresses, and beyond a certain point oxide fracture occurs. Oxidation then continues with rapid linear kinetics. Zircaloys and zirconium niobium alloys were developed deliberately to suppress the breakaway phenomenon. But even they are subject to it, albeit at a higher temperature.

An interesting twist can put this process to practical use. In a procedure developed by Watson, the zirconium alloy of fairly light cross section is exposed rapidly to breakaway oxidation at a temperature where creep of the substrate will occur readily.[7] The cream-colored breakaway oxide then stretches the substrate to a predictable extent, but remains fully protective. The result is a zirconium alloy core encapsulated in a solid and highly protective oxide. This can be finished by grinding to give an excellent hard surface for a bearing that can be used with water lubrication in high temperature and high pressure water. Other competing materials are not easy to fabricate to particular shapes, and most are hot water-soluble to a greater extent than ZrO_2.

The Watson approach can give fully protective post-breakaway coatings of 0.0005 to > 0.009 inch (1 to 20 m) in thickness. Optimum thickness for friction and wear is 0.002 to 0.003 in.(5 to 8 m). Provided the zircaloy part being oxidized is sufficiently thin to be subject to creep under the influence of oxidation-generated stress, the process may be followed by reference to Figures 5.04 to 5.06.

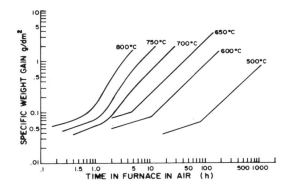

FIGURE 5.04   *Oxidation of glass shot blasted zircaloy-2 in air at different temperatures.*[7]

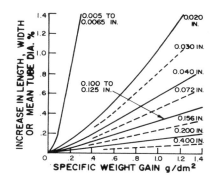

FIGURE 5.05   *Increase in wall thickness of zircaloy-2 and zircaloy-4 during oxidation at 650°C (1,250°F) in air.*[7]

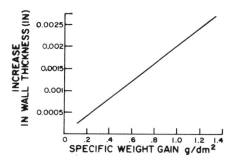

FIGURE 5.06   *Dimensional changes of zircaloy-2 or zircaloy-4 parts oxidized in air at 659°C (1,218°F).*[7]

Watson's analysis of the stresses generated in a thin-walled tube is given in the following.[7] A tube wall thickness of 0.120 in. (3 mm) is assumed for the model.

As zircaloy oxidizes, there are two stages to be considered. The diffusion layer would lead to a volume (V) 1.01 times that of the original material (Vo) while the fully oxidized layer would have a volume 1.56 times the original value:

$$\frac{V}{Vo} = 1.01 = 1 + 3\epsilon \qquad (5.05)$$

Where ϵ is the peripheral strain (assumed isotropic) that would be experienced by the diffusion layer if free to expand. Thus:

$$\epsilon = 0.0033 \text{ in. } (8.4 \text{ } \mu m) \qquad (5.06)$$

If this strain is shared between the tube and its diffusion layer:

$$\epsilon_T \text{ (tensile) } + \epsilon_{DL} \text{ (compressive) } = 0.0033 \text{ in. } (5.07)$$

Also, from the condition of equilibrium:

$$\epsilon_{DL} E_{DL} W_{DL} = \epsilon_T E_T W_T \qquad (5.08)$$

Where E_{DL} and E_T = Young's modulus for the diffusion layer and tube, and equal 14×10^6 psi in each case, and:

$$W_T = \text{tube thickness} = 0.120 \text{ in. (assumed unchanged)} \qquad (5.09)$$

And W_{DL} = diffusion layer thickness = 0.004 inch for each side for a total of 0.008 inch. Where:

$$\epsilon_{DL} = 15 \, \epsilon_T \qquad (5.10)$$

And:

$$\epsilon_T = \frac{0.0033}{16} = 0.00021 \text{ in. } (0.52 \text{ m}) \qquad (5.11)$$

The corresponding tangential stress in the tube σDL is given by:

$$\sigma DL = E_{T\epsilon T} = 14 \times 10^6 \times 0.00021 = 2,940 \text{ psi} = 20.5 \text{ MPa} \tag{5.12}$$

Now it is necessary to calculate a tangential stress σDL corresponding to the stresses stemming from the oxidized layer. This occupies 1.56 times the volume of the original metal and has a thickness of 0.0003 inch; i.e., a double thickness of 0.0006 inch, with E_{OL} having a value of 40×10^6 psi. Here:

$$\frac{V}{Vo} = 1.56 (1 + \epsilon)^3 = 1 + 3\epsilon + 3\epsilon^2 + \epsilon^3 \tag{5.13}$$

This gives:

$$\epsilon = 0.16 \tag{5.14}$$

So that:

$$\epsilon T + \epsilon OL = 0.16 \tag{5.15}$$

And:

$$\epsilon_{OL} E_{OL} W_{OL} = \epsilon_T E_T W_T \tag{5.16}$$

So that:

$$\frac{E_{OL}}{E_T} = \frac{14 \times 10^6 \times 0.120}{40 \times 10^6 \times 0.0006} \tag{5.17}$$

And:

$$\epsilon_{OL} + \frac{\epsilon_{OL}}{70} = 0.16 \tag{5.18}$$

So that:

$$\epsilon_{OL} \approx 0.16 \tag{5.19}$$

And the tangential stress:

$$^\sigma OL = E_{OL \epsilon OL} = 40 \times 10^6 \times 0.16 = 6,400,000 \text{ psi}$$
(5.20)

It is unlikely, however, that such a high compressive stress could be supported without yielding. $^\sigma YO$ denotes the compressive yield stress of the oxide layer, then:

$$^\sigma OL = {}^\sigma YO \frac{W_{OL}}{W_T} = {}^\sigma YO \frac{0.0006}{0.120} = 0.005 \; {}^\sigma YO \quad (5.21)$$

So if the yield stress of the oxide is assumed to be 500,000 psi there would be a tube stress:

$$^\sigma OL = 0.005 \times 500,000 = 2,500 \text{ psi} = 17.5 \text{ MPa} \quad (5.22)$$

Thus, the total tangential tensile stress in the tube will be given as the sum of the $^\sigma OL$ and $^\sigma OL$ components:

$$^\sigma TOT = {}^\sigma DL + {}^\sigma OL = 5,400 \text{ psi} = 38 \text{ MPa} \quad (5.23)$$

The principal assumptions in the preceding treatment are: (1) The volumetric growth of the oxide is not directionally sensitive; (2) The axial shortening of the tubular oxide layers has no effect on the final stress condition; (3) The oxidizing process will progress to maintain constant stresses in the tube.

Pressure Tubes in Nuclear Reactors

The CANDU nuclear reactor system employs heavy water as both coolant and moderator, along with zirconium alloy pressure tubes as the principal pressurized component. The weakest link in the system, which nevertheless ranks first worldwide in percentage of rated power delivered on a long-term basis, is the pressure tubes. The problem relates to the hydriding of the pressure tubes. It was found that Zircalloy 4 was marginally inferior to zirconium-niobium in this regard. In addition, the performance of zirconium-niobium can be further enhanced by texture control so the hydride that forms eventually will be oriented so it is less damaging in terms of crack formation.

Volatile Oxides

A few metals have oxides that are much more volatile than the metals themselves. These are poor in resistance to oxidation at temperatures where the oxide has appreciable vapor pressure. Molybdenum, osmium, and ruthenium are examples of refractory metals whose oxides are appreciably volatile. The noble nature of the last two metals cited is not able to overcome the oxide volatility problem. They cannot be exposed to air at high temperature. Rhodium also suffers from this defect, but to a lesser extent. As a consequence, the long-term stability of platinum rhodium thermocouples is affected.

Liquid Oxides

In most cases of high temperature oxidation, the oxides produced are solid, although they may approach their sintering temperatures. However, the higher temperature applications can lead to liquid or partially liquid oxides, particularly where the impurity level resulting from combustion is significant. It is then more appropriate to consider the oxides as slags.

Many sets of otherwise refractory oxides are capable of undergoing eutectic reactions that show a much lower melting temperature than either component. Where polycomponent eutectics exist, there is a real chance of additional depression of the melting temperature. Where metals have oxides with many valence states, the multicomponent situation is achieved readily.

Iron, a component of many alloys of interest, has three different oxides, FeO, Fe_3O_4, and Fe_2O_3. These cannot exist concurrently. The element with most oxides that is likely to be found in a combustion device is vanadium, with V_2O, VO, V_2O_3, V_2O_4, and V_2O_5 all being possible. Given the presence of iron, vanadium, and the ubiquitous sodium, many relatively low melting combinations are possible. This is at the heart of the problem for superheater tubes in oil-fired boilers.

The vanadium content of residual oils has been increasing gradually. Any step calculated to lead to a greater recovery of light fractions must inevitably lead to greater sulfur and vanadium content in the residues. The net result is that the corrosion limitations dictate the maximum energy conversion that can be attained because of the necessary limitations of T_H.

Virtually all known engineering metals have an unacceptably high corrosion rate in slags where possibilities for redox reactions abound. The best material seems to be a Co-Cr binary. Even this would have a life of only a few months, and the alloy can be obtained only as a casting.

The problem appears to be the low melting range of a complex vanadium bearing slag. The solution must be to eliminate vanadium from the system or tie up the vanadium in higher melting compounds. For the latter technique, the addition of Ca or Mg compounds can be helpful. However, when this is done, it is difficult to keep the superheater tubes and other components free of deposits and to keep environmental emission of vanadium compounds as fly ash sufficiently low. Elimination of vanadium from the fuel also is expensive as it is in the form of organovanadium compounds, which are hard to crack.

Sulfur is not quite as much of a problem as vanadium. Sulfates or pyrosulfates can contribute to slagging. Calcium or magnesium compound additions can tie up about 90% of the sulfur.

Removal of sulfur compounds from stack gases was first demonstrated about 1934 at the Battersea Power Station in London and has been employed continuously since. The original reason for the anti-pollution measure was the concern of the Royal Physician for the health of King George V since Buckingham Palace is downwind from Battersea.

Liquid Metal and Fused Salt Corrosion

High temperature corrosion by liquid metals and salts can involve both dissolution and chemical mechanisms. The rationale for using either liquid metals or salts is to take advantage of their high capability for heat transfer. Nuclear reactor systems involving both liquid metal and fused salt coolants have received serious study while liquid metal coolants have been used in aircraft engine valves and the like.

Fused salts can be expected to have high ionic conductivities, especially at high temperatures. Only in cases such as phosphate or silicate melts, where large complexions can be formed, are the conductivities lower and the corresponding viscosities higher. Thus, if they occur at all, corrosion reactions can be expected to be rapid. Presence of oxidizable or reducible ion species helps to prevent polarization and enhances the rate of corrosion. Any corrosion process that would occur at lower temperature in aqueous media can be expected at high temperature in the fused salt.

In addition to the corrosion per se, many salts can dissolve metals to some extent, resulting in metal ions and electrons in solution. This also can accelerate corrosion.

In the case of liquid metals, solution, rather than corrosion, tends to be the principal mode of attack. The solution process can involve grain boundaries, various defects, or grain faces. Where grain boundaries are susceptible, the interfacial tension between solute metal and the grain is important. Solution processes in fused salts are governed by similar considerations.

Even where metal loss by solution proceeds at a tolerable rate, there may be deposition of metal in dendritic form in cooler parts of the system, possibly causing deterioration of overall heat transfer, if not complete blockage. The complication is to be expected more in systems that circulate coolant.

Other than in the specialized cases where fused salts are deliberately present, a high corrosion rate can be expected in any system where fused salts are present accidentally. The most common exposure to fused salts is in metallurgical refineries, where the slags are typically silicates of high enough molecular weight and viscosity that corrosion is not intense.

Where fused salt electrolysis is used for reactive metal recovery, corrosion of the refined metal is usually easier to control because of the applied cathodic depositing potential. This results in cathodic protection.

References

1. J.C. Scully, *The Fundamentals of Corrosion*, 2nd ed. (Pergamon Press, Ltd.), p. 31.
2. J. Stringer, *Werkstoffe und Korrosion* 23, Part 9 (1972): pp. 747-755.
3. N.B. Pilling, R.W. Bedworth. *J. Inst. Met.* 29 (1923): p. 529.
4. S. Mrowec, A. Stoklossa, *Werkstoffe und Korrosion* 21 (1970): p. 934.
5. S. Mrowec, T. Werber, *Gas Corrosion of Metals*, NTIS Transla-

tion TT 76-54038 (Washington, DC: NTIS, 1976).

6. R.C. John, W.T. Thompson, I. Karakaya, CORROSION/90, paper no. 279 (Houston, TX: NACE, 1990).

7. R.D. Watson, "Procedure for Oxidizing Zircaloy 2 and Zircaloy 4, AECL, Ltd., Report 9AECL-7552 (February 1982) and J.G. McManus, D.J. Gorman, R.D. Watson, "Stresses Induced by Surface Oxides as a Possible Cause of Diametral Growth of Oxidized Zirconium Alloy Pressure Tubes," AECL, Ltd., Report 9AECL-7530 (February 1982).

6

Synergistic Modes
of Attack

Corrosion Fatigue

Corrosion in combination with other factors such as fatigue can lead to more rapid deterioration than would be expected from either corrosion or fatigue separately. This is one example of a synergistic process. In corrosion fatigue, the alternation of tensile and compressive stresses in a corrosion environment can lead to failure at a surprisingly low load. Tensile stress appears to be the damaging component.

Fatigue in the absence of corrosion will reduce the endurance limits of many steels to about half the ultimate properties disclosed by tension testing. A much greater reduction results from concurrent exposure to fresh or salt water, or even to moist air. The endurance limit in salt water could be as little as six or seven of the ordinarily determined ultimate tensile strength. Even worse, many superior low alloy steels seem to have a lower corrosion fatigue limit in salt water than do the plain carbon steels.

A classic example of this effect can be drawn from a North Atlantic convoy experience in World War II. The main shafts of the Victory ships had been failing with undesirable consequences in the Atlantic Ocean by a corrosion fatigue mechanism. The solution, according to a misguided authority, was to replace the steel shafts with alloy steel shafts and thereby obtain a longer service life for the class of ships. Critical materials were diverted, alloy shafts were installed at great expense, and there was no improvement in the shaft failure rate. In this case, dire economic and personal consequences stemmed from an engineering judgment made in ignorance of corrosion principles and pressured by the wartime emergency situation.

Strictly speaking, there is no fixed endurance limit in a corrosion fatigue situation, though a stress level corresponding to a given number of reversals to failure can be predicted. Where corrosion fatigue is observed, the effect is so damaging that the environment should be modified to confer immunity, or the material should be changed to one that is inherently immune. Inhibitors and cathodic protection can, if properly applied, convert a corrosion fatigue case to one of dry fatigue, which is more amenable to adequate action in the design office.

It should be remembered that many laboratory measurements of fatigue involve exposure to the ambient atmosphere. One would not expect the same data from a laboratory in the Mojave Desert as for another on the Miami waterfront. It is better practice to reduce all fatigue test work to a common basis by using air below 40 relative humidity, or by immersion of the test piece in an inhibited oil.

Fatigue failures in service often fall into a grey area between dry fatigue and corrosion fatigue. If the crack that led to final failure is not obviously corroded, the failure is usually classed as dry fatigue rather than corrosion fatigue. Parkins has covered the topic of corrosion fatigue.[1]

Corrective measures for corrosion fatigue are primarily directed toward reducing the stress level to the point where it can be tolerated for the expected structure life. Sometimes the situation can be improved by giving the part in question a compressively stressed skin (e.g., by shot peening). This causes a dramatic increase in life, at least until the compressively stressed surface has corroded away. A better technique is to use cathodic protection or suitable inhibitors. This removes or drastically reduces the corrosion component of corrosion fatigue.

Where corrosion fatigue is possible, nondestructive testing can be helpful in determining the presence of cracks before total failure has occurred. This could run from the use of a hammer sounding on railroad axles in days of yore to any modern crack-detecting device. The cost and other consequences of failure will determine the sophistication of examination that can be justified.

The morphology of fatigue and corrosion fatigue failures is interesting. The alternating stresses lead to extrusion of slip bands on some surfaces and intrusion on others. A characteristic striation pattern can be observed, particularly on steel samples. For many nonferrous metals, the striation marks can only be seen at much higher magnification, for example, with the scanning electron microscope (SEM). Examples are shown in Figure 6.01.

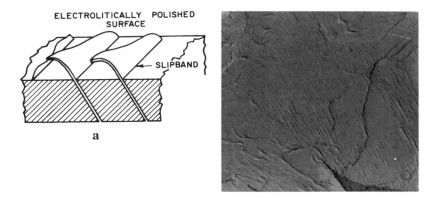

FIGURE 6.01   *The appearance of fatigue failure: (a) slip band extrusion (after Forsyth and Stubbington[2]) and (b) fatigue fracture surface of a failed titanium valve (SEM). (Figure 6.01b is repeated and discussed as Figure 17.07 in Chapter 17.)*

Much information can be gained from a study of the fatigue fracture surface (Chapter 17). The origin of the failure often can be identified by the crack front emanating from it. Each marking corresponds to the amount by which the crack front moves in one cycle so it is possible to estimate whether high or low cycle cumulative processes are involved. The final area of failure is usually ductile and corresponds to some sort of overload. The relative size of this portion identifies the loading level at failure. This array of information often results in recommendations for measures to avoid similar failures by design modification and other action. It also can define proper schedules for examination by nondestructive tests or proper intervals for the replacement of a component on a preventive maintenance basis. Accurate and complete records are needed.

Stress Corrosion Cracking

Stress corrosion cracking (SCC) is a dangerous form of corrosion in which a combination of a small and apparently insignificant amount of localized corrosion combines with tensile stresses to cause premature failure. Typically, the failure is sudden and occurs with little warning. It must be emphasized that SCC is a borderline phe-

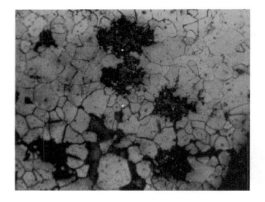

FIGURE 6.02
Intergranular corrosion of steel by caustic soda. This is an example of caustic embrittlement.[3] (Used with the permission of McGraw-Hill Book Co.)

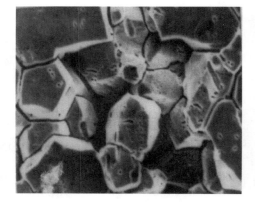

FIGURE 6.03
Corrosion of type 304 stainless steel in boiling 65% nitric acid (Huey test) (SEM).

nomenon and occurs where there is little, if any, superficial evidence of corrosion.

Intergranular corrosion is the form of localized corrosion often involved, although pitting also can be a culprit. Figure 6.02 shows intergranular corrosion of steel by caustic alkali as seen in cross section under the optical microscope; Figure 6.03 shows a similar attack on type 304 stainless steel in boiling 65% nitric acid, as seen by SEM. Both examples show grain dropping, although the latter shows the process more clearly. It should be noted that intergranular attack can be much more deep seated than is evident from the amount of grain dropping. Grain dropping has been convenient to study only since the advent of the SEM. But it may be an important tool in determining whether intergranular attack is merely superficial and of little importance or when it is the harbinger of more serious consequences.

If any grain dropping at all can be observed in the short term, there likely will be potentially serious SCC in longer term service exposure where tensile stresses are involved.

In any event, pitting and intergranular attack can both produce stress raisers. In combination with tensile stress, cracking is possible. The immediate consequences of the crack can be calculated by applying the principles of fracture mechanics. In general, there will be a period of subcritical crack growth in which the risk of failure is negligible. Both rate of growth and critical crack length for sudden failure can be calculated. In service, the crack must be detected and the rate of growth determined by nondestructive testing while it is still innocuous. As in the case of corrosion fatigue, early crack detection can avert sudden failures that could lead to danger to personnel and/or major economic losses. Once again, systematized inspection and record-keeping is vital.

SCC is highly specific. Particular metal environment systems will crack while others will not. A helpful compilation of susceptible combinations is given by Logan and Johnson[4,5] (Table 6.01). Unfortunately, there is no obvious logic to finding the susceptible cases. Experience seems to be the only guide. A partial list of some more common problem areas is given in the table. Studies of SCC susceptibility always should be made when new materials are proposed for a chemical plant or where new combinations of chemicals are involved.

SCC has been reviewed by both Evans[6] and Parkins.[1] Parkins has developed the stress corrosion spectrum, which shows the range of phenomena covered by SCC. Where stress is the major factor, crack-assisted rupture is observed. Where corrosion is a major factor, more typical SCC occurs. Identification of the origin of the stress is not always simple — it may involve residual stress from manufacturing and other processes in addition to the more obvious service stresses.

SCC may be either intergranular or transgranular in nature. Typically, the countermeasure for SCC is avoidance by use of a nonsusceptible material or by modification of the environment to render it innocuous. It is not entirely wise to attempt to define the allowable tensile stress level. This is because of the difficulty of determining residual tensile stresses, which add on to the known applied loads. It also is difficult to either analyze or test cases involving triaxial tensile loads. Because of the high disaster potential of SCC, a conservative design basis is in order.

TABLE 6.01

Alloy Corrodent Combinations in Which Stress Corrosion Cracking Has Been Reported*

Alloy	Environment	Alloy	Environment	Alloy	Environment
Aluminum Base		Cu-Ni	Moist SO_2 : $Cu(NO_2)_2$, H_2SO_4, HCl, HNO_3 solutions		(c) $MgCl_2$, $CoCl_2$, NaCl, $BaCl_2$ solutions
Al-Zn	Air	Cu-Zn plus minor amounts of Al, As, Be, B, Cd, Co, Au, Pb, Mn, Ni, Pd, Ag, Sr, Tl, Sn, Sb, Ba, Bi, Ca, Ce, Cr, Fe, Mg, P, Si, Te, Tl, Zr, Li, Nb, Mo, K, Se, Na, S, Ta	Moist NH_3 solutions		(d) CH_3CH_2Cl + water
Al-Mg	$NaCl + H_2O_2$, NaCl solutions; air				(e) LiCl, $ZnCl_2$, NH_4Cl solution
Al-Mg					(f) $(NH_4)_2CO_3$ solutions
Al-Cu-Mg	Seawater				(g) NaCl, NaF, NaBr, NaI, NaH_2PO_4, Na_3PO_4, Na_2SO_4, $NaNO_3$, Na_2SO_3, $NaClO_3$, $NaC_2H_3O_2$ solutions
Al-Mg-Zn					(h) Steam + chlorides
Al-Zn-Cu	NaCl, $NaCl + H_2O_2$ solutions				(i) H_2O solutions
Al-Zn-Mg-Mn					(j) $NaCl + NH_4NO_2$ solution, $NaCl + NaNO_2$ solution
Al-Zn-Mg-Cu-Mn	Seawater				(k) Polythionic acids
Al-Cu-Mg-Mn	$NaCl + H_2O_2$ solution	Cu-Ni-Si	Moist NH_3 atmosphere		
Al-Cu	$NaCl + H_2O_2$ solution	Cu-Al-Fe	Steam		
Al-Cu	$NaCl_2$, $NaCl + NaHCO_3$, KCl, $MgCl_2$,	Cu-Be	Moist NH_3 atmosphere		
Al-Mg	$CaCl_2$, NH_4Cl, $CoCl_2$ solutions				
		Iron Base		*Nickel Base*	
		Mild Steel	(a) HNO_3, NaOH, HF solutions	Ni	(a) $NaOH + Na_2SiO_3$
			(b) Distilled water		(b) $Ca(NO_3)_2$, NH_4NO_3 & $NaNO_3$ solutions
Magnesium Base				Ni-Cr-Fe	NaOH, KOH solutions; fused NaOH
Mg-Al	(a) $NaCl + H_2O_2$ solution			Ni-Cu	NaOH + sulfide solution, steam
Mg-Al-Zn-Mn	(b) Coastal atmosphere; $NaCl + K_2CrO_4$ solution				Fused NaOH, H_2SiF_6 solution, chromic acid, sulfonated oil, steam

TABLE 6.01 (Continued)

Alloy	Environment	Alloy	Environment	Alloy	Environment
Mg	(c) Moist air + SO2 + CO2		(c) HCN + SnCl$_2$ + AsCl$_2$ + CHCl$_3$	Ni-cu-Al	
			(d) Na3PO4 solution	Ni-Cu	
			(e) Pure NaOH solution	Ni-Al	HF acid vapor
Copper Base			(f) Nh3 + CO2 + H2S + HCN		
Cu-Zn	NH$_3$ vapors and solutions		(g) NaOH, KOH solutions; Monoethanolaine solution + H2S + Co2 + Fe(AlO2)3 + CaO solution	Ni-Cr-Fe	
				Ni-Cr-Fe-Ti	
Cu-Zn-Sn	NH$_3$ vapors and solutions			*Miscellaneous Alloys*	
Cu-Zn-Pb	Conc. NH4OH		(h) HNO$_3$ + H$_2$SO$_4$	Au-Cu-Ag	FeCl$_2$ solutions
Cu-Sn-P	Amines		(i) MgCl$_2$ + NaF solution	Cu-Au	HNO$_3$ + HCl, HNO$_3$, FeCl$_3$, NH$_4$OH solutions
Cu-Zn			(j) Anhydrous liquid NH$_3$		
Cu-Zn-Ni			(k) H$_2$S media	Ag-Pt	HNO$_3$ + HCl, HNo$_2$, FeCl$_3$ solutions
Cu-Sn	NH3 vapors and solutions		(l) FeCl$_3$ solution	Pb	FeCl$_3$ solutions
Cu-Sn-P	Air	Fe-Cr-C	(a) NH$_4$Cl, MgCl$_2$, (NH$_4$)H$_2$PO$_4$ Na$_2$HPO$_4$ solution	Pb	(a) Pb(OAc)$_2$ + HNO$_3$ solutions
Cu-As			(b) H$_2$SO$_4$ + NaCl solution		(b) air
Cu-P, -As, -Sb, -Ni -Al, -Si, -Zn	Moist NH$_3$ atmosphere		(c) NaCl + H$_2$O$_2$ solution, sea water	Ti Alloys	Solid NaCl, temp>550°F (290°C)
			(d) H$_2$S solutions		
Cu-Si-Mn		Fe-Ni-C	(a) HCl + H$_2$SO$_4$ solution, sea water	Ti-6Al-4V	Electrolytes; ambient temps.
Cu-Zn-Si	Water vapor				Liquid N$_2$O$_4$
Cu-Zn-Sn-Mn	Water	Fe-Cr-Ni-C	(b) H$_2$S solutions	Zr	FeCl$_3$ solutions
Cu-Au	NH$_4$OH, FeCl$_3$, HNO$_3$ solutions		(a) NaCl + H$_2$SO$_4$ solution, sea water		
Cu-Zn	Water				
Cu-Zn-Mn	Moist SO$_2$; Cu(NO$_2$)$_2$ solutions				

* This table, except for minor additions, is taken from Johnson.[5] Shown here from Logan.[4]

89

The most famous early case of SCC in plain carbon steel is the caustic embrittlement of boilers. The pioneers of steam technology treated boiler water with alkali to reduce the more obvious danger of acid attack. Some rivet holes would be subject to leakage and evaporative concentration of caustic followed by cracking and final explosion of the boiler. The solution to this problem is to maintain alkalinity in the boiler by either a buffered (phosphate) system or with a volatile amine (Chapter 7). In either case, the drastic rise in pH in crevices or leaks is avoided. Now that modifications necessary to the boiler water systems are known and boiler water systems are controlled, explosions are rare. Boiler and pressure vessel inspection codes are stringent (Chapter 13). This is proper because of the risk of catastrophic failure.

Exposure of steel to hot alkali is not an obvious trigger for SCC; the Pourbaix diagram merely identifies an area of corrosion. But, having identified a problem with SCC, one can then try to avoid it.

The season cracking of brass is another well-documented case of SCC. This was observed in artillery shell casings in the Napoleonic era. It was customary to store these shell casings adjacent to stabling areas. In this case, the corrodent was ammonia from urine. The problem continued until horse-drawn transport gave way to the internal combustion engine. Stressing in this case resulted from either the manufacturing process of the shell cases or from firing a round and then reloading.

A more modern and less spectacular example is the SCC of a variety of high-strength aluminum alloy components in marine service. Naval architectural considerations demand that the superstructure of a ship be as light as possible. High-strength aluminum silicon alloy castings for items such as guard rail stanchions and hatch and bulkhead hardware became commonplace. The strongest alloys judged to have acceptable corrosion resistance were selected. As it turned out, this criterion was inadequate, and SCC was observed. Since failure of a guard rail stanchion could cause a sailor to fall overboard in icy waters with zero survival possibilities, this case received the most study. The final solution was a stanchion of an alloy of more moderate strength and more generous dimensions. A somewhat similar application of the original high strength casting alloy in scaffolding clamps also suffered SCC, this time in an industrial rather than a marine atmosphere. The alloy in question is rarely specified today.

As the examples in the last paragraph show, it is possible for a sophisticated design team reasonably knowledgeable in corrosion to overlook the possibility of SCC. In general, any application involving the user of a material of premium mechanical properties must employ a stress level such that if SCC occurs at all there cannot be disaster potential. Many practical applications can provide mechanisms for the local concentration of corrodents by evaporation and other processes so test environments should be much more aggressive than would be suggested by simple-minded considerations.

The unwanted environment can be hard to avoid. The nuclear industry is well aware of SCC problems that could arise from chloride contamination of boiler waters. This can arise from leaks of cooling water into the condensers under the influence of the normal pressure differential if the condensers have any problem areas. Thus, the apparently noncritical condenser must also be built to exacting specifications, if the overall system is to be fully reliable. In any boiler room, leaks from asbestos-insulated items can be a hazard to whatever receives the drips. Possible SCC of zircaloys in nuclear reactor cores also has had considerable study. Fission product iodine seems to contribute to the problem.

Another unwanted environment can plague aircraft operators. Dead storage of military aircraft in desert areas has been used to limit corrosion. However, serious SCC of undercarriages can be a significant problem. The source of corrodent was the guard dogs used by the security patrol. Urination by dogs on aircraft wheels and other parts certainly was not a concern of the original design team.

A somewhat similar problem exists when sled dogs or other animals are airlifted. Spills in galley and washroom areas of aircraft pose similar problems, but are much more predictable to the designer and are less likely to escape early detection. On the ground, lampposts also are subject to damage from dogs.

Fretting

Fretting is a subject that has received inadequate study. There is only one book of note that deals with the subject, the monograph by Waterhouse.[7] Fretting may be observed as a distinct phenomenon, or in conjunction with fatigue processes. Corrosion products resulting from fretting normally have a distinctive appearance.

Typically, fretting involves vibratory rubbing contact of inadequately lubricated surfaces. The sequence leading to damage is:

pressure welding of asperities in contact; breaking these welds by relative motion of the two surfaces; rapid oxidation of the freshly broken surface; abrasion of the surfaces by oxides and debris; followed by rewelding of the asperities. The net result is the accumulation of atypical corrosion products and more or less rapid deterioration of the interfaces. The proper countermeasures are lubricating and/or clamping the surfaces.

Generally, aluminum alloys are prone to fretting; therefore, coils of sheet products are oiled and clamped for shipping. Problems have been caused by stacked aluminum boxes, trays, etc. Ammunition boxes in World War II were one example. Stacks of these boxes were delivered in a variety of adverse conditions, and the black oxide or suboxide produced by fretting was evident. Unfortunately, this oxide could be pyrophoric under certain conditions. Other examples of frettage of aluminum were common in the food industry. The black oxide was unsightly and detrimental.

Bearings of many types designed for service in rotation can be damaged severely by vibration in shipping. Air compressors delivered by Caterpillar train in the Arctic and automobiles delivered thousands of miles by rail or road transporters have shown this problem. The bearings need rotation for lubrication to be effective and do not get it in transit. In this case, a thin coat of lead on the bearing surfaces solved the problem. The lead was quickly worn away in service but served to eliminate the fretting problem in shipping.

Galvanized products also can suffer from fretting in delivery by road or rail. The corrosion product in this case consists of "white rust"; this reduces the ability of the galvanizing to resist early development of normal rust spots in service. Poor on-site storage seems to contribute to the deterioration, particularly if there has been prior fretting damage. The sheets should be separated in storage to allow free access to the air and should be protected adequately for shipping. Oiling and clamping is not a frill for long distance shipping.

Cases of fretting or fretting fatigue have been found in surgical implants under screw heads and other components. The corrosion behavior of such implants needs further study. Unfortunately, samples for study are notoriously difficult to obtain possibly because of potential liability considerations for the surgeon involved.

Fretting fatigue is a troublesome phenomenon that is not always easy to detect. It involves a synergistic combination of fretting and fatigue, and it can lead to a dramatic reduction in the fatigue endurance limit. A classic example occurs where there is a press fit of a wheel onto a shaft and the shaft is subject to bending loads, as in railroad wheel axle assemblies. In service, the shaft flexes more than the hub of the wheel, causes some rubbing at the wheel to hub contact, which triggers the fretting damage; fatigue soon takes over. A remedy based on eliminating the stress concentration by machining a smooth groove in an axle is shown in Figure 9.08 in Chapter 9. The insidious nature of this attack arises from the fact that the fretting site coincides with the region of maximum stress concentration. In extreme cases, there can be a tenfold reduction in fatigue strength. This extreme was reached in a large low-pressure steam turbine with shrunk-on wheels. The bending stress due to the weight of the unit was enough to trigger fretting fatigue and eventual failure.

Hydrogen Damage

Hydrogen is a factor in many cracking situations and can result from many causes. Corrosion product hydrogen, hydrogen from over-zealous cathodic protection, hydrogen from pickling operations, or hydrogen from welding with damp electrodes can be sources of trouble. Electroplating also can lead to hydrogen pickup. All plating operations are potentially suspect, but metal deposition under conditions where there is a high overvoltage, such as bright plating with zinc, are particularly dangerous. Plated coatings also may hinder the later escape of hydrogen.

As an interstitial element in the body-centered cubic (bcc) ferrite lattice, hydrogen can contribute to a number of mechanical problems for steels. Any interstitial solute can cause an increase in the brittle to ductile transition temperature. This will make the steel inherently brittle up to a somewhat higher temperature than would otherwise be the case.

Delayed fracture is the main manifestation of hydrogen damage. The typical test for this is to have a notched tensile specimen loaded to some fairly high percentage of its notched ultimate tensile strength (UTS). In the presence of a damaging amount of hydrogen, sudden failure would occur after the load had been applied for some time, usually a few hours. The process of fracture is time-sensitive and seems to require time for hydrogen to diffuse to sites where it can contribute to crack growth.

Welding with damp electrodes is a typical means of ingress for hydrogen. The reaction:

$$Fe + H_2O \rightarrow FeO + 2H \qquad (1)$$

is responsible. Atomic hydrogen can dissolve in many solid metals, including α iron.

Some fraction of the contained hydrogen is able to diffuse away and escape, particularly if the workpiece is not under load. In any event, there will be a period of about 48 hours at ambient temperature in which some hydrogen escapes. This reduces the tendency to hydrogen damage to some extent. Some fraction of the hydrogen is taken up irreversibly, however, and will never diffuse out. Shorter times at higher temperatures will be equally effective in removing that part of the hydrogen that is removable.

Hydrogen cracking often was observed in high-strength steel undercarriages for commercial airliners in the early 1950s. The hydrogen probably originated from cleaning and plating techniques used in the application of cadmium plating specified for corrosion resistance to the undercarriages. Fortunately, none of these failures occurred on landing, despite the fact that landing conditions correspond to maximum stressing. Typically, the classic type of delayed failure occurs after the aircraft has been standing for some time at the gate.

Hydrogen damage can be expected in any steel for which the UTS exceeds about 100,000 psi. Lower strength materials are affected more rarely. Zinc-plated wood screws, particularly in the heavier gauges, are prone to hydrogen damage. The hydrogen results from poor pickling and plating techniques, such as trying to obtain bright plating on an excessively large barrel load. Any other operation likely to increase hydrogen overvoltage also will increase the possibility for hydrogen damage. Mistreated screws three or four inches long can fail in brittle fashion in the time required to secure them with a hand-operated screwdriver. Unfortunately, it is no longer possible to purchase unplated screws.

Detection of hydrogen damage is difficult. The delayed fracture test is tedious and time-consuming. For applications in aircraft, etc. it is customary to call up detailed specifications for finishing and plating operations and to bake or boil the work produced. This seems to be an effective procedure.

The hydrogen content of steel produced in the mill in periods of high indoor humidity, as in summer heat waves, poses an interesting problem. With processes such as ladle degassing becoming more common such concerns will become less important.

Erosion-Related Phenomena

Many applications require the flow of process streams or cooling waters in pipes. To achieve economy, the flow rate should be the maximum that is consistent with good corrosion performance. In many cases, it will be necessary to remain in the laminar flow regime. Typical flow rates would be 1.2 m/s for waters in steel, 1.5 m/s for copper, and around 7.5 to 9 m/s for stainless steel. Often, limitation on velocity will be set by damage to throttling valves and downstream from valves, fittings, etc. Figure 6.04 shows severe erosion of a cast steel valve body. This sort of effect can be cured only by a reduction of the flow velocity to a level appropriate for cast steel. Note that perforation has occurred where eddy action has led to highest flow velocity.

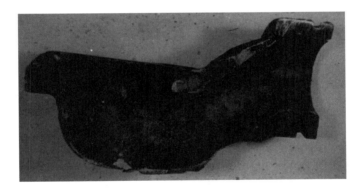

FIGURE 6.04 Erosion of a cast steel valve body.

For example, if a process calls for aqueous flow of 2.5 to 3 m/s, plain carbon steel would be inadequate and would fail rapidly by erosion. The remedy is to restrict the flow to about 1.2 m/s by reducing the quantity of flow or by increasing the pipe size. Alternatively, a material such as stainless steel, which is tolerant of higher velocities, could be used.

A good example of the importance of velocity effects can be given when a plain carbon steel tubular heat exchanger eventually failed due to external corrosion of the tubes. The shell side carried water, and the process material, which was not very corrosive, was on the tube side flowing under pressure at 1.2 m/s. To prolong the service life of the heat exchanger, the wall thickness of the tubes was increased using the axiom, "The thicker the tube wall, the longer it will last." This unit was installed and failed sooner than the old one. Why? Erosion at 1.2 m/s in the old unit was no problem, but by increasing the wall thickness of the tube while maintaining the same outside diameter the velocity increased proportionately to the reduction in surface area of the tubes. The change from a one-in. 18 Birmingham Wire Gauge (BWG) (1.6 mm wall) to a one-in. 12 BWG (2.56 mm wall) reduced the cross sectional area by almost 25%, resulting in a corresponding increase in velocity and premature failure.

Copper is favored for heat exchangers because of its high conductivity. Its ability to tolerate higher flow rates is enhanced by the addition of alloying elements, such as nickel or aluminum (particularly if a little iron is added). For example, an iron-modified 90-10 cupronickel can tolerate a 3 m/s flow rate of seawater. The role of the iron is to develop an oxide film of improved resistance to flowing seawater. Interestingly, the iron can either be added to the alloy, provided from periodic additions of $FeSO_4$, or from a corrosion site for iron upstream from the cupronickel. The latter cannot be recommended as a design strategy. It is more or less inevitable that some bright "improver" will discover and remove the offending iron on their own initiative.

The behavior of nonpassivating and passivating metals when exposed to flowing corrodents is shown in Figures 6.05 and 6.06. In effect, this involves oxygen for passivation maintained at or above a given flow rate, in the normal case, e.g., cooling water containing dissolved oxygen. Stagnant conditions can be disastrous for stainless steels exposed to chlorides, etc.

FIGURE 6.05
Corrosion of a normal metal.

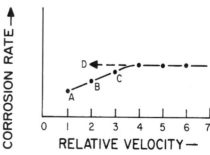

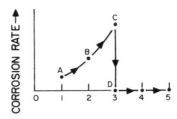

FIGURE 6.06 *Corrosion of passivating metal.*

It is assumed in Figures 6.05 and 6.06 that the process is controlled by diffusion of oxygen to cathodic sites, as is often the case. In practice, the effect of turbulence also is significant. The most likely trouble spots will be downstream from pipe fittings, valves, poorly fitted gaskets, etc. The effect of the turbulence, with or without the scouring action of suspended particulates, will be to wear away the corrosion product film more rapidly than would occur in its absence. The rate of corrosion will then be maintained at a rate corresponding to the rather high initial rate rather than the slower rate characteristic of a metal that carries a protective film. As the flow velocity increases so does the corrosion damage, and the otherwise protective film can be worn away rapidly.

At extreme but impractically high flow velocity regions in which the pressure is below the vapor pressure of the flowing liquid or below the partial pressure of dissolved gases can occur. Provided that proper nucleation conditions are met, this will lead to the formation of low-pressure bubbles in local regions of the most rapid flow. When these bubbles pass into regions of less rapid flow (often near boundaries) they collapse. This can cause extremely high local impact loads on exposed objects or surfaces. In the extreme case, there is no cure for this, and any exposed material will ultimately be destroyed. However, from an engineering point of view, there is no excuse to construct or design equipment to operate this regime, which can be termed cavitation erosion.

In competent engineering practice, cavitation is far less extreme, and it is merely capable of damaging the thin corrosion product films. The net appearance of the damage in this cavitation corrosion regime is similar to that for cavitation erosion. There is, however, a significant difference. If the corrosion component is brought under control by cathodic protection, inhibitors, and so forth there is no more "erosion." With competent design, it is rare for a device to fall outside the cavitation corrosion regime. Failure to distinguish between cavitation corrosion and cavitation erosion is a source of great confusion in the literature.

An example of practical interest involved naval harbor tugs in Halifax Harbor in the early 1950s. Because of damage by ice and flotsam, bronze propellers were not practical so steel ones were employed. These had to be heavily repaired after six months and replaced after one year because of "typical" erosion damage. However, the tugs were used for development of paint systems compatible with cathodic protection. While under cathodic protection, "erosion" of the propellers vanished, and they lasted as long as they could be mechanically straightened, following the inevitable abuse in service. Cathodic protection has enabled the tugs to enjoy long-lived propellers.

This raises interesting questions about propeller materials for ships in general. Complex bronzes were instituted because ferrous propellers failed by "erosion." A major factor in the good service of bronze propellers is cathodic protection at the expense of the steel hull plating (Chapter 2). Now that cathodic protection of ships is universal, steel propellers should give as good service as bronze propellers, but at a much lower cost. A secondary benefit would be to reduce the current demand for the cathodic protection system. Perhaps the incredible conservatism of marine insurers eventually will be overcome, allowing the most cost-effective material to be used.

There is another cure for cavitation. By analogy with supersonic flight, supercavitation is possible. For appropriate screw form and speed of rotation, cavitation bubbles can be generated that do not collapse until after they have cleared the trailing edge of the propeller. This is an elegant solution to an old problem, and it does call for precise engineering. It is not applicable to piping systems.

Microbiological Corrosion

Microbiological involvement in corrosion does not involve new principles. It involves additional avenues by which aggressive ions can be generated, and it introduces new methods by which corrosion reactions can be accelerated. More complete accounts can be found in works by Booth[8] and Parkins.[1] The appearance of biological or microbiological attack is often characteristic, as shown in Figure 6.07.

Large pits of somewhat unusual appearance often are found. Scrupulous examination often is required to identify the type of organism involved.

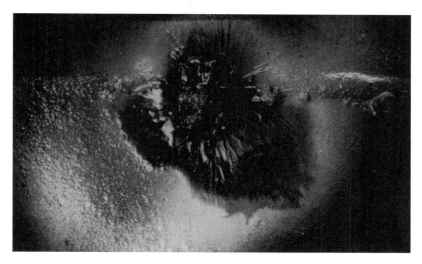

FIGURE 6.07   *Pitting caused by microbiological corrosion on the inside of a stainless steel storage tank.*

Recirculating cooling water systems are becoming more and more common, particularly with increasingly stringent environmental regulations. Biocidal techniques, such as pH control, intermittent chlorination, or dosage with quaternary ammonium compounds or organo-metallic tin compounds, are becoming increasingly necessary. However, many organisms can adapt to specific toxins, and control is rarely straightforward. A more promising strategy is to discover and eliminate trace elements necessary for the healthy growth of the troublesome species. There have been examples where the elimination of zinc or vanadium has been helpful.

By growth and metabolism, microbes can introduce species such as acids, sulfides, etc. into a given situation. The microbes can participate directly in an electrochemical reaction in a corrosion cell or furnish an alternate route for such a reaction. Most microbes of consequence to corrosion processes involve sulfur. Hydrogen sulfide can be oxidized to sulfur or sulfates by bacteria. Other species can reverse the process.

Thiobacillus thiooxidans is a versatile bacillus capable of oxidizing any other sulfur species to sulfate. The final pH can be 0.6 or less. The presence of oxygen is necessary for its metabolism. Sulfate reducers, such as the genus *desulfovibrio*, can only operate anaerobically, and at a redox potential around -100 mV relative to hydrogen. Their normal product is H_2S. This, in turn, can lead to corrosion product films that can support high corrosion currents. Bacteria also can stimulate corrosion by setting up differential aeration cells that can be maintained as corrosion proceeds.

Bacterial corrosion rarely occurs when corrosion of nonbacterial type is unlikely. But it leads to much higher rates of attack than would otherwise be expected and can lead to major degradations of concrete, limestone, and other materials.

A characteristic of microbiological corrosion is that it is rare for a single species to be effective. Lab tests involving a single purified strain of a bacterium often give negative results. On the other hand, infection from a sample that is already corroding is almost always effective; while this may be predominately a single species, it is usually a consortium of several species.

Bacterial corrosion of aluminum alloy fuel tanks can show crystallographic pitting.

Bacterial corrosion of stainless steel can sometimes be a major problem. Typically, there will be an increase in chloride concentration in the infected nodule. As little as 10 ppm Cl- can lead to SCC, particularly of weldments.

A fairly recent example involved a telephone exchange in the Ottawa area.[9] A pyritic shale provided a breeding ground for bacterial formation of H_2SO_4, which, in turn, caused the shale to degrade and swell. The basement floor in the exchange was heaving to an alarming extent as this occurred. The necessary control measures involved pH control with alkali to suppress the bacterial processes. In practice, control by pH or cathodic protection normally is effective. Mildly alkaline pH levels, whether generated by cathodic protection or added chemicals, will inhibit bacterial growth of the type that caused this problem.

Another interesting case of bacterial corrosion was noted a few years ago on the track of a railway in northern Ontario, Canada.[2] The ballast material was the float (reject) component of a sink-float separation at a neighboring iron mine. Unfortunately, many small pieces of rock in the float were flecked with pyrite. After a couple of years there was significant bacterial infection, and the H_2SO_4 led to significant corrosion of the underside of the rail flange, where there was no chance to wash off the acid with rainwater. The ballast material had to be changed.

Bacterially accelerated corrosion of buried pipe is fairly common. When present, cathodic protection is almost obligatory, and care must be taken to ensure that the secondary wrapping materials are not liable to bacterial attack. Use of crushed limestone as backfill also provides some measure of control. Where bacterial corrosion is involved, the normal criteria for cathodic protection may not be adequate to stop corrosion. More cathodic potentials are required.

Primitive organisms can tolerate surprisingly acid solutions. Cases have been reported of infection of acid copper sulfate plating tanks.

Epilogue

Microbiologically induced corrosion (MIC) is beginning to mature as a subject in its own right. It is becoming increasingly clear that its full understanding calls for expertise in microbiology as well as corrosion science. Two important recent reviews on the electrochemical aspects of MIC have been published by Dexter et al.[10]

It is difficult to generalize about the mechanism of MIC. There will, of course, be microbiologically induced changes in a particular environment, which may be general or highly localized. These changes may lead to a characteristic form of corrosion, or they may establish conditions that will allow another form of corrosion, such as crevice corrosion, to proceed. It is, therefore, necessary to learn about the mechanisms that lead to a corrosion-prone situation as well as to monitor and, hopefully, to control corrosion once it has started.

Measurements of the corrosion potential E_{corr} by themselves can give no information on mechanism. They should at least be accompanied by polarization resistance and redox potential measurements, and surface analytical techniques should be used as appropriate. But there may be pitfalls. Whether biofilms influence the behavior of the reference electrode needs to be checked. The influence of light is another potential factor since many biological processes are photosensitive. The reviews should be consulted for further details.

An example of an indirect form of MIC in stainless steel cooling water systems was reported by Tverberg et al.[11] The problem was associated with a number of strains of manganese fixing bacteria that are more common in, and perhaps restricted to, the South. These can form an insoluble deposit on the inner surfaces of stainless steel or other piping systems that circulate cooling water. Nothing much happens until the system is subjected to chlorination.

Then there is rapid and massive crevice corrosion associated with the manganese-containing deposits. The problem does not occur if the tube surfaces can be kept clean. The simplest control may be a flow rate of 6 ft/s., where applicable. If mechanical cleaning is used, care must be taken to ensure the cleaning process cannot deposit fragments of carbon steel as these would depolarize the stainless steel and lead to major corrosion troubles by another mechanism. Chemical cleaning agents must, of course, be benign to stainless steel.

Deterioration of Nonmetallic Materials

Deterioration of materials other than metals by corrosion or otherwise noncorrosive deterioration of metals also can be important economically, though this is not often treated as part of a study of corrosion. Other than mechanical wear, possibilities include the following.

Concrete can be damaged by freezing and thawing cycles, particularly in the presence of deicing salts. This will be considered as part of the treatment of corrosion of reinforcing steel (Chapter 10). Concrete also is subject to attack by acids; rainwater contaminated by SO_2 and CO_2 is one source of trouble, but much more concentrated acids can result from bacterial action.[4] For example, concrete sewer pipe can be seriously attacked. Natural stones with substantial calcite content are affected similarly.

Polymeric materials are prone to degradation, particularly in the presence of ultraviolet radiation or ozone produced by such radiation. The common effect is excessive additional condensation reactions or oxidation to yield unduly hard and brittle surface layers. The most common remedy is to pigment the material with carbon black to exclude the radiation from all but the surface layers. Automobile tires are one example of this approach. Where excessive polymerization follows a free radical mechanism, it is also possible to inhibit the process by deliberate addition of free radical getters. An example of the problem is polyolefin rope. For typical "on deck" service, the rope loses its properties more rapidly than does the hemp rope, which it normally would replace.

The mechanical stability of plastics also can be a problem. All pipe sizes are implicated, from small gas distribution lines to large size sewer pipe. The latter case calls for great care to ensure transverse thermal gradient and stresses do not cause problems. Very careful analysis is required.

Another problem area is in pressure vessels of fiber-reinforced plastics. Failures are occurring, but the mechanism of deterioration is not clear. Creep probably is involved. The problem is considered in more detail in Chapter 15.

Wood, another natural polymer, can deteriorate in a number of ways. For structural applications, it should be treated to inhibit the biological agents responsible for the process. Microorganisms and insects most often are involved. A variety of small mammals can cause damage by chewing, usually on wood or plastics, although aluminum is occasionally involved.

Polymeric materials also can be damaged by solvents or their vapors. In most cases, fairly long periods of exposure are needed. Certain paint thinners or solvents can cause stress cracking of hard hats, for example.

The harsh environment of the northern winter creates a number of real problems for both materials and personnel. First is the low-temperature embrittlement of bcc materials, such as steel. This can be solved, albeit at some cost, by ensuring a very fine grain size and a very clean steel. Special care also is needed with welding. Ductile to brittle transition temperatures in the -50 to -70°C (-58 to -94°F) range are needed. Other limitations are: the effectiveness of winter clothing, which sets a limit of -45 to -50°C (-49 to -58°F); the glass transition temperature of the electrical insulation on cables, etc., often around -50°C (-58°F); and the stiffening point of water-free hydrocarbon lubricants, again around -50°C (-58°F).

Components for remote transmission lines and other structures must remain ductile, even at the minimum temperatures that can be envisaged. Only in this way can northern mines, tar sands operations, oil exploration and recovery, and other operations be economically viable.

References

1. R.N. Parkins, *Corrosion Processes* (London, UK: Applied Science Publishers, 1982).
2. P.J.E. Forsyth, C.A. Stubbington, *J. Inst. Met.* 83 (1954): p. 395.
3. M.G. Fontana, N.D. Greene, *Corrosion Engineering* (New York, NY: McGraw-Hill, 1967).
4. H.L. Logan, *The Stress Corrosion of Metals* (New York, NY: Wiley,1966).
5. H.E. Johnson, Thesis, University of Alberta, Edmonton, Alberta. 1964.
6. U.R. Evans, *The Corrosion and Oxidation of Metals*, 2nd supplementary volume (London, UK: Arnold, 1976).
7. R.B. Waterhouse, *Fretting Corrosion* (London, UK: Pergamon Press,1972).
8. G.L. Booth, *Microbiological Corrosion* (London, UK: Mills and Boon, 1971).
9. Anon, *Science Dimension* 4, 1 (1972): pp. 4-9.
10. S.C. Dexter, L.N. Moettus, K.E. Lucas, *Corrosion* 41 (10)1985: pp. 598.
11. A. Tyverberg, *Publication of South African Corrosion Institute*.

7

Control Measures — Modification of the Environment

Control measures can be considered under either electrical or chemical techniques. The most important electrical technique is cathodic protection, in which the potential of the corroding structure is moved to a value where the metal is thermodynamically inert. This involves a significant electrical operating cost, but is universally applicable. A secondary electrical technique, anodic protection, is applicable only to metals that can be passivated (Chapter 4). Of the chemical control measures, the use of inhibitors already has been treated. The remaining techniques involve a gross control of water chemistry and the humidity level of the atmosphere.

Cathodic Protection as a Control Measure

Cathodic protection has a long history. It is the principle behind the effective action of galvanizing and was first applied in specific form by the team of Sir Humphrey Davy and Michael Faraday in 1824. In their application, zinc protector plates were applied to the copper sheathing on the oak hulls of ships in the British Navy. Copper sheathing was necessary to prevent the attack of the hull by marine borers. The copper also was sufficiently toxic to prevent any significant attachment of most fouling organisms. This early application of cathodic protection was an unqualified success.

By the time steel hulls replaced earlier materials, some 40 to 50 years later, zinc plates had become traditional and continued to be applied. In the light of later knowledge, these plates were far too small to significantly affect the corrosion of steel. But by that time they were required by tradition and continued to be used.

Effective modern application of cathodic protection of ships was pioneered in the Canadian Navy by K.N. Barnard and co-workers in Halifax soon after World War II. Barnard established that ship hull potential should be maintained at about 850 mV with respect to the

Ag/AgCl reference electrode. This could be achieved with galvanic or impressed current anodes; careful attention to detail was required to ensure electrical continuity of the anode connections for long periods and proper current distribution to the hull by anode placement and insulating shielding. For mechanical and hydrodynamic reasons, the preferred location for anodes was on the bilge keel.

Anode materials evaluated by the Barnard group included zinc, aluminum, and magnesium as galvanic anodes with impressed current anodes of steel, graphite, lead, duriron, and platinum also being studied. The resulting naval specifications selected AZ63 Mg alloy, with resistance control, for small installations, and a Pb 2% Ag alloy for use on larger ships. The group also extended its work to cover the protection of steel jetties. Later developments by other workers have recommended specialty zinc and aluminum alloys for galvanic anode systems, and platinum-coated titanium or tantalum anodes for impressed current systems. Trailing wire anodes also have been proposed, e.g., for icebreakers.

Although cathodic protection was first applied to ships, its most common use is for mitigating corrosion of pipelines and other buried metallic structures, such as tanks and tank bottoms. The key issue is that cathodic protection can protect the environment better than any alternative. An increasingly important application is the protection of reinforcing steel in concrete exposed to chlorides, either from road salt or in a marine environment. Peabody's monograph[1] and the second edition of Morgan's book[2] are the standard works on cathodic protection.

Cathodic protection is well-established and is required by law for the protection of pipelines and underground storage tanks for petroleum products. The principle of cathodic protection, as outlined in Figure 7.01, calls for the potential of the originally cathodic parts of the structure to be polarized to the point that the mixed potential of the entire structure is a little more anodic than the potential of the originally most

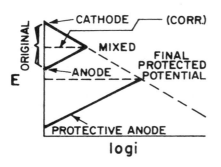

FIGURE 7.01 *Schematic illustration of the principle of cathodic protection.*

effective anodes. A considerable current, often more than twice the original corrosion current, is required. It does not matter how the current is supplied, but it must be more or less uniformly distributed. The final protected potential must be in the immunity region (Figure 2.04). A common criterion is 850mv with respect to the copper sulfate electrode. But this may not be adequate where bacterial activity is prevalent.

Protection of Underground Structures

Impressed current systems with insoluble anodes are most commonly applied for cathodic protection of pipelines. Applied voltages of a few tens of volts are applied to the anodes and the potential of the line with respect to a $Cu/CuSO_4$ electrode, and the system is monitored and kept at suitable levels. Anodes are normally inserted in a carbonaceous backfill. In one technique, lubricated and carefully sized granules are used so the backfill can be fluidized to make anode placement and replacement easier and more economical.

Potentials of a few tens of volts are commonly applied to the anodes. This can result in a dangerous step potential at the surface above the anode bed, which could be lethal to animals of various kinds, particularly in wet weather. The hold-down potential for DC is higher than for mixed AC and DC so rectifiers for cathodic protection require highly efficient filtering. It is good practice to bury anodes so deeply that the surface step potential is trivial since security fences cannot be guaranteed to keep small boys or livestock permanently away from the vicinity of anode beds.

Galvanic anodes also can be used for pipeline protection. This method is generally more expensive than using the impressed current types. It is restricted to remote areas where electricity cannot be obtained, or to congested areas where minimal electrostatic fields can reduce electrical interaction with "foreign" pipelines, etc.

Several cases of interaction with foreign pipelines are worthy of note. Any protected pipeline will be at a more cathodic potential than the corrosion potential of bare steel in a similar environment. Hence, the electrostatic field will stimulate corrosion of adjacent metal, as shown in Figure 7.02. The electrolytic current between the protected and unprotected line tends to stimulate corrosion of the latter since an anodic area is induced electrostatically. The best way to resolve the problem is to bond the two lines metallically to eliminate stray current damage. This will require careful negotiation with the owner of the foreign line. The best solution involves cathodically protecting both lines. In this case, the bonding will serve to eliminate major problems if either cathodic protection systems suffers a power outage. Stray currents can be particularly troublesome where pipelines run parallel to each other. The logical solution is to protect both.

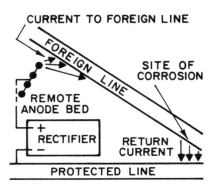

FIGURE 7.02 Corrosion of a "foreign" pipeline.

Somewhat similar considerations obtain when a pipeline passes close to any sizeable buried metallic structure. Small galvanic anodes are helpful in such cases. The potential resulting from a galvanic anode is small, and the resultant electrostatic field is much smaller than for the standard anode beds with applied current. Protection can then be achieved with minimal interference, albeit at a somewhat higher cost.

Once cathodic protection is applied, initial variations in pipe to soil potential, from whatever cause, cease to be troublesome. The most common causes for these differences in pipe-to-soil potential are differential aeration cells. In these cells, the aerated pipe would have been the cathode, and the nonaerated pipe, the anode. Clay near loam or gravel, passages under roadways, etc. would set up such cells. In addition, bacteria-loaded sites in swamps and similar environments set up bacterially stimulated cells of other types.

The inherent cost of cathodic protection is much higher than for anodic protection. The current requirement will be about twice the normal corrosion current, often something like 6 ma/ft.[2] Since this is a perpetual requirement, it makes good economic sense to coat the pipeline, ship, etc. with a suitable wrap or paint system so cathodic protection is only needed for the holidays in the coating. The coating must be alkali-resistant to withstand cathodically generated alkali.

Cathodic deposit of such compounds as basic calcium or magnesium carbonate can be formed at potentials of about 1,000 mv or higher rather than at 850 mv, which comes close to conferring complete protection. Full protection without cathodic deposit can be achieved at lower cost in many cases, for ships and jetties in particular. For pipelines with high applied protective potentials at infrequent intervals, cathodic deposit is more or less inevitable at holidays in regions close to the anode beds.

A word of caution about hydrogen damage to cathodically protected structures: Potentials sufficient to cause cathodic deposit also can drive hydrogen into the underlying steel. Thus, it is wise to use steels that have some tolerance for hydrogen in cases where the cathodic protection system can produce cathodic deposit. This may place constraints on pipelines exposed to low ambient temperatures since the ductile-to-brittle transition temperature can be raised markedly by interstitial hydrogen. Careful testing should precede major installations. A dramatic incident along these lines occurred when a harbor buoy was being cathodically cleaned in its normal environment of saltwater. Its high tensile steel mooring cable, being used as a conductor, disintegrated violently as a result of the operation.

In certain cases, cathodic protection can call for unusual planning. In one Eastern Ontario location, two chemical plants are linked by two pipelines carrying liquified ammonia and concentrated nitric acid, the former in carbon steel and the latter in 304L stainless steel. A complication arose because nitric acid is a better conductor of electricity than the pipe that contains it. For this reason, a potential gradient in the pipe is to be avoided. These lines also cross a mainline railroad with associated communications circuitry.

The solution to this problem was to bond the pipelines to each other and to a substantial conductor from the ground bed. In addition, the lines were electrically isolated at each end. The rail line facilities also were bonded into the system.

Pipeline leaks can be considered from a number of points of view. If the cost and environmental impact of a leak can be tolerated, it is possible to predict the proper time to apply cathodic protection from a plot, as shown in Figure 7.03. Assuming an effective mean cost to repair a leak, the protection system is justified when the costs of leaks in the absence of cathodic protection would balance the annual cost of cathodic protection. If the insult to the environment caused by leakage cannot be tolerated, cathodic protection should be applied from the outset. This is required by law in many jurisdictions.

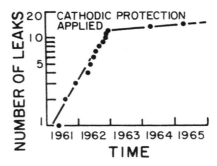

FIGURE 7.03 *Semilog plot of leak curve showing dramatic improvement in leak incidence following application of cathodic protection.*

Even cathodically protected structures can be influenced by stray currents from high-voltage sources. Telluric currents of somewhat obscure origin are one possibility. Others are surges from lightning strikes, electric traction systems, and the effects of high-voltage DC transmission lines. High voltages can be drained effectively by the use of a series of large electrodes in an electrolytic conductor, such as aqueous potassium hydroxide.

Alternating currents also can cause corrosion. The effect is much less than for direct currents. Large currents (such as would result from electrically powered trains) are potential sources of difficulty.

From time to time, cathodic protection of car underbody parts has been proposed. This is an attractive concept. The main problem is to ensure an adequate throw of protective current via the thin electrolyte film present on the car. The practical conclusion seems to be that effective local protection can be achieved, but that the number of anodes required for total protection would be unreasonably large.

Cathodic Protection of Reinforcing Steel

The salt-enhanced corrosion of reinforcing steel was first recognized as a problem in the 1940s in work for the South African Navy on dockside structures.[3] Other studies showed that the difficulties were found in many other tropical or subtropical marine locations.

110

At a somewhat later stage it became evident there also were major problems in any location, such as the northern US or Canada, where the public had demanded extensive use of road salt to keep the roads clear in winter. By about 1960 the associated deterioration of bridges, overpasses, and elevated highways had become the major contributor to corrosion costs continent-wide. Parking garages were soon added to the list.

Initial response was that all would be well if the concrete placement technique were better controlled. Unfortunately, this only led to a marginal improvement. Even with proper rebar placement and cover, traffic loads will eventually cause cracks and provide an entry path for saline solutions. The next remedies proposed were the use of epoxy-coated rebar and application of cathodic protection.

The coating of rebar was most successful if it used bars made in a mini-mill that used electric furnace practice. But the mills never set out to produce rebar on a regular basis because their other product lines were more profitable. Typical rebar has quite a poor finish; preparing it for a thick epoxy coating would be much more expensive and probably prone to a higher holiday count.

The remaining method of protection, cathodic protection, can be highly effective, but tends to be costly. More research is needed on the most appropriate criteria for cathodic protection so costs can be optimized. It is difficult to measure the potential of the bar, and factors of safety tend to become very expensive. However, this cathodic protection system differs from others in that there will be insignificant corrosion if the chlorides can be driven out and kept out. Cathodic protection achieves this; but perhaps once this has been effected the criterion for protection should not be maintenance of a particular potential, but rather the maintenance of the potential gradient necessary to prevent chlorides from reentering.

The cathodic protection of parking garages must be achieved without obstruction to the headroom, which is often severely constrained. Conductive paint coatings or specially designed low-profile anodes have to be used.

Design of Cathodic Protection Systems

For cathodic protection to be effective it is necessary to maintain the protected structure at an appropriate potential. Where the underground structure is coated with an insulator, the current demand is small and the total power costs are insensitive to the potential selected. But where the structure is uncoated or poorly coated, the current demand is large and is very sensitive to the potential selected. A "factor of safety" can be very costly.

Two alternative views on how cathodic protection works for large structures have been presented. In the 1930s, the postulate of Mears and Brown,[4] also supported by Hoar,[5] was that, when the applied cathodic current is high enough, the localized anodic current drops to zero. There is a net cathodic current over the whole surface. An alternative view was promulgated by LaQue in 1965, suggesting that as cathodic current was being applied the area of the anodes was reduced but their current density was substantially constant.[6] The former theory suggests that protection occurs when the whole surface is polarized to the potential of the local action anodes. The latter theory, on the other hand, requires polarization to the potential of the local action cathodes to ensure sporadic localized corrosion ceases.

The issue has been reexamined by Dexter et al.[7] along with careful examination of the actual corrosion that occurred at local anodes for steel and aluminum. Their work lent support to the Mears and Brown view and suggests that partial cathodic protection will lead to some reduction in overall attack.

This leads to problems for those who pass laws and draw up regulations for matters such as pipeline safety. Adequate treatment for a pipeline through a desert area with a sandy soil might not require cathodic protection or even coating. On the other hand, a line through a typical temperate region would need cathodic protection as secondary protection for holidays in the original coating. In the Arctic, the ground rules are again different. Frozen soil is not corrosive, but if the line carries a warm product, or if there is seasonal thawing, cathodic protection is needed. It must be remembered that both the cost of power and the cost of cleaning up spills can be extremely high in remote northern locations.

Electrostatics and Cathodic Protection

Successful design of a cathodic protection system involves the maintenance of an appropriate electrostatic potential in and around the protected structure. If it is not possible to effect this on the basis of prior experience, it will be wise to fall back on suitable theoretical models.

112

Any theoretical treatment of cathodic protection must stem from an electrostatic model, this being the appropriate element of a more generalized potential theory. There does not appear to be a treatment based on cathodic protection; rather, the literature refers to electroplating, the field in which current distribution has the greatest obvious economic impact. A critical review of the literature, prepared by Kronsbein as part of an American Electroplaters Society research report, covers pre-1950 literature in considerable detail.[8] The most significant contributions to the field are contained in a series of five papers on "The Theory of the Potential and the Technical Practice of Electrodeposition" by Kasper.[9-13] This set of papers outlines, in mathematical form, the application of potential theory to electrolytic solutions and applies the theory to electrodeposition, making the assumption that the solutions involved were homogeneous and, in the first two papers, that there was negligible polarization of the cathodic process.

The first Kasper paper introduces the topic and deals with the restricted cases of uniform current flow.[9] The second paper deals with the more practical cases of point-plane and line-plane systems.[10] Planes that are insulating as well as conducting are considered, along with planes that have one or two right angle bends. The concept of imaging is introduced. The relevant equations are solved, and numerous graphs and equations are used to illustrate the solutions. This treatment assumes no polarization.

The next paper adds the complication of polarization to some of the line-plane systems.[11] Linear polarization is assumed in which the polarization is proportional to the current density. Laplace transform methods are required for the solutions. The fourth paper deals with current flow between and to circular cylinders, both with and without polarization.[12] The final paper extends the treatment to more complex two-dimensional rectangular enclosures.[13] This is of less significance in the cathodic protection field.

A significant limitation of the Kasper treatment is that he assumed an even deposition to the edge of the workpiece and made no allowance for the phenomenon of edge buildup. It is well-known that there is a higher current density at edges; this was addressed in a later paper by Wagner.[14]

When the Kasper treatment is used for the design of actual cathodic protection systems, it is probably appropriate to assume there is no polarization. As has been pointed out by Webster, the effects of polarization will then constitute an engineering safety factor.[15]

Water Treatment

The two most obvious factors in corrosion by water are the pH of the water and its oxygen content. Secondary factors include the scale-forming ability of the water and its ability to develop biological fouling growths in cooling water systems and the like. The topic of corrosion by waters is covered in considerable detail in Butler and Ison's specialized text.[16] This is a necessary reference book for any professional in the field of water corrosion.

In once-through cooling water systems little can be done to treat the water because of cost. The major effort should go to removing suspended solids that would otherwise cause silt deposits. Biological fouling can be combatted by measures such as intermittent chlorination, although this will make extra demands on the corrosion resistance of the tubing material.

Scaling tendencies are, of course, important in once-through cooling systems. A numerical indication of scaling tendencies is the so-called Langelier Index, the determination of which is detailed in the *NACE Corrosion Engineer's Reference Book*.[17] The treatment enables an estimate to be made of the temperature and pH at which scaling will commence for a water of known calcium hardness and alkalinity. A positive Langelier Index indicates scale-forming tendencies while a negative index shows scale will not form. In the latter case, corrosion is to be expected when dissolved oxygen levels are appreciable.

In recirculating cooling water systems, there is more scope for treating the water. Scale formers should be eliminated by deionizing or otherwise softening the water, and inhibitors should be added. Since many inhibitors have a slightly alkaline reaction, pH control is normally more or less automatic. The choice of inhibitors may be restricted on environmental grounds; if this is not a factor, chromates or phosphates would be the normal choice (Chapter 4). Measures to combat fouling also may be necessary. Despite its corrosion ramifications, chlorination is a real possibility. Another choice is the use of organotin compounds. Some of these are highly specific poisons for the lower forms of life with reasonably low mammalian toxicity. Another elegant technique is to use ion exchange resins to maintain an essentially zero concentration of essential trace elements, e.g., vanadium, for the particular fouling organisms. Heavy metal ions such as Cu++ or Hg+ also are effective toxins, though there may be corrosion and environmental objections to their use. Domestic water supplies often are not treated from a corrosion point of view.

Control of waters in backyard swimming pools requires that the pH be maintained at a comfortable level, around 6.7. In addition, the water must be absolutely clear and must not be aggressive to exposed metal components or to the pool wall or liner. For concrete-lined pools there must be enough calcium in solution for incipient precipitation of a scale, but this is not as necessary for pools with a vinyl liner. About 0.5 ppm of available chlorine is required, preferably in stabilized form, along with a small amount of a wetting agent that inhibits algae formation. Despite these precautions, it also is necessary to give the water a "shock treatment" of 3-4 ppm chlorine at one- to two-week intervals. Small indoor pools tend to use bromine rather than chlorine-based sterilants.

Speller's text has more detail on water treatment than any modern general book.[18] In essence, the most important factor in corrosion by domestic waters is the oxygen content, particularly for hot waters. Figures 7.04 and 7.05 show the oxygen solubility and corrosion rate

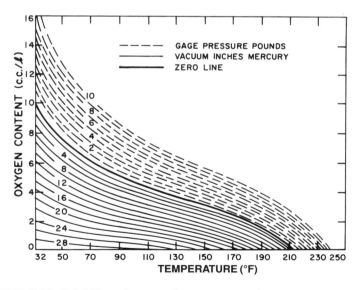

FIGURE 7.04 *Solubility of oxygen in water at various temperatures and pressures.[18] (Used with permission of the McGraw-Hill Book Co.)*

for hot waters. The latter shows total corrosion of steel in 150 days for a closed system using 22°C (73°F) tap water.

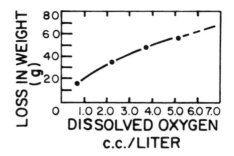

FIGURE 7.05 *Corrosion at various oxygen concentrations of steel in water at 22°C (72°F) for 150 days.[18] (Used with permission of the McGraw-Hill Book Co.)*

By nature, domestic water supplies cannot be given much treatment. Soft waters can be treated with a little lime, and hot waters can be deaerated or deactivated by reaction with a large area of bare steel for about 45 minutes. Circulating domestic hot water systems are most troublesome because of continuing makeup. In one apartment house case studied carefully by Speller, the oxygen content was reduced to one sixth of its value in the absence of treatment by a deactivation technique. In the modern context, copper piping should be used for circulating hot water systems with most waters.

The common mistake of using steel or galvanized steel for hot water systems for high-rise buildings warrants detailed comment. Many of these have galvanized water piping for the larger sizes that is buried in concrete and virtually impossible to repair or replace. The smaller sizes would be copper. But with hot water recirculation through a mixed copper and steel system the galvanized coating would soon be gone. However, there would be early warning signs of rust staining before destruction of the whole system is imminent. The ultimate remedy, of course, is to exclude steel or galvanized steel as a permissible material for recirculating systems in the building codes or design specifications.

For existing buildings, all that can be done for a potable water system is to restrict oxygen content. The early method was Speller's deactivation procedure.[18] The modern equivalent would be to install deaeration equipment, assuming this would be more economical than total replacement of steel by copper, or by a polymeric material if one can be found that is suitable for hot water service.

Treatment of Boiler Waters

The treatment of boiler waters has been practiced since the early days of steam technology. Both calcium carbonate scales and acidic conditions in the boiler were found to cause costly failures so softening (later deionization) and pH control were introduced early. However, if the boiler water was alkaline and unbuffered, there was local caustic buildup in the vicinity of leaks at rivets and so forth, and the water conditions would drift into the alkaline corrosion zone   (Figure 2.04). As discussed in Chapter 6, this triggers the form of SCC known as caustic embrittlement, and earlier resulted in a number of boiler explosions. The obvious solution was to buffer the boiler water at the optimum pH of somewhat below 10 using phosphates. Where schedules of phosphate-containing boiler waters can be tolerated environmentally, phosphate treatment is still a preferred treatment method.

Modern boiler practice requires high temperatures to achieve the best attainable thermodynamic efficiency for electricity generation. These high temperatures dictate large unit sizes, and whether in fossil-fired or nuclear plant make water control critical. The effect of pH is emphasized in Figure 7.06. This shows the influence of vari-

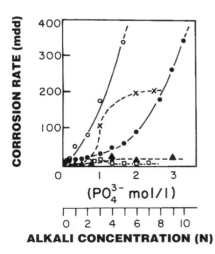

FIGURE 7.06

Corrosion rate of carbon steel in various alkalis at 315 °C (590 °F).[19]

117

ous alkaline salts on the corrosion rate of steel at 360°C (680°F). Note the good characteristics of Na_3PO_4 and LiOH. Closely related to this is the solubility of magnetite, shown in Figure 7.07.

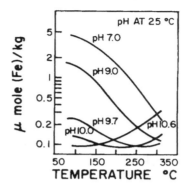

FIGURE 7.07 *Magnetite solubility. (Used with permission of the* Journal of Chemical Thermodynamics. © *by Academic Press, Inc., Ltd., London.)*[20]

Having established a target pH for boiler water, it is wise to examine the orthophosphate system to see how the target can be attained. Figure 7.08 shows the relationship between phosphate content of the boiler and pH for a variety of values of the Na/PO_4 ratio. For practical levels of phosphate addition, the optimum $Na:PO_4$ ratio is around 2.6.

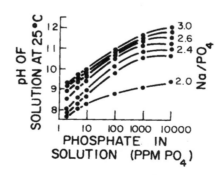

FIGURE 7.08 *pH of orthosphosphate solutions having various sodium to phosphate molar ratios.*[21]

118

The physical form of any internal boiler scale also is important. The intent is that anonadherent sludge rather than an adherent scale is formed. Blow down can then eliminate the sludge. The difference between the sludge and scale depends on a nucleation process, and any technique that favors homogeneous (rather than heterogeneous) nucleation is desirable. Adsorbable boiler additives should adsorb on the heat-transfer surfaces and inhibit heterogeneous nucleation if they are to be effective.

The ideal is to have a boiler for which the water is of controlled chemistry and without entrained solids. In practice, a solids loading of 50 ppm is probably as good as can be achieved easily, at least for nonnuclear boilers. Nuclear boilers require much cleaner waters to minimize transported radioactivity levels.

An alternative to the phosphate treatment is the so-called zero solids treatment using amines. The boiler water is carefully purified by ion exchangers, and alkalinity is achieved by the addition of ammonia or amines. These are sufficiently volatile that they also report in the steam so brass must be eliminated from all condensate return lines and other parts of the steam system. Where steam is used for domestic heating, there will be restrictions on the use of amines (including hydrazine) because of the danger of toxic leaks.

The toxicity of hydrazine has resulted in its being banned in steam plants for domestic heating in many jurisdictions. This has led to research on hydrazine and potential substitutes. [22,23] This work has shown that hydrazine is only an indifferent oxygen scavenger; it should be regarded as a passivating inhibitor that can only be effective in the presence of a trace of oxygen. This opens the way for the use of other passivating inhibitors that are less toxic than hydrazine. High pressure boiler operations, particularly in load-following service, are appropriate for this strategy.

Whatever form of water treatment is used, the elimination of oxygen is essential. Deaerating heaters remove most of it, but it must finally be removed with an oxygen scavenger. The first such scavenger to be used was sodium sulfite, but hydrazine is more commonly used in higher temperature boilers. In atomic reactors, either hydrogen or ammonia will act as an oxygen scavenger when activated by an intense radiation field. Transient presence of free radicals complicates the situation.

The chief cause of poor chemical control in boilers is leakage of untreated cooling water from the condenser into the recirculating boiler feed water. The negative pressure here means that inward leaking is more or less inevitable, unless the condenser design is unusually stringent. Clearly, the water treatment facility must be able to cope with whatever level of leakage is accepted as trivial or inevitable. Larger leaks require at least a prompt warning signal so remedial measures can be taken before much damage has been done. Nuclear power stations, of course, call for stringent measures to detect and minimize leakage.

Corrosion does not stop with the boiler, however. The steam turbine and the condenser also must be considered. For a phosphate-treated boiler, there will be little carryover of buffering salts in the steam, and adsorbed moisture films on the turbine components will be at near neutral pH. For amine-treated boilers there will be some carryover of volatile amine in the steam so that the adsorbed film pH will be closer to that in the boiler.

There is increasing evidence that some turbine materials, particularly in the larger units (600 MW), may be susceptible to cracking in the steam environment. In any event, turbine shafting should be selected for low crack propagation characteristics, and the shafting should be monitored as closely as practical. The difficulty seems to relate, at least in part, to the increasing difficulties of manufacturing large metallic components of appropriate metallurgical quality. Design detail should be such as to avoid fretting fatigue.

Corrosion in the condenser tubes is much more straightforward and better understood. In any event, the results of a leak here would be less drastic. However, if amines are present, copper alloy tubing should not be used.

Condensate Lines

Where a centralized power plant provides steam heating over an extended area, as on a plant site, university campus, etc., there can be special problems with corrosion of the condensate return lines. In practice, it is virtually impossible to prevent some in-leakage of air to the condensate. Oxygen and carbon dioxide are the components of air that cause trouble.

A recent study has helped clarify the problem by avoiding the generalizations in some earlier treatments.[24] Where soft water is involved, CO_2 can depress the pH and cause the normally protective film to dissolve. If oxygen is available as a depolarizer, corrosion

120

can be expected to continue. Deaeration of the condensate, or chemical treatment compatible with the boiler water treatment in use, may be appropriate and should certainly be evaluated at the design stage.

Atmospheric Control

Dehumidification is the key to atmospheric corrosion control. At or below 40 relative humidity, there is negligible corrosion of any metal of engineering interest. But the techniques for obtaining such humidity control call for painstaking design, except in cold spells in winter.

The key to humidity control is a vapor barrier of some kind. Many plastic films can actually dissolve molecules such as O_2 or H_2O, which can then diffuse through and reappear on the other side. A metallic layer is usually necessary to reduce water vapor permeation to near zero values. Packages for potato chips and other junk food closely follow the state of the art in impermeable packaging. Multilayers of different plastics are typical, backed up with a vacuum-evaporated layer of aluminum. This latter replaces the earlier and more costly foil layer.

Shipping packages can consist of impermeable foils with an internal desiccant and external mechanical protection for the foil. This essentially gives the tropical package that first came into major use in World War II. A more sophisticated version of the impermeable protected package was used by Atomic Energy of Canada, Ltd. (AECL) for shipping assembled reactor calandrias to Argentina for the CANDU reactors being built there. In this case, there was an inert gas blanketing system, deliberate dehumidification, and meticulous recording of conditions actually attained. The ship's captain was made personally responsible for meeting the humidity target.

A rather extensive use of atmospheric control is involved in the various naval programs for "moth balling" inactive ships. In this technique, the necessary maintenance on the ship is performed in advance. The interior is then sealed, with all possible piping and machinery spaces opened to the internal atmosphere. Dehumidification equipment and suitable humidity recorders are then installed. Long experience with this operation shows that humidity can be kept acceptably low for long periods, and corrosion is virtually eliminated. The only humidity excursions noted were traceable to breakdowns of equipment or to the occasional activity of watchmen. With the external ship hull under cathodic protection, the mothballed fleet is available for return to active duty on a prompt and predictable basis.

When large structures such as water towers are to be coated internally in the field, it may be appropriate to dehumidify the internal air for both the preparation and coating steps. This can be achieved with equipment currently available, either via refrigeration or desiccant dehumidification. In the latter case, the ambient temperature of the dried air is higher. This may allow a shorter curing time for the coating so the structure can be returned to service earlier.

The clean rooms used for instrument assembly belong in the same category. The cost of protection normally can be justified on economic grounds. Less obvious is the in-transit and on-site protection of major items of heavy equipment prior to commissioning. Perhaps more should be done in this field.

References

1. A.W. Peabody, *Control of Pipeline Corrosion* (Houston, TX: NACE, 1967).
2. J. Morgan, *Cathodic Prevention*, 2nd edition (Houston, TX: NACE, 1987).
3. D.A. Lewis, W.J. Copenhagen, *Corrosion* 15, 1959: p. 382-388t.
4. R. Mears, R. Brown, *Trans. Electrochem Soc.* 74, 1938: p. 519; and 81, 1942: p. 455.
5. T.P. Hoar, private communication, 1962.
6. F. LaQue, private communication, 1968.
7. S.C. Dexter, L.N. Moettus, K.E. Lucas, *Corrosion* 41 (10) (1985): p. 598.
8. J. Kronsbein, *Plating* 8(1950): pp. 851-854.
9. C. Kasper, *Trans. Electrochem. Soc.* 77, 1940: pp. 353-363.
10. C. Kasper, pp. 365-384.
11. C. Kasper, pp. 131-146.
12. C. Kasper, pp. 147-161
13. C. Kasper, *Trans. Electrochem. Soc.* 82, 1942: pp. 143-185.
14. C. Wagner, *J. Electrochem. Soc.* 98, 1951: pp. 116-128.
15. H. Webster, private communicatiion, 1979
16. G. Butler, H.C.K. Ison, Corrosion Prevention in Waters (New

York, NY: Van Nostrand Reinhold, 1966).

17. R.S. Treseder. *NACE Corrosion Engineer's Reference Book* (Houston, TX: NACE, 1980).

18. F.N. Speller, *Corrosion, Causes and Prevention*, 2nd ed. (New York, NY: McGraw-Hill, 1935).

19. H.A. Klein, Presentation at Les Renardieres, France, July 8, 1970.

20. F.H. Sweeton, C.F. Baes, *J. Chem. Thermodyn.* 2(1970): p. 496.

21. V.M. Marcy, S.L. Halstead, *Combustion*, Vol. 84, No. 7, p. 45.

22. W.L. Trace, *Materials Performance* 20 5(1981): pp. 46-49.

23. S.T. Costa, S.B. Dilcer, J.L. Walker, CORROSION/89, paper no. 71 (Houston, TX: NACE, 1989).

24. G. McIntire, J. Lippert, J. Yudelson, *Corrosion* 46, 2(90): p. 91

8

Control Measures — Protective Coatings

Surface Preparation

Painting is one of the long-established methods of corrosion control. If the environment can be effectively excluded, a paint can do its intended job. It takes good user technique to be sure a paint works properly. Otherwise, it can be a waste of money. The object of painting is to furnish a barrier coating that will exclude the environment and prevent its premature adverse reaction with the substrate. All paint systems fail eventually, but avoidance of premature failure is needed to minimize the annual cost.

The first and most important step in assuring good paint performance is surface preparation. If there is oil or grease contamination, this must first be removed by solvent or vapor degreasing with, for example, a chlorinated hydrocarbon, or by alkali or emulsion cleaning, and so forth. The degreased surface can then be sandblasted or pickled.

Paint failure normally involves a combination of oxidation and ultraviolet light. There may be a change in appearance, such as loss of gloss, or there may be a reduction in the film thickness remaining, etc. Premature failure is usually characterized by a loss of adhesion, either with the substrate or between successive paint layers. Loss of adhesion to the substrate also can be a secondary process resulting from corrosion.

Paint Adhesion

To avoid these problems, adequate cleaning must be done to remove greasy soils of various kinds, poorly adherent prior coatings, corrosion product salts, and solid corrosion products, such as millscale. Primers that are to be topcoated must be completely cured; manufacturers are tempted to underestimate the time required for this. Topcoats on primers or other existing coatings must be compatible. As a general rule, two paint coats will be compatible if the plots of their solubility parameter vs their hydrogen bonding index are appropriately close.

Solvent cleaning and water washing may both be required prior to processes designed to remove oxides, pickling and abrasive blasting being the most common. Sandblasting has been the norm, but is environmentally objectionable. Use of steel shot, crushed walnut shells, etc., in place of sand is more costly. Water blasting with very high pressure water is another possibility, as is wet sandblasting (sand washing). Pickling is usually practical only in the steel mill. This would be followed promptly by rinsing, drying, and priming. If the primer is soft, it needs to be protected by a thin, but hard, topcoat to minimize shipping damage. Only minor touchup work is then needed in the field.

Old work needs to have all loosely adherent coatings removed. Hand cleaning with wire brushes and so forth is the least effective, followed by power tool cleaning, commercial sandblasting, and blasting to white metal, in order of increasing cost and efficacy. All of these processes are labor-intensive. A further variant is flame cleaning. This can cause oxide or mill scale to crack because of differential thermal expansion. It should be followed by power tool cleaning and priming while the surface is still warm. This is only practical for relatively small areas.

An interesting case of high quality surface preparation arose during the construction of the Forth Bridge in Scotland. A complete surface treatment shop was set up on site, and all steel work was subjected to abrasive cleaning, zinc spraying, and painting immediately prior to actual installation. This counteracted the vagaries of the British climate and assured minimum damage to the intended finish during delivery. Subsequent maintenance costs on the bridge have been exceptionally low, despite the marine environment.

As mentioned in the previous chapter, it is possible to control the humidity inside tanks, etc., being coated in the field.

From time to time, claims are made that a given brand of paint can be applied to rusted steel. The bare fact is that any and all paints give best performance on adequately cleaned steel. Paints with an inhibitive primer, such as the environmentally undesirable red lead pigmented types, will be somewhat more tolerant of rust than other types of paint. Still, painting on rust is never recommended. Advertising that recommends painting on rusty steel is misleading.

Two classes of painting should be recognized. The first is cosmetic painting, for example, on fire mains for identification purposes. For noncorrosive indoor applications, a solvent wipe may be the only justified pretreatment, and the coating thickness is not important. The second class is intended to protect from corrosion; here the pretreatment is necessarily expensive and thorough. Thickness also is important for optimum performance and should be a minimum of 3-12 mils for air-dried coatings, depending on the type of coating used and the intended service.

Protective Coatings — Paints

For best overall performance, the first coat of paint should be applied at the steel mill. At the mill, it is more practical to set up a high quality finishing line; pickling is economical only for a large throughput and should be followed by a reasonably prompt priming step. Normally, a weldable primer often pigmented with iron oxide is used. The primer also should be hard enough to withstand handling en route to the assembly site with minimal damage. Alternatively, a thin (but hard) top coat can be applied prior to shipping to protect a softer primer.

Steel that has been pickled or sandblasted will rust rather rapidly. Consequently, a phosphate conversion step often precedes priming. The object is to replace the superficial oxide with phosphate, which then acts as a good paint base. An alternative is to combine phosphoric acid with a specialized primer, giving the so-called etch primer. This, in turn, is covered with a normal primer.

Essentially similar steps are required for painting in the field. However, it is much more difficult and usually more costly to achieve a consistently good prime coat in the field than in the shop. Best practice calls for a shop-applied prime coat with subsequent coats in the field.

When old paint is recoated, it is first necessary to remove everything that is loose or nonadherent. Where there has been local damage or imperfections in the paint coating, all defective material must be removed, and the uncoated portions suitably feathered into the surrounding sound coating.

Sandblasting to bare metal is preferred for damaged areas. The feathering should be done (e.g., with fine-grained sand, -60 mesh) with the nozzle at least 1 m from the surfaceand with the sand directed at near grazing incidence. This minimizes damage to otherwise sound paint in the feathering zone. For some coatings, solvent wiping may be necessary. In any case, a highly penetrating low viscosity primer is applied, preferably by brush, after which more or less normal painting schedules can apply. It must be noted that this primer is the key to the original primer and the original topcoat. It may well be necessary to adopt a primer and repair top coat of a different type from the systems used in the original coating.

Compatibility between a resin and a solvent system or between a paint and an existing polymeric coating is a somewhat difficult matter to judge. The existing coating should be swelled somewhat by the solvent system of the intended topcoat but should not be swelled excessively or be completely soluble. The extent of the swelling can be judged by the use of a plot of the hydrogen bonding index vs the solubility parameter. Examples of such plots are shown in Figures 8.01 and 8.02.[1]

The paints most difficult to recoat are ones that are, or have become, highly polymerized and crosslinked. This may occur in the normal curing process or on longer exposure to an aggressive combination, such as ultraviolet light and oxygen. Such coatings with effectively high molecular weight present the greatest difficulties with recoating. Many early epoxy formulations fell in this category. Partial removal by sandblasting would tend to lead to subsurface damage and make successful recoating impossible. For details on recoating on difficult substrates refer to Munger.[2]

Organic Coatings and Their Classification

In general, organic protective coatings are applied to a surface in liquid form and dried to give a continuous solid film. The drying process can involve chemical reactions, often polymerizations, or merely consist of solvent evaporation. The properties of the dry film are affected by: nonvolatile plasticizers to improve flexibility; pigments for cosmetic and other purposes; binders to improve coherence and adherence; and more or less inert fillers. The role of pigments is complex; many function as inhibitors, red lead being a prime example. Flake or leafing pigments will tend to align with their flakes overlapping and parallel to the surface as the film dries, drastically reducing rates of diffusion through the film. Aluminum and mica are examples.

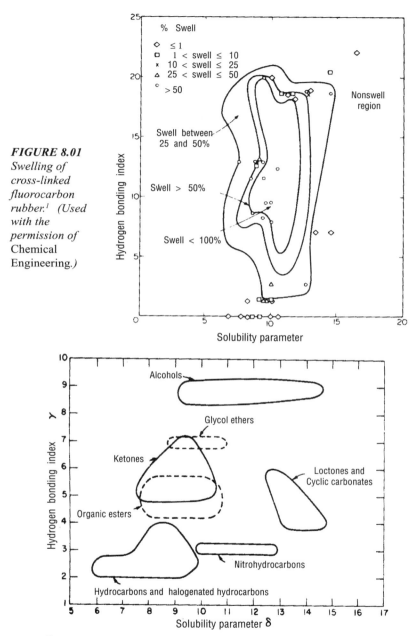

FIGURE 8.01 *Swelling of cross-linked fluorocarbon rubber.[1] (Used with the permission of* Chemical Engineering.*)*

Within the figure:

% Swell
◇ ≤ 1
□ 1 < swell ≤ 10
× 10 < swell ≤ 25
△ 25 < swell ≤ 50
○ > 50

Nonswell region

Swell between 25 and 50%

Swell > 50%

Swell < 100%

Hydrogen bonding index

Solubility parameter

Within Figure 8.02:

Alcohols

Glycol ethers

Ketones

Loctones and Cyclic carbonates

Organic esters

Nitrohydrocarbons

Hydrocarbons and halogenated hydrocarbons

Hydrogen bonding index

Solubility parameter δ

FIGURE 8.02 *Parameter locations for major solvent groups.[1] (Used with the permission of* Chemical Engineering.*)*

Pigments also can affect surface potential on the inside surfaces of the inevitable micropores in the film; this will determine whether positive or negative ions find the film more permeable.

A lacquer is the most straightforward organic coating. In lacquer, the film-forming resin is dissolved in a solvent, and the film is formed by solvent evaporation. Varnishes are similarly nonpigmented but involve a drying reaction as well, classically the oxidation/polymerization of a so-called drying oil. Other condensation reactions may occur with the various synthetic resins.

Generally, paints involve both a solvent evaporation or emulsion collapse mechanism as well as a condensation reaction. The extent of the latter defines the molecular weight of the film former in the final dried surface. If the molecular weight is excessively high — particularly if crosslinking in the paint film is extensive (as in some early epoxy formulations) — the paint can never be recoated satisfactorily.

For all classes of coatings, the plasticizers must stay put for the life of the coating. Ideally, there should never be evaporation or exudation. Minor losses of plasticizers are, in practice, inevitable.

Application of Paints

Paints can be applied by dip, brush, roller, spray, and airless spray techniques. The distinction between spray and airless spray is important. In the former, the paint is aspirated into a stream of compressed air, and the paint formulation must have low viscosity; hence, the final coat will be relatively thin, often less than one or two mils. In airless spray, the paint is pressurized to about 100 atm; this allows a more viscous formulation to be used, and dry film thicknesses of up to 10 mils become possible. Airless spray is rapidly becoming the standard technique for many anticorrosion applications. A comparable device suitable for home use is the centrifugal applicator. This also employs a high-viscosity product.

Combining an electrostatic charge with dip or spray painting can lead to better covering of sharp corners, etc., than can otherwise be achieved. Electrodeposition of paint can be regarded as a special case of dip painting, and it is effective for coating internal, as well as external, surfaces. Paint electrodeposition is practiced most often on phosphated surfaces.

Selection of Paints

The selection of proper combinations of primers and topcoats calls for good judgment. Manufacturer recommendations are a good starting point in making a selection.[3] Published specifications also are helpful. The Steel Structures Painting Council periodically publishes a Steel Structures Painting Manual which details many useful specifications. The most recent edition of this work is an important source of specifications, as are publications of national bodies, such as the Canadian Government Specification Board. An advantage of such specifications is that the system specified will work. A disadvantage is that newer and possibly better systems may be disallowed for awhile.

After surface preparation, the most important factor for assuring a performance is the thickness of the applied film. The choice of paint systems comes next.

Where paint is required for anticorrosion rather than cosmetic purposes, the cost of preparation plus materials and labor for application can be justified only for a dry film thickness approaching 10 mils. Such thickness can be achieved most economically by the use of high-build formulations in airless spray equipment.

There are a number of special considerations concerning paints and components of paint. Toxic pigments, such as lead and cadmium compounds and chromates, are banned entirely or severely restricted in use. Lead-based paints are not suitable for aluminum alloys. High loadings of metallic zinc can yield a primer that is electrically conductive and can confer cathodic protection to its substrate. Antifouling coatings contain either a leachable form of a toxin, such as cuprous oxide, or an ion exchange resin that can inhibit development of attached growths by interfering with trace elements in their metabolism.

Where special problems exist, it may be necessary to identify the particular chemical species that penetrate the film and cause the problem. Normally, there will be diffusion or migration through the everpresent pores. If the troublesome species carries a charge, it may be possible to add pigment to the paint that will lead to the development of like charge on the internal surfaces of the pores. This can exclude the unwanted species.

Maintenance Painting Contracts

In the more highly industrialized areas, it is usually possible to contract out the entire responsibility for maintenance painting to a major paint manufacturer. This has the advantage of predictable costs and avoidance of difficulties in defining liabilities in the event of poor paint system performance. It is the responsibility of the paint manufacturer to locate and train painting contractors and to ensure that specifications for the entire operation are met. Where this arrangement is possible, it has the advantage of freeing the maintenance engineer from the need for technical expertise in a peripheral area.

A recent paper by Morgan suggests a related but alternative procedure.[4] Morgan advocates single source responsibility programs for maintenance painting. This also takes care of the case where the manufacturer wishes to introduce a new product believed to be improved, but which only has the results of preliminary testing to support this view.

Paint and the Automobile

Automobile painting is a subject that often provokes strong opinions. Ideally, the paint coat should remain in acceptable condition for as long as the rest of the functional parts are reasonably serviceable. The collective judgment of the manufacturers seems to be that this can be achieved with less coating thickness than the 10 mils quoted earlier in this chapter. If the preparation of the automobile for painting is efficiently performed, and such techniques as application by electrocoating and the use of galvanizing or zinc rich paints in critical areas are used, the paint performance for the film thickness actually employed is optimized. There seems little doubt that manufacturers now ensure that money spent on the paint system is well spent. Whether sufficient money is spent on a cost-benefit basis for the hidden parts of the paint system for the median consumer is more open to question. The present trend for government intervention by way of statutory forms of guarantee is an indication legislators sense real customer dissatisfaction.

An episode of poor internal paint performance of most cars produced by a major manufacturer seems to have been related to inadequate test methods for assessing paint performance. Paint that looked good when tested in the salt spray cabinet showed poor performance in the field.

A modern trend is to more extensive use of either zinc-rich primers or galvanizing for critical areas of body steel. Difficulties with welding galvanized steel have tended to cause manufacturers to weld uncoated steel then apply a zinc-rich coating. The critical question then becomes whether the laps generated by spot welding can be sealed adequately. It is significant that Rolls Royce persists with galvanizing and a more exacting welding technique.

Control Measures — Metallic Protective Coatings

As in the case of painting, cleaning is a vital part of preparation for deposition of a metallic coating. The object of cleaning is to achieve complete removal of all foreign material from the metal surface while retaining as much surface finish as possible. Therefore, sand blasting is not used unless a final matte finish is acceptable.

Typical cleaning cycles will involve a preliminary degreasing in a vapor degreaser or emulsion cleaner, treatment in hot alkali of a strength appropriate to the particular metal, and a pickling operation to remove oxide without attacking the metal itself, followed by rinsing or rinsing plus neutralizing steps. The neutralizing step is necessary where alkaline plating is to follow an acid pickle.

One technically significant application of nickel is as an electrodeposit on the inside surfaces of piping and process equipment. This offers a reasonable improvement in corrosion performance at a modest increase in cost. However, there are some problems in the

FIGURE 8.03

Unsuccessful weld of nickel-plated steel equipment showing undercutting of the nickel layer by corrosion of the underlying carbon steel.

133

welding of nickel-plated equipment. Considerable nickel is required at all joints so no underlying steel is exposed and a sound weld without iron dilution can be made to nickel or monel piping or equipment. The so-called "buttering" technique has to be adopted. Figure 8.03 shows an unsuccessful weld of this nature. The weld cracked and permitted corrosion of the underlying steel to undercut the nickel layer.

Hot Dipping

Metal coatings traditionally applied by hot dipping have been tin, aluminum, and zinc. Tin, however, has become more expensive, and its application by hot dipping is rare. Aluminum and zinc are cheap enough that dipping is still a practical operation. However, in the case of aluminum the elimination of oxide is a problem, and careful selection of complex fluoride fluxes and operating conditions is necessary. Galvanizing by hot dipping is a much less critical application. One complication is that customers expect a galvanizing operation to produce parts with a spangled appearance. This is usually called for, though it cannot contribute anything to the performance of the zinc coating.

Galvanized steel also is valuable as a paint base. Once the galvanizing has weathered somewhat, it can accept a reasonably wide range of primers, and the painted galvanized steel then has a much better corrosion resistance than ordinary steel with a comparable coating. Where unweathered galvanized steel is to be painted, it may be necessary to treat it with acid to give a slight etch on the surface.

Aluminum-coated steel is one acceptable option for automobile mufflers and other applications where high-temperature oxidation resistance is sought at a moderate cost premium over untreated steel. Hot-dipped galvanized steel also is widely used. The zinc confers cathodic protection on the underlying steel so galvanized articles do not rust until the zinc has been substantially consumed. Galvanized steel has useful resistance to atmospheric corrosion, and painted and galvanized steel is used extensively in building siding, and so forth with every prospect of long life. Galvanizing and painting are used extensively in the more corrosion-prone areas of automobiles.

Electrodeposition

The most obvious example of electrodeposition is the chromium finish on automobile bumpers and trim. The earliest manufacturing technique for bumpers applied a fairly heavy copper coating, which was then buffed to a high finish, followed by 0.3 to 0.4 mil nickel and a thin chrome plate. In some cases, the nickel had to be touched up by buffing.

During the Korean war, nickel shortages led to the use of much thinner nickel coating and poorer corrosion performance of the bumpers. Since then, much effort has gone into finding techniques for achieving good corrosion performance of the plating with less nickel. This has been combined with the use of a starting material with a better finish so the preliminary, but costly, buffing operation could be eliminated.

Two successful techniques for optimizing the corrosion resistance of chromium plate are the use of duplex nickel and microcracked chromium. In the former, the bumper is given a flash coating of copper, followed by a coat of semibright sulfur-free nickel, then a coat of bright nickel (using addition agents containing sulfur), and the usual flash coating of conventional chromium. With this combination, the inevitable pitting at the cracks in the chromium plate cannot go beyond the bright nickel layer until it is all used up since the bright nickel is anodic with respect to the semibright layer of sulfur-free nickel. Therefore, rust spots cannot develop at an early stage. Microcracked chromium has a crack pattern so fine that deep pits cannot develop from a starting crack. This achieves good performance by another route since a great many tiny pits for which the anode to cathode ratio is moderately large are not objectionable. Another technique involves replacing nickel plating with alloy plating of a Ni-Fe alloy. This gives equivalent thickness and more or less equivalent corrosion resistance with less consumption of nickel. This is a successful technique.

The trend toward less weight in the automobile has led to an interest in aluminum bumpers, plastic trim, etc., with a chromium finish for color match with the rest of the trim. From a corrosion standpoint, plated aluminum is always a potential disaster so thick coatings of nickel would be essential (5 to 10 mils). Plated aluminum has been tried occasionally on bumpers in the past with less generous thicknesses of nickel. Pitting occurred in a few months, followed by undermining and dropping out of chunks of metal 550 mm in diameter. The customers were not happy. It seems to be more practical to finish aluminum bumpers by anodizing, rather than by plating.

In addition to the family of operations needed for chromium plating, many other metals, such as copper, tin, and zinc, often are electrodeposited. Cyanide electrolytes are becoming less common, and even pyrophosphate electrolytes are falling out of favor because of environmental considerations. In many cases, these baths are being replaced by acid or neutral baths, such as chloride baths for zinc deposition. These baths have no inherent detergency; also, the maintenance of a sufficient hydrogen overvoltage is difficult. Consequently, these baths are more difficult to operate profitably than the cyanide zinc baths they replaced.

Many other metals can be electrodeposited. Some of the more important in corrosion applications are precious metal deposits, used to decrease contact resistance in microelectronic circuitry; lead plating in bearings to improve fretting resistance; and the familiar silver plating on brass or nickel silver for uses in the home.

Miscellaneous Coating Techniques

Chemical reduction plating is a common technique for initiating metallic coatings on nonmetals, or for coating metallic objects where provision of electric circuitry for electroplating would be impractical. A chemical reducing agent, such as sodium hypophosphite or hydrazine, is introduced to an appropriate pregnant metal solution, and conditions are set so that heterogeneous nucleation occurs on the desired surface. For coating plastics, the surface is cleaned, lightly etched, then activated, often with a trace of palladium salt. The metal most commonly used for the coating is nickel, and sodium hypophosphite is the reducing agent normally employed. The nickel deposit is amorphous and contains appreciable phosphorous; it may be used as a basis for normal subsequent electroplating steps. Many items of plastic trim on automobiles are treated in this fashion, finishing with a chromium-plated surface. These techniques were developed originally in the National Bureau of Standards (NBS) laboratories in Washington by a team headed by Abner Brenner, who is responsible for coining the term "electroless plating" as a name for the process.

Applications of chemical reduction plating in the corrosion field include items such as tank interiors of various kinds, i.e., coating the internals of railroad tank cars with nickel. Activation for coating ferrous metals is virtually automatic since all the Group VIII metals are catalysts for the heterogeneous reaction. The Ni-P alloy deposited in this way is exceptionally pore-free and is a good candidate for many applications where pure nickel would be suitable. It shows no structure and can probably be termed a metallic glass.

An earlier version of chemical reduction plating was the use of mild reducing agents, such as tartrates, to reduce silver salts and yield mirrors on glass. Prior to World War II, this was the only method available for making mirrors. With the advent of modern vacuum equipment, mirrors are now made by the vacuum deposition of aluminum evaporated from a hot filament or basket.

Other techniques for applying metallic coatings include: tumbling in a barrel with metal powders; vacuum evaporation; vapor plating by the dissociation of a volatile compound; chemical immersion plating where a more noble metal is deposited on a less noble one; explosion bonding; metal spraying; and overlaying with weld metal. Only the last three are important in corrosion applications. Zinc spraying is common for articles too large to galvanize, but where the advantages of galvanizing are sought. The entire steel work for the Forth Bridge in Scotland is an example, as noted earlier.

Weld cladding is common for applications of heavy duty coatings that are not mechanically workable. Most power shovel teeth, bulldozer blades, etc. for heavy duty service will be overlaid with super alloys (e.g., stellites) for wear resistance under corrosive conditions. The deposits have to be shaped for grinding. Such techniques also can be used for a wide spectrum of repair procedures.

Explosion bonding calls for careful technique but achieves a sound metallurgical bond even for metals that could form harmful intermetallic compounds in any bonding process involving heat. Properties of such explosion claddings can approach the best available by any technique, but the process is expensive.

Composites of various compatible sets of metals also can be prepared by roll bonding and other methods. Usually, one layer is present for mechanical reasons, and it is protected by a relatively thin layer of more costly, but highly corrosion-resistant, metal or alloy.

Protective Coatings — Inorganic

The deliberate formation of oxide or other coatings on metals is sometimes practiced as a corrosion control measure. The conversion coating may serve as a control measure in its own right, provide a better paint base, or enhance the value of a coating already in place.

Anodizing

The most versatile of the conversion coatings is achieved by the process of anodizing, and aluminum is the metal most commonly anodized. The initial cleaning steps for anodizing or for other conversion coatings must be thorough and resemble those used in preparation of electroplated coatings.

In anodizing, the clean metal is immersed as anode in a suitable acid solution, and the anodic potential is either maintained at an appropriate value or gradually increased to a selected maximum value, following a prescribed time schedule. Anodizing voltages of a few tens of volts are typical. For aluminum, the anodizing acids could be sulfuric, phosphoric, chromic, oxalic, or boric acid. The sulfuric acid anodizing process is the most common; properties of the anodic film vary from hard (when formed below ambient temperature) to a somewhat softer and more porous deposit that can be sealed for optimum corrosion resistance, or colored and sealed for decorative purposes combined with corrosion resistance.

The structure of the anodic film is shown schematically in Figure 8.04. At the metal/oxide interface is an essentially nonporous thin barrier layer. Atop this is a honeycomb structure which has a set of pores within the oxide that go from the barrier layer to the outerface of the anodic oxide. When the anodized film is heated in steam or

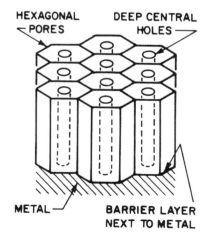

FIGURE 8.04 Pore structure on anodized aluminum.

boiling water, the film swells and fills the pores so the final sealed film has negligible porosity. Pigments or dyes may be introduced into the pores prior to sealing. The sealed film then assumes the color of the pigment or dye. Most dyes suitable for textiles can be used in anodizing. The stability of the color on long exposure to light is a problem with many of them.

Corrosion resistance of anodized film is good. However, if defects develop, there can be deep pitting of the underlying metal. This pitting tends to be deeper than would be expected for a similar non-anodized material. Anodized films, particularly when produced in boric or oxalic acid, have high resistance to the passage of current in the direction of the original anodizing current. This is the basis for the production of electrolytic condensers; tantalum or niobium are materials of choice in this application.

Chromic acid anodizing leads to a rather dark anodic film that is an excellent paint base. It is not used often since a chemical conversion coating in a solution containing phosphates will give an equivalent paint base at lower total cost.

Chemical Conversion Coatings

A variety of formulations involving phosphates, chromates, fluorides, etc. can be used to develop conversion coatings on clean metals, such as steel, aluminum, magnesium, and so forth. These coatings typically improve the corrosion resistance of the metal and may furnish a good paint base. The better painting schemes typically involve forming a conversion coating and then giving an initial paint coat with a paint containing an inhibitive pigment. Zinc chromate is one example of such a pigment. As with the other chromates, there are restrictions on its use because of environmental concerns. Virtually all primers, including zinc-rich inorganics, are compatible with the various conversion coatings. Paint systems on conversion coatings generally give good performance.

A somewhat related treatment is the use of chromic acid dip to confer some measure of passivity on zinc or galvanized coatings. Treated work is more resistant to picking up fingerprints. Most work that has been galvanized by electrodeposition also should be treated with chromic acid since electrogalvanized films are normally quite thin. Their corrosion resistance is enhanced by the passivating step.

References

1. F. Rodriguez, *Principles of Polymer Systems*, 2nd. ed. (New York, NY: Hemisphere, 1982).
2. C.G. Munger, *Materials Performance* 19, 2 (1980): pp. 46-52.
3. Larry J. Van de Walle, ed., *Efficient Materials and Coating for Improved Design and Corrosion Resistance,* Metals & Processing Congress, Chicago, November 1979 (Metals Park, OH: ASM, 1981).
4. J.R. Morgan, CORROSION/89, paper no. 90 (Houston, TX: NACE, 1989).

9

Control Measures —
Action at the Design Stage

Corrosion control at the design stage does not just happen — it must be planned. For a major project, as much lead time will be required for the corrosion aspects of the design as for other considerations. If the technology of the application is established, there has to be careful selection of a known solution with meticulous attention to details that happen to be new. If new corrosion technology has to be developed, protracted testing will be necessary so reasonable choices can be made.

Material Selection

The material sought is the one that will lead to the most economical solution to the design problem. Often, this leads to use of a nonpremium material with a reasonably generous corrosion allowance at a modest stress level. Nonpremium materials such as steel must be considered first. Material performance in such cases can be predicted with some degree of certainty. The relative merits and costs of a protective scheme, such as painting or cathodic protection, also are likely to be known. There should be no surprises.

With a premium material, particularly where the material or its application is novel, there will be a tendency to help justify its use by using high stress levels. This normally implies that synergistic modes of attack are more likely to be encountered, and that performance will be much less predictable. Failures could be potentially dangerous. For such applications, careful and extensive testing is in order.

Detail of Design

In a nutshell, the design detail should embody all corrosion principles as well as conform to appropriate codes and regulations (Chapter 13). Above all, the detail calls for common sense. Consider welding as an example. First, a material that is weldable and for which welds do not suffer from corrosion shortcomings should be selected. The weld bead should be somewhat cathodic to the structures being joined. The weld must be in a location that allows for easy maintenance and avoidance of stress concentrations. The joint must be such that there are no exposed crevices. Examples of good and bad practices are given in Figure 9.01. Dissimilar metal welds call for particular care (refer to the discussion of poison pads in Chapter 16).

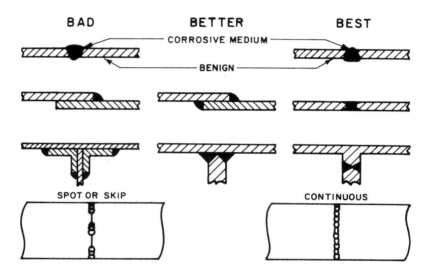

FIGURE 9.01 *Examples of weld detail.*

Welding on plate that has attached millscale is a guarantee of corrosion disaster. The scale spalls off near the weld and leaves a small anode to large cathode situation.

Paintability also is an important consideration. An effective coating cannot be achieved on sharp edges or sharp interior angles. These sites must be rounded. Members must beset far enough apart to allow for the use of a paint brush or spray gun, as shown in Figure 9.02. The use of galvanized sections or of sections pickled with a weldable primer may be appropriate.

Drainage is another concern. Any detail that can trap water is to be avoided. Examples are given in Figures 9.03 and 9.04.

The design and support of tanks is an important area. There must be provision for the proper mixing of contents without undue erosion; the support must not trap water; the tank must be drainable; and insulation detail must be appropriate (Figures 9.05 and 9.06).

When dissimilar metals are used in a corrosive environment, it is necessary to insulate them. The insulation must be complete; a bolt requires a sleeve and washers of an insulating material. Incomplete insulation may be even worse than none at all. In any event, it gives a false sense of security. Mechanical joints must have load -bearing and insulating properties. The joint must not trap corrodent or heavy metal bearing drips from the cathodic component (Figure 9.07).

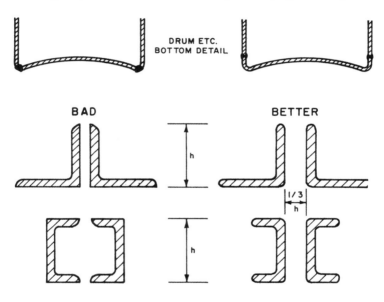

FIGURE 9.02 Design for paintability.

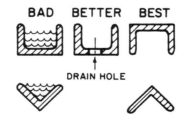

FIGURE 9.03 Arrangement of profiles.

143

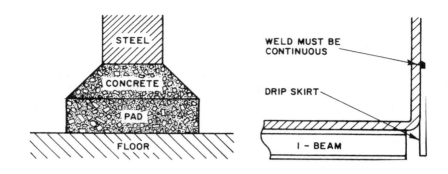

FIGURE 9.04 *Proper detail for supports.*

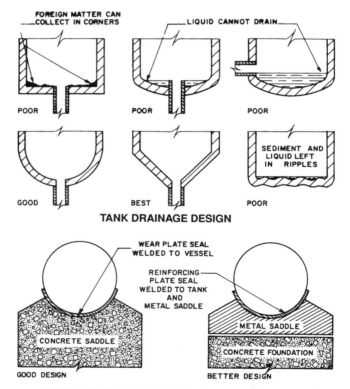

TANK DRAINAGE DESIGN

METAL SUPPORT PADS FOR HORIZONTAL TANKS

FIGURE 9.05 *Tank design details. (Courtesy du Pont de Nemours & Co., Inc. Canada.)*

144

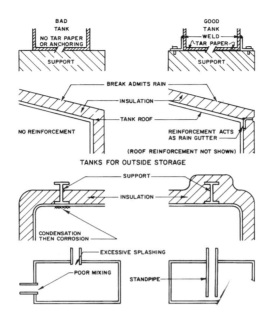

FIGURE 9.06 *More tank design details.*

BAD   BETTER   BEST

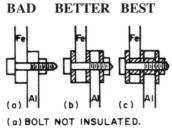

(a) | Fe   (b) | Fe   (c) | Fe
| Al | Al | Al

(a) BOLT NOT INSULATED.
(b) INSULATING WASHERS ONLY.
(c) INSULATING WASHERS AND
    SLEEVES.

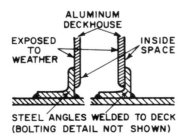

ALUMINUM
DECKHOUSE

EXPOSED   INSIDE
TO   SPACE
WEATHER

STEEL ANGLES WELDED TO DECK
(BOLTING DETAIL NOT SHOWN)

FIGURE 9.07 *Joining dissimilar metals.*

The problem of coping with crevices in sensitive material is closely related to the joining of dissimilar metals. The crevice has to be neutralized in some way. Possible solutions are: galvanizing; sealing the crevice with chromate, etc., inhibitor loaded sealant; or the use of anodic protection techniques with a precious metal coating (on stainless steel, etc.). Wherever possible, the crevice should be avoided rather than neutralized.

As mentioned in Chapter 6, fretting fatigue can be a problem with press fit wheel shaft assemblies. For the railroad axle case, the solution is shown in Figure 9.08.

In this case, provision of a smoothly formed groove adjacent to the press fit caused a substantial increase in fretting fatigue life for railroad axle wheel assemblies, as used in the London Underground system. The effect of the groove is to relocate the position of the maximum stress concentration from the shaft to wheel contact to the base of the machined groove where it can cause no particular harm. The elimination of a synergistic process is the key concept in this remedy.

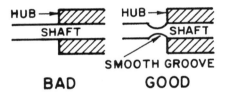

FIGURE 9.08 *How to avoid fretting fatigue.*

Influence of Design Detail on Automobile Corrosion

Automobile corrosion elicits strong reactions. As will be seen in the next chapter, premature replacement of the automobile because of corrosion is the largest component in the total cost of corrosion in the United States. It is the corrosion cost item that is most obvious and of most direct concern to the median consumer and to the corrosion engineer alike.

An important formulation of measures to reduce the extent of automobile by design was made by the Society of Automotive Engineers in 1964. A summary of significant recommendations follows.

The underbody surface should be designed to stay dry; ledges, flanges and pockets that could accumulate and hold moisture or moistened dirt must be avoided. All joints should be and remain watertight. Solder-filled double lap joints are preferred where appearance is of primary importance. Joints should be sealed with a mastic type compound, and riveted joints should have the entire faying surface covered. Special protective measures are required for lap joints in line with wheel splash so that water and dirt will not be driven in. Dissimilar metal joints should be avoided as much as possible.

Open construction, rather than box sections and enclosed areas, are preferred. Where box sections or enclosed areas are used, there must be sufficient openings to allow for a successful painting operation and for subsequent drainage. Adequate drainage must be provided in doors and other body areas having movable windows. Electrical connections must be kept free of moisture. Fuel tanks and other fluid-containing components should be designed to limit the need for corrosive solder fluxes.

The provision of openings for painting in partially enclosed spaces calls for some comment. The manufacturer can be expected to rely on electrostatic priming to optimize painting costs and efficiency. But the intended advantage of electrostatic priming will only be realized if the electrostatic field can "throw" into all interior spaces. This requires much more open area than would be needed for drainage alone.

Ease and Frequency of Maintenance and Inspection

The cost for any item must include an allowance for periodic inspection and/or maintenance as well as first cost. Indirect costs, such as lost production, may have to be included. The design of the item can influence these costs; occasionally, an estimate of such costs is imprecise, but it should be made.

For pressure vessels, inspection techniques and intervals are defined by legal requirements. Other items, such as pumps or nonpressurized vessels, have inspection schedules set by proprietor policy, presumably in response to real safety and cost factors.

For pressure vessels, it is normal to design inspection nozzles to admit Borescopes, etc. If stainless steel is used, the end of the pipe that contributes the inspection part must be seal-welded to avoid end face attack, as shown in Figure 9.09.

Inspection of structures such as water towers can be difficult.

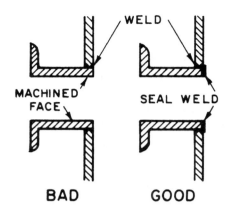

FIGURE 9.09 *Stainless steel inspection nozzle detail.*

Some bright young engineer and a helper have to climb a long ladder and cope with test equipment, collapsible canoe, paddle, etc. The detail of the layout at the top, including the size of the manhole, can have quite an effect on the scope of the task, and, hence, its cost. Yet, a new water tower can be selected on a low-bid basis by a purchasing process that gives scant attention to ongoing cost.

More information on the subject matter of this chapter can be found in V.R. Pludek's monograph.[1] This is the most complete treatment of the subject available. A helpful chapter also can be found in both Wranglen[2] and Gellings.[3]

References

1. V.R. Pludek, *Design and Corrosion Control* (London, UK: Macmillan, 1977).
2. G. Wranglen, *An Introduction to the Corrosion and Protection of Metals* (Stockholm, Sweden: Institut fur Mettallskydd, 1972).
3. P.J. Gellings, *Introduction to Corrosion Prevention and Control for Engineers* (Leiden, The Netherlands: Delft Univ. Press, 1976).

10

Corrosion
Economics

Corrosion economics is at the heart of the subject of corrosion engineering. It calls for a wide range of information if the best decisions are to be made. The ground rules can be different for different sectors and periods of the economy. Goals defined by the public must be respected. Protection of the environment is one of these goals, and it may be found that energy and materials conservation will come to merit increasing attention. Safety must be an overriding priority. Such considerations obviously will limit free choice on a purely economic basis.

In the industrial sector of the economy, the corporate tax structure has a large influence on anticorrosion measures. The large difference, for taxation purposes, between expenses which are written off in the current taxation year and capitalized expenditures which are tied to rigid depreciation schedules means that industries must have a bias in favor of short, rather than long, life equipment, particularly when high interest rates make capital expensive. The corporate taxpayer, therefore, willingly accepts a policy which tolerates rather high maintenance expenditures provided tax savings are not wiped out by costs arising from reduced or lost production. Obviously, the tax savings of industry resulting from this strategy redistribute but do not diminish the overall taxation burden. Irrational prejudices also have some weight, particularly where the company manufactures a candidate material of construction.

The government sector has its own foibles. It can be obsessed with spending in the current fiscal year and pay scant attention to long-term cost-effectiveness or conservation. The overriding consideration is the actual amount of the estimates and expenditures for a particular year. Future economies can rarely be justified by additional expenditures in the current year since depreciation is often not admitted. Such items as cathodic protection systems for docks tend to be postponed more or less indefinitely since bureaucrats do not view future reductions in their own department as a priority. The bureaucrat target is to spend all of the current year's budget, thus protecting the amount budgeted for the coming year.

Inflation has an important influence on project evaluation: It complicates efforts to determine the most cost-effective alternative. A rate of inflation has to be postulated and set into the calculations. Consider an oversimplified case in which the annual inflation rate is 100% and the real interest rate is 10%, exclusive of inflation. If $100 is borrowed, it will have to be repaid as $200 (in terms of the then current nominal dollars), and recover $20 more as interest. The nominal interest rate will be 120%. We must be careful to distinguish between real and nominal dollars and real and nominal interest rates. True dollars and true interest rates are based on constant dollars (usually as of day one in the calculations). Nominal dollars and interest rates are the sums which change hands, and include effects of the inflationary process (including anticipation of inflation). All calculations must be consistent. Either real or nominal values must be used throughout. On no account can they be mixed, or it becomes impossible to discount future expenditures to present values.

There is another complication. Say the (nominal) bank interest rate is 15% at a time when the inflation rate is 10%. This results in a real interest rate of 5%. But this is not the whole story. If there are competing investment opportunities that would yield a real interest rate of 10%, this value, rather than the real (inflation corrected) bank rate, should be used for discounting purposes. This competing rate is termed the real opportunity cost rate.[1] This might reasonably be set around 10% if it has to be estimated. Other levels might be set by company fiscal policy.

The relationship between interest rate and inflation rate also merits scrutiny. If money is borrowed at a market (nominal) interest rate r, its unit cost is $1 + r$. This, in turn, can be broken down into the inflation component $1 + I$, and a true interest component $I + R$ such that:

$$1 + r = (1 - R)(1 + I) \text{ and} \qquad (1)$$

$$r = R + I + RI \qquad (2)$$

---

[1] For example, refer to S.H. Hanke, P. Carver, and P. Bugg. "Project Evaluation During Inflation in Benefit-Cost and Policy Analysis," an Aldine Annual on Forecasting Decision Making and Evaluation (Pub City, 1974).

150

Note that many analyses neglect the cross product term RI. This is only appropriate when I is relatively small, but leads to the simplification of r = R + I.

The simplest, and hence preferred, form of financial analysis is to use real terms for both dollar costs and interest rates. The interest rate in this case is not the (nominal) bank rate, but the deliberately estimated real opportunity cost rate. Note that expectations of revenue will not always be increasing at the same rate as the real opportunity cost rate. Technological improvements and competition both tend to hold nominal revenues in check.

In the following example, real dollars are used with an estimated real opportunity rate of 12% per annum. The example is taken from a paper by T.R.B. Watson.[1] A corporate tax rate of 50% is assumed, and the depreciation is set at a constant percentage (20%) of the undepreciated value in a given year. This is the only method permitted by Canadian tax authorities. Standard methods are used in the following calculations.Tables 10.01 to 10.07 give details.

TABLE 10.01
Economic Factors Based on 12% Annual Interest

Year	Value Factor	Yearly Cost Factor	Sinking Fund Factor
1	0.8929	1.1200	1.0000
2	0.7972	0.5917	0.4717
3	0.7118	0.4164	0.2963
4	0.6355	0.3292	0.2092
5	0.5674	0.2774	0.1574
6	0.5066	0.2432	0.1232
7	0.4523	0.2191	0.0991
8	0.4039	0.2013	0.0813
9	0.3606	0.1877	0.0677
10	0.3220	0.1770	0.0570
15	0.1827	—	0.0268
20	0.1037	0.1339	0.0139
25	0.0588	—	0.0075
26	0.0525	—	—
27	0.0469	—	—
28	0.0419	—	—
29	0.0374	—	—
30	0.0334	0.1241	0.0041

Formula

$PV = F \dfrac{1}{(1 + I)^n}$ $AC = PV \dfrac{i(1 + i)^n}{(1 + i)^n - 1}$ $AC = F \dfrac{i}{(1 + i)^n - 1}$

TABLE 10.02

Capital Cost Factor for Constant
Percentage Depreciation

Formula Used: CCF = 1 - td/i + d

i = Interest Rate = 12%; t = Tax Rate = 50%; d = Depreciation Rate

Class	Description	Depreciation Rate	Capital Cost Factor
2	Generating Equipment Pipelines Utilities	6%	0.883
3	Buildings Plants	5%	0.853
8	Machinery Equipment Furniture	20%	0.688
10	Automotive	30%	0.643

TABLE 10.03
Stainless Steel Heat Exchanger Work Sheet

		Cash Flow		Tax Factors				Present Value	Total Present Value	Equiv. Annual Cost
Item	Yr.	Capital	Expense	Capital Cost Factor (Table 10.05)	Expense Factor	Present Value Factor (Table 10.01)	Calculation	Value	Value	Cost
Capital	0	300,000		0.688		$PV_0=1.000$	$300,000 \times 0.688$		206,400	
Maintenance	1		100		0.5	$PV_1=0.8929$	$100 \times 0.8929 \times 0.5$	44		
Maintenance	2		150		0.5	$PV_2=0.7972$	$150 \times 0.7972 \times 0.5$	60		
Maintenance	3		200		0.5	$PV_3=0.7118$	$200 \times 0.7118 \times 0.5$	71		
Maintenance	4		250		0.5	$PV_4=0.6355$	$250 \times 0.6355 \times 0.5$	79		
Maintenance	5		300		0.5	$PV_5=0.5679$	$300 \times 0.5679 \times 0.5$	85		
Maintenance	6		350		0.5	$PV_6=0.5066$	$350 \times 0.5066 \times 0.5$	89		
Maintenance	7		400		0.5	$PV_7=0.4523$	$400 \times 0.4503 \times 0.5$	90		
Maintenance	8		450		0.5	$PV_8=0.4039$	$450 \times 0.4039 \times 0.5$	91		
Maintenance	9		500		0.5	$PV_9=0.3606$	$500 \times 0.3606 \times 0.5$	90		
							Total	**699**		
Retube	10	50,100		0.688		$PV_{10}=0.3220$	$50,100 \times 0.3220 \times 0.688$		11,099	
Salvage	10	(682)		0.688		$PV_{10}=0.3220$	$(682) \times 0.3210 \times 0.688$		(151)	
Maintenance	11-19					$PV_{10}=0.3220$	699×0.3220		225	
Retube	20	50,100				$PV_{20}=0.1037$	$50,100 \times 0.1037 \times 0.688$		3,574	
Salvage	20	(682)				$PV_{20}=0.1037$	$(682) \times 0.1037 \times 0.688$		(49)	
Maintenance	21-29					$PV_{20}=0.1037$	699×0.1037		72	
Salvage	30	(4,500)				$PV_{30}=0.0334$	$(4,500) \times 0.034 \times 0.688$		(150)	
							Total		**221,022**	

Equivalent Annual Cost = Present Value × Annual Cost Factor (Table 10.03) = PV × ACF_{30} = 221,022 × 0.1241 = $27,428

153

TABLE 10.04 - Carbon Steel Heat Exchanger Work Sheet

Item	Year	Cash Flow		Tax Factors		Present Value Factor (Table 10.01)	Calculation	Present Value	Total Present Value	Equiv. Annual Cost
		Capital	Expense	Capital Cost Factor (Table 10.05)	Expense Factor					
Capital	0	260,000		0.688		$PV_0=1.000$	$260{,}000 \times 0.688$		178,880	
Maintenance	1		400		0.5	$PV_1=0.8929$	$400 \times 0.8929 \times 0.5$	178		
Maintenance	2		500		0.5	$PV_2=0.7972$	$500 \times 0.7972 \times 0.5$	198		
Maintenance	3		650		0.5	$PV_3=0.7118$	$650 \times 0.7118 \times 0.5$	231		
Maintenance	4		900		0.5	$PV_4=0.6355$	$900 \times 0.6355 \times 0.5$	286		
Retube	5	20,150		0.688		$PV_5=0.5674$	$20{,}150 \times 0.5674 \times 0.688$	7,866		
Salvage	5	(143)		0.688		$PV_5=0.5674$	$(143) \times 0.5674 \times 0.688$	(56)		
							Total	**8,703**	**8,703**	
Maintenance and Retube	6-10					$PV_5=0.5674$	$8{,}703 \times 0.5674$	4,939		
Retube	11-15					$PV_{10}=0.3220$	$8{,}703 \times 0.3220$	2,802		
Retube	16-20					$PV_{15}=0.1828$	$8{,}703 \times 0.1828$	1,590		
Retube	21-25					$PV_{20}=0.1037$	$8{,}703 \times 0.1037$	902		
Maintenance	26		400		0.5	$PV_{26}=0.0525$	$400 \times 0.0528 \times 0.5$	10		
Maintenance	27		500		0.5	$PV_{27}=0.0469$	$500 \times 0.0469 \times 0.5$	11		
Maintenance	28		650		0.5	$PV_{28}=0.0419$	$650 \times 0.0419 \times 0.5$	13		
Maintenance	29		900	0.688		$PV_{29}=0.0374$	$900 \times 0.0374 \times 0.5$	17		
Salvage	30	(2,520)				$PV_{30}=0.0334$	$2{,}520 \times 0.0334 \times 0.688$	(58)		
							Total		197,810	

Equivalent Annual Cost = Present Value × Annual Cost Factor (Table 10.03) = $PV \times ACF_{30}$ = $221{,}022 \times 0.1241 = \$27{,}428$

TABLE 10.05 - Stainless Steel Scrapped in 10 Years

| Item | Year | Cash Flow | | Tax Factors | | | | Calculation | Present Value | Equiv. Annual Cost |
		Capital	Expense	Capital Cost Factor (Table 10.05)	Expense	Present Value Factor (Table 10.01)	Annual Cost Factor (Table 10.03)			
Capital	0	300,000		0.688		1.000		$300,000 \times 0.688 =$	206,400	
Maintenance	1-9				0.5			From Alternative 2	699	
Salvage	10	(4,500)		0.688		$PV_{10} = 0.1770$		$(4,500) \times 0.688 \times 0.3220 =$	(977)	
								Total	**206,102**	
								$ACF_{10} = 0.1770 \quad 206,102 \times 0.1770 =$		36,480

155

TABLE 10.06 - Incoloy Heat Exchanger Work Sheet

Item	Yr.	Cash Flow		Tax Factors				Calculation	Equiv. Annual Cost	Present
		Capital	Expense	Capital Cost Factor (Table 10.05)	Expense Factor	Annual Cost Factor (Table 10.03)	Sinking Fund Factor (Table 10.04)			
Capital	0	400,000		0.688		$ACF_{30} = 0.1241$		$400{,}000 \times 0.1241 \times 0.688 =$	34,152	
Maintenance	1-30		100		0.5				50	
Salvage	30	(10,000)		0.688			$SFF_{30} = 0.0041$	$(10{,}000) \times 0.0041 \times 0.688 =$	(28)	
								Total	**37,174**	
						$ACF_{30} = 0.1241$		$37{,}174 \div 0.1241$		

156

TABLE 10.07
Comparison of Alternatives

	Initial Cost	Present Value	Equiv. Annual Cost
Carbon Steel	$260,000	$197,810	$24,548
Stainless Steel	300,000	221,022	27,428
Stainless Steel Scrapped in 10 years	300,000	206,102	36,480
Incoloy	400,000	275,374	34,174

TABLE 10.08
Cash Flow Details for Watson's Example

	Carbon Steel	317L Stainless	Incoloy
Initial Cost	$260,000	$300,000	$400,000
Cost of Tubes	7,150	34,100	95,700
Labor and Materials	13,000	16,000	20,000
Total for Retubing	20,150	50,100	115,700
Salvage on Tubes	143	682	1,800
Final Salvage	2,520	4,500	10,000

Example

A heat exchanger used in a nuclear power plant to cool the heavy water moderator may be constructed of carbon steel, Type 317L stainless steel, or Incoloy. In each case, the unit is designed to last 30 years, but the carbon steel exchanger will have to be retubed every five years and the stainless one every 10 years. The Incoloy tubes are expected to last the full 30 years. Maintenance for the carbon steel unit for each of the four years following retubing will be $400, $500, $650, and $900 per year. For the stainless unit, maintenance will be $100 per year, increased by $50 each year until the next refit. The Incoloy exchanger will require only $100 per year for the whole period. Details of the cash flow are given in Table 10.08.

Alternative Number 1-Carbon Steel. As detailed in Table 10.01, all expenditures and income from salvage are converted to present value after discounting for tax credit. The computation could be made by listing the cash flow every year for 30 years and multiplying by the present value factor for each year. However tedious, procedure becomes unnecessary when it is realized the same items occur every five years. Thus, the present value of the maintenance and retubing for the first five years is totalled, and for the next five years this total is multiplied by 0.5674, the present value factor for year 5. This puts the whole group of transactions five years further into the future. Similarly, for years 11 to 15, the five year total is discounted another 10 years by multiplying by PV_{10}, and so on. Since the last five years does not include retubing, the maintenance is discounted separately to present value, as is the final salvage.

Alternative Number 2-Stainless Steel. This example is treated similarly to the first alternative, except that the retubing and salvage are discounted separately from the maintenance.

Alternative Number 3-Incoloy. Since the cash flow in this case takes place at the beginning and ends with maintenance a fixed annual cost, it is preferable to reduce everything to an equivalent annual cost and convert this total to present value.

A comparison of the alternatives shows the carbon steel unit to be the cheapest, despite the frequent refits. This demonstrates that the longer expenditures can be delayed, the cheaper they become. The Incoloy alternative, though trouble-free, requires a large present expenditure, which is expensive.

The three alternatives are similarly rated, whether compared to the total present value or the total equivalent annual cost. This is because the life of each unit is the same. Consider the comparison between the Incoloy exchanger and the stainless one if the stainless is scrapped after 10 years. Table 10.07 shows that the Incoloy choice is cheaper on the basis of equivalent annual cost, although the present value is greater. Equivalent annual cost is the only way to compare alternatives of differing lives.

Surveys of Corrosion Costs

Direct costs of corrosion are difficult to gauge. There has to be a reference condition to define hypothetical costs in the absence of corrosion. For the automobile, for example, there must be a definition that assigns a certain time or mileage lifetime to the vehicle for existence in a corrosion-free world; indirect costs are more elusive.

Most of the major industrial nations have taken a serious look at their own corrosion costs and have subsequently made more serious attempts to come to grips with corrosion. In general, the more detailed the estimate of corrosion costs, the higher the figures seem to be.

One significant item in any survey of corrosion cost is the interest rate assigned to an investment in corrosion prevention. Should the rate be the bank rate, bank rate adjusted by the annual rate of inflation, or the real opportunity cost rate expected by investing the available money elsewhere? Unfortunately, a highly subjective assumption has to be made which has a profound effect on the survey.

The corrosion costs in the United States have been the subject of a painstaking study commissioned by Congress on a substantial scale.[2] The point of departure for the study was a review of what other countries had done. While the other national studies varied considerably in methodology and scope, they identified corrosion costs as from about 2 to 4% of the gross national product (GNP), and usually identified about 25% of those corrosion costs as avoidable. The most comprehensive report included in the preliminary survey was the Hoar Commission in the United Kingdom, which identified corrosion costs as 3.5% of the GNP, of which 23% was identified as avoidable if best current techniques were used.[2]

The United States study was performed jointly by economists and corrosion experts, and the data was interpreted by two independent groups at Battelle Columbus Laboratories (BCL) and the National Bureau of Standards (NBS).[3] The methodology involved discounted cash flow in an input-output model and was based on three "worlds" for the study of 1975. Data of this year was adjusted to a full employment basis. World I is the real world of corrosion thus modified. World II is a hypothetical world in which corrosion does not exist and the cheapest available materials will suffice. World III is a hypothetical world in which everyone uses the best corrosion practices. Neither World II nor World III postulate full employment.

Clearly, it is in the public interest to minimize the overall costs of corrosion. It also is in the public interest to minimize overall energy and materials consumption. Again, it is hard to see how this can be achieved without a tax structure that at least removes disincentives. The present tax structure rewards corrosion expense with tax deductions, but does not encourage investment for reducing corrosion costs over a long period. This policy needs reexamination. The net effect of the present system is that the taxpaying public meet a significant fraction of industrial corrosion costs, justified or not. Some corrective action by the government may be necessary.

On the other hand, individuals who encounter corrosion costs are not normally able to obtain tax relief from such expenses. Their view of corrosion costs in an automobile will, therefore, differ from that of (for example) the purchaser of a fleet of taxicabs. The individual consumer wants to minimize the sum total of all costs associated with the operation of a family car. The government is taking a direct, though belated, interest in the consumer's ability to meet this goal. It is also looking at ways to minimize energy consumption, but in a superficial fashion. The energy consumed in the operation of a vehicle has come under relatively more scrutiny than the large total energy required for initial manufacture and replacement after the vehicle has rusted out. A more comprehensive view is required.

It is evident that the automobile can be taken from its present corrosion status to one more acceptable to reasonable consumers and consumer groups at a cost increase of about 10%. Much of the additional cost would involve specific action at the manufacturing stage, such as the increased use of galvanizing and more attention to a number of design details like the effective sealing of spot-welded laps and improved specifications for protective treatment of interior surfaces. It is significant that one North American manufacturer began in 1980 to guarantee his products for five years against rust perforations, partly as a result of bringing a major rust-proofing organization into the factory.

Recent governmental action has led to consumer warranties stating there shall be no rust perforations on the body of an automobile in three years. Surely this is only a first step on the road to protecting the public. More attention to safety is needed. A more adequate three-year criterion would be whether cars after that time still give sufficient lateral impact protection to their occupants. The structural integrity of a stressed skin design, in which the skin is significantly thinned at many of its seams, is open to question as is the proper duration of the consumer warranty.

The economy was broken down into 130 sectors with an appropriate growth rate for each and with a reasonable estimate of interest rates, all on the basis of the 1975 estimate. Indirect costs or savings are included in the study. If an item has longer life in World

II or III, for example, a smaller number of items will provide the same level of service, and one saving will be the elimination of redundant units. Unusual major corrosion disasters are not included in the study.

The final result was an overall BCL metallic corrosion cost estimate of $82 billion (4.9% GNP), and an NBS estimate of $70 billion (4.2% GNP) ± 30%. The currently avoidable corrosion cost was roughly 15% of the total, but could be from 10 to 45%. The error in the avoidable cost is greater than the error in the total. One reason for this is the difficulty in defining the performance of the automobile in Worlds II and III. The differences between the BCL and NBS estimates involve something like $10 billion of avoidable corrosion cost, or 0.6% of the GNP if $1.677 billion is involved.

In passing, we should note that these figures can be extrapolated to Canada. Given the 1979 GNP of about $260 billion, the overall cost of corrosion would be about $10 billion. The preventable component would be $2 billion, or a little more.

Perhaps the findings of the corrosion cost survey can be understood better by a more complete consideration of the private automobile. In this case, a surprisingly small fraction of the total corrosion cost goes along with replacing mufflers, water pumps, corroded exterior metal work, etc. Well over 80% of the total cost is more or less hidden in "premature replacement" and associated costs. The effect is that the vehicle has to be replaced more often than would be the case in a world where corrosion did not exist or in a world where optimum anticorrosion technology was applied. Of course, the study has to exclude cars replaced because of collision damage or mechanical wear, and it attempts to separate voluntary replacements of cars with outmoded styling from involuntary replacements of corroded-out vehicles. Clearly, there are strongly subjective elements in the corrosion cost survey. The additional cost to achieve "optimum corrosion technology" has been estimated as about $550 per vehicle. Such an option is available only from one new car manufacturer.

Beyond the corrosion costs per se are the overall effects of good corrosion practice on the economy. Eventual removal of "tax" of .5 to 1% of the GNP will give the economy as a whole a direct boost. However, if at the same time there are reductions in the sale of new cars, etc., it follows that automobile manufacturers may be forced to diversify operations — perhaps by mass producing solar heating units or some other essentially new product line.

In response to these studies, virtually all industrialized nations are taking corrosion seriously. Corrosion resource centers and the like are springing up with government initiative in an attempt to conserve national resources and energy. The emphasis is generally on making sources of corrosion expertise both obvious and relatively accessible to small and medium-sized industries.

Spectacular Corrosion-Related Disasters

The direct costs of particular corrosion-related disasters are not included in any inventory of corrosion costs. The most widely publicized of these in Canada was the Glace Bay heavy water plant, as originally installed. The plant never became operational for a variety of reasons. The major corrosion component was the pitting of stainless steel condenser tubes. It should be noted that there was a similar incident in private industry on the West Coast at about the same time that got less publicity.

A European disaster involved a blast furnace stove in a steel plant. The search for higher productivity dictated a higher blast temperature and, hence, a hotter stove. The resultant increase in thermal production of oxides of nitrogen led to nitrate stress corrosion cracking of the shell of the stove, and it blew up. Possible solutions to this problem would be to reduce the stove temperature (and, hence, the productivity of the furnace) or to increase the temperature of the stove shell to above the dew point of nitric acid, possibly by adding external insulation. In any event, extra costs will be incurred. These will show as an element of corrosion cost in any future survey. It is unfortunate the disaster had to occur before the problem was identified.

Road Salt and Its Effects

Corrosion of reinforcing bar and pretensioning members in bridge decks, elevated highways, and parking garages is one of the major examples of continuing corrosion losses in Canada and the northern United States. As corrosion proceeds, a build-up of bulky corrosion products typically causes the concrete to spall and, consequently, increases the corrosion rate. Deicing salts are the primary culprit, though the problem has also existed under marine conditions.

One of the earliest substantial studies on the corrosion of reinforcing steel in concrete in a salty environment is in a paper by Lewis and Copenhagen.[4] This outlines tests performed to follow up on over two decades of experience with bridges in marine locations in Natal Province in South Africa. Cdr. Copenhagen's early work on jetties and dockside structures, while well-known to commonwealth naval scientists, is largely unpublished.

A variety of factors, including traffic loads, can cause an initial crack in the concrete cover over reinforcing steel on highway bridge decks. Such cracks will permit the ingress of water or aqueous solutions, and subsequent freeze thaw cycles will cause cracks to extend. The problem is more pronounced on bridge decks because there are more freeze thaw cycles than on highway surfaces backed up by a large thermal mass, as is the normal situation. Good technique in placement of concrete can postpone problems but cannot effect a cure.

Once the crack network has begun to develop, it will progress inward and open a crack path to the reinforcing steel. The corrosion of steel causes formation of a bulky oxide that enhances the cracking process, and deterioration of the bridge deck accelerates.

Measures to combat this form of deterioration must arrest either the cracking or the corrosion process, or both. Cracking, as a result of traffic load, is probably inevitable. Air-entrained concrete is more resistant to freeze thaw cycles because the increase in volume that accompanies freezing can be better accommodated locally without resulting in further crack growth. A final solution must involve making the reinforcing bar immune to corrosion or effectively excluding the corrosive solutions.

The most straightforward measure to exclude the corrodent is to top the deck with a thick layer of impervious asphalt which, in turn, is covered by an adequate layer of load-bearing asphalt. Other techniques to control the corrosion rely upon ensuring that reinforcing steel does not have a chance to corrode. One manufacturer recommends a thick epoxy coating on the rebar. This is most effective on a premium grade of rebar produced by a mini-steel mill with electric furnace practice. Unfortunately, this is only available when more lucrative orders for specialty products are not available. Typical rebar is difficult to coat effectively.

Galvanizing and cathodic protection are other palliatives, though galvanizing is only effective in the short term. For cathodic protection to be effective, the reinforcing steel must be bonded and connected electrically to the anodes. The use of conductive asphalt layers may be required. The cathodic protection route appears to be favored by the Ontario Department of Highways, at least for extending the life of structures which already have significant corrosion damage.

As is to be expected in an identified area of high corrosion costs, there is considerable current research and development work. Calcium nitrite appears to be a helpful inhibitor in concrete,[5] though nitrites can cause cracking in high strength steels. There has been a determined search for a less corrosive deicing salt. The currently favored candidate is calcium magnesium acetate,[6] though its cost is a problem. The cost of cathodic protection of reinforcing steel in highway bridges is of concern to the various highway authorities. One view is that since many structures do not show significant corrosion the use of cathodic protection (with its associated costs) should be reserved for cases where repairs are needed.[7] It is not clear whether this strategy will ultimately be appropriate. However, it certainly will be in order to develop more efficient and cost-effective ways to achieve and maintain cathodic protection of vulnerable structures.

The total incremental corrosion costs associated with road salt damage to pretensioning and reinforcing steel, concrete road surfaces, motor vehicles, parking garages and other adjacent buildings need to be added to the cost of the insult to the environment by deicing salts, together with the cost of the salt itself. These costs need to be compared with the global costs that would result from the use of tire studs or from the use of, say, calcium magnesium acetate as a deicer. What is needed is a highly competent and detailed evaluation rather than an *ex cathedra* selection of the use of sodium chloride as deicing salt without a complete cost analysis.

References

1. T.R.B. Watson, "Corrosion in the Power Industry," NACE Regional Conference (Montreal, Canada, 1977).
2. T.P. Hoar, *Report of the Committee on Corrosion and Protection*, HMSO (1979).
3. "Economic Effects of Metallic Corrosion in the US," *NBS Special Publication 511-1* (1978).
4. D.A. Lewis, W.J. Copenhagen, *Corrosion* 15 (1959).
5. N.S. Berke, CORROSION/89, paper no. 445 (Houston, TX: NACE, 1989.)
6. R.L. McCrum, CORROSION/89, paper no. 12.
7. H.C. Schell, D.G. Manning, CORROSION/89, paper no. 385.

11

Corrosion Testing

There has been an ongoing attempt to quantify corrosion losses and to assess the value of all possible remedial measures. Corrosion tests are necessarily as diverse as corrosion itself. Corrosion test pieces are immersed, buried, exposed to atmospheres, and exposed to known industrial or artificial environments judged to simulate particular practical conditions. If mechanical factors are known to be significant, they are incorporated in the tests in a controlled fashion.

The most common criterion used in corrosion testing is the weight loss (or gain) of a sample of known area. This sample must be thoroughly cleaned to remove oxide films and grease, and be in appropriate metallurgical condition. The sample is weighed before and after exposure and also after cleaning by techniques that remove only corrosion product, not the base metal. The simplest technique is soap and water cleaning with a soft bristle brush. The chemicals used as an alternative are normally inhibited acids. A related procedure is to follow electrical resistance changes in a sample in the form of a wire. The most convenient compilation of many details of such tests is H.H. Uhlig's *Corrosion Handbook*.[1] More recent information on particular tests can be found in NACE and ASTM standards. L.L. Shreir's *Corrosion* also has a strong chapter on testing.[2]

Where finishing systems are to be evaluated, other performance criteria are involved. Rust staining, pitting, discoloration, chalking, and gloss retention are some. Once again, it is important that the tests be standardized. Where pitting is under study, it is important that the samples be large enough to give statistical pitting probability close to unity.

To maintain a proper perspective on corrosion testing, its purpose must be kept clearly in mind. One objective is to determine whether an item is sufficiently corrosion-resistant to be sold as fit for its intended use. Buyer and seller must agree on a test. This test must give at reasonable cost and in acceptable time, an unambiguous result which either qualifies or disqualifies the item. Test specifications must be followed with meticulous care. Unfortunately, such tests do not always accurately predict the service lifetime of an item in its intended function. Even so, the testing must go on at least until a better test is developed and agreed upon.

A second objective is directed toward improvement of a product or a piece of process equipment. In this case, there is more leeway in the cost or time of the test, and there is more emphasis on the accuracy of its findings. In general, developmental testing has to be supported by a deliberate ongoing evaluation of service performance.

A third objective is more impersonal in nature. Here, the attempt is to increase the total data base of corrosion performance of a wide range of items. Such testing can cover the whole spectrum from relevancy to triviality. The key criterion is whether the new information justifies the effort and cost of the program.

The following discussion examines atmospheric corrosion testing and materials selection in light of the preceding comments.

Atmospheric Corrosion Testing

The assessment of atmospheric corrosion has traditionally involved the use of large sample racks constructed (as are the samples themselves) to rigid specifications. Protection of samples on even remote sites is by no means simple. A site on MacNab's Island near Halifax, for example, suffered predictable annual invasions of pickers in the blueberry season. The cost of lost or damaged specimens or of the alternative of policing easily can get out of hand.

Preparation of samples also can be a source of difficulty. Psychologically, samples prepared for a test program will attract more care and selectivity than would be the case for "run of the mill" techniques in the field. For example, test pieces with minor blemishes that would be accepted for practical use might well be rejected for test purposes.

A traditional difficulty with atmospheric corrosion testing has been the influence of the original conditions. Samples which experience fine weather at the start of the test can be expected to show lower corrosion rates than those which start off in foul weather. A possible improvement is to use electrical sensors to monitor total time of wetness. The correlation between time of wetness and total corrosion seems to be less sensitive to initial conditions.

Drift in test site severity also seems inevitable. Industrial sites are becoming less severe as environmental regulations come to have more clout. Remote locations, on the other hand, become more severe with the spread of "acid rain." Long term tests will, of course, become less attractive if suitable alternatives at lower cost can be adopted.

A further problem with atmospheric testing performed at industrial sites arises from "over the fence" contamination. A chemical plant might be downwind from another which either produces or uses ammonia, for example. Exceedingly small amounts of ammonia can invalidate the testing of copper or copper alloys. Such possibilities must always be borne in mind.

A variant of atmospheric testing has been proposed in which the increase in volume that occurs as a metal corrodes is monitored.[3] The samples are in the form of a stack of steel washers, and corrosion is followed by measuring the height of the stack. It appears possible to correlate the results with normal atmospheric tests.

The Legault and Preban approach to atmospheric corrosion testing (Chapter 4), if it lives up to its original promise and can be extended to metals other than steel, is one of these. Another less costly alternative is Alcan's spool test.[4] In this test, there is an inconspicuous wire wound spool of the metal under investigation. The spool is exposed on a utility pole to evaluate both the corrosion of the wire and of its contact with the spool. The cost of this test is low, and the survival rate of the samples is close to 100%.

In view of the preceding, the authors are of the opinion that conventional atmospheric testing should be restricted to large established sites where security can be maintained (from all but hurricanes) and to small, but specialized, sites on roofs where public access is impossible. Large new programs of atmospheric testing are not easy to justify.

Materials Selection for the Process Industries

This section deals with corrosion testing with a view to selecting materials of construction and finishes exposed to a wide variety of environments, ranging from the atmosphere to aggressive chemicals. The key concept in corrosion testing is that all relevant factors, including cost, are considered carefully before the tests commence. Too often actual performance of the material selected through corrosion testing has been disappointing, corroding either too quickly or too slowly. The last statement may raise some eyebrows; however, considering that corrosion engineers are paid to do a job as engineers, the material that does not corrode at all may be overly expensive if cheaper, but adequate, material were available. This section provides some guidelines in the workings of corrosion testing.

The ideal corrosion test should be simple, rapid, low cost, and able to accurately predict long term service behavior. Since the ideal is rarely attained, some compromises have to be made. Where mass production is involved, a test is selected that will give precise results in a reasonably short time. Good judgment is involved in estimating how well the test ranking will parallel in-service behavior. Regrettably this does not always happen as automakers rediscover from time to time. Unfortunately, supporting in-service test results may come too late to avoid embarrassment. Short-term tests tend to be more accurate in determining that a given finishing schedule has been applied properly than in evaluating relative rankings of competing schedules.

Where production of a single costly item is involved, the approach must be to optimize the predictability of results. First, the obviously bad alternatives are eliminated by simple short term tests, and the serious candidate materials are examined in greater depth by increasingly complex test procedures, including pilot plant studies. When the final choice has to be made, it is not uncommon for a supporting in-service test of good alternatives to be conducted as insurance.

Corrosion Testing of the Automobile Body

Since the cost of premature automobile body corrosion is so high, a reliable test for this type of corrosion is desirable. The largest causative factor is exposure to saline conditions, whether coastal or deicing salt in origin.

For the latter case, the major factors are severity of the winter and extent of the use of salt by the local authorities. Driver-related variables include whether the car is driven in all weathers, whether the driver consistently avoids puddles, if time of wetness is increased by the use of a partially heated garage, whether the car is washed with freshwater or at a car wash where recirculating water picks up salt, and so on.

With so many variables, a statistical test involving many cars would be needed. Unfortunately, results would not be available until the particular model year is long gone.

Philosophy

The original approach to corrosion testing is governed by two main considerations: (1) To select the most suitable material of construction; or (2) to control the corrosion of equipment in service. The former deals mainly with tests for the most suitable material from a number of viewpoints, such as corrosion resistance, cost, and compatibility with other materials or with the process. The latter deals with the actual ongoing corrosion in the process. Usually, corrosion specimens or probes are installed in the process stream and are evaluated from time to time. Hence, representative information is obtained regarding the corrosion rates of operating equipment. Furthermore, corrosion tests are used to verify the quality or metallurgical condition of the material of construction (e.g., Huey test ASTM-A-262-88T).[5] A salt spray test may be used to study pitting or discoloration of aluminum or stainless architectural panels. Newly developed alloys having superior corrosion resistance in a particular application must be tested extensively before being released for actual service.

There may be a question as to whether a specific material will contaminate a process stream due to the release of specific ions which are detrimental or poisonous to the process, or, in the atomic industry, if radioactive corrosion products migrate to undesirable locations. Corrosion tests often are useful in the search for a less aggressive environment where measures such as lowering a concentration, temperature, changing velocity, or providing aeration could be beneficial. The effect of the type and quantity of inhibitors also can be studied. A whole array of information, however, must be considered from the point of view of reliability and cost.

Test Methods

The selection of the appropriate test method is governed mainly by reliability and cost; however, other factors, such as available time (urgency), opportunity, and the availability of adequate facilities also may play an important role. Safety in testing is a paramount concern. Such systems as Ti in red fuming nitric acid must be set up with the possibility of violent reactions in mind. Prior to commencing the corrosion test, it must be decided what key information is desired — penetration, appearance, effect of operation, contamination, or effect on mechanical or physical properties? The probable consequences of a corrosion failure also have a bearing on the test selection. Four major types of test methods are used in the industry. They are: (1) service test; (2) field test; (3) laboratory test; and (4) electronic or linear polarization test.

Service Test

The service test is a corrosion test whereby the actual equipment is exposed to operation conditions. Usually, this is done by installing a spool piece in a process line or bypass which, after suitable exposure, is removed and its condition evaluated and/or measured. This test is expensive mainly because of the maintenance cost of removing and reinstalling the spool piece. The reliability of the information is high, provided that service conditions such as temperature, velocity, and concentration are well-specified and maintained. If any of these conditions change with or without intention, the results of these tests become less significant. Also, most of the service corrosion tests are long term. They may suffer or lack precision in interpretation, and may be subject to electrochemical effects when different materials are used for the tests. Contamination of the product by the test spool piece made of an incompatible material sometimes creates problems where it may affect the purity of the process stream and/or cause problems with the final product.

Above all, however, the safety of the system must be considered carefully. If a spool piece made from a material with a lower modulus of elasticity, lower temperature resistance, or poor corrosion resistance is installed, the spool piece may fail catastrophically, adversely affect utility of operation, and injure personnel. To alleviate some problems mentioned with this test method, a bypass system often is used (Figure 11.01). There, the spool piece can be taken out of service, measured, and reinstalled without interrupting the process. The bypass spool piece must be exposed to the exact operating conditions.

Field Test

The next test is the so-called field test, which is carried out by simply installing a corrosion sample holder into a process line or vessel. Such samples may be evaluated in any convenient fashion.

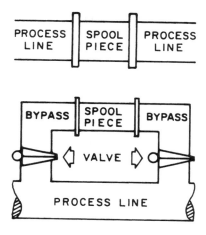

Figure 11.01 *Fixed spool piece and the bypass system.*

Weight loss determination would be normal, though electrical resistance or polarization resistance also may be used to monitor corrosion.

The main advantage of this test is that, although it may not be quite as reliable as a service test, a number of materials can be tested at one time. The corrosion holder is simply inserted into the process or a bypass, left for a predetermined time, removed, cleaned, and the corrosion rates calculated by an accepted method. But note that the corrosion holder itself and the means for securing it must be totally resistant to the process stream. It is obvious that this test offers a good opportunity to screen a number of candidate materials in a rather rapid fashion. Since the corrosion specimens are usually relatively small (a few square inches) metallographic or stereoscopic examination of their structure and/or surface is needed to reveal information with regard to intergranular attack and/or surface conditions, e.g., pitting or crevice corrosion. It should be noted that the good condition of small samples cannot guarantee absence of pitting on a larger scale. If pitting is the main concern, weight loss is not a reliable indicator. Also, if pits are found on a small sample, their depth is not a good indication of the maximum pit depth found on a larger item. An increase of at least 3x in maximum pit depth would be expected.

It also is possible to install stressed specimens (usually U bends) to investigate the materials' resistance to stress corrosion cracking.

Failure to obtain accurate information from this type of test often is caused by improper installation. A correct decision is needed on where to install the corrosion holders in the system — should they be in the vapor phase area or in the liquid phase area, or both, etc.? If there is a degree of uncertainty with regard to location, the best alternative usually is to install corrosion holders at several locations. There is nothing worse than taking a test at a location that is not representative of the most severe actual service conditions. For instance, it is not unusual for a corrosion study of a large distillation column to require 4 to 10 corrosion holders installed at different locations.

Often, problems are encountered with the fixation of the corrosion samples onto the corrosion holder. If the small nut holding the sample on the holder comes loose, the corrosion sample will drop into the process stream and can end up in a circulating pump with ensuing disaster. By the same token, the material of construction of the holder and the fasteners must be corrosion-resistant and designed so vibration will not cause fatigue failure. Some problems have been experienced where corrosion holders were installed in a line of too small a diameter, and plugging and/or flow restriction occurred. It is obvious that both plugging and restriction (usually exhibiting high-velocity patterns) will produce erratic and unreliable results.

Most of the time a number of different candidate materials are used on one corrosion holder. This implies that galvanic corrosion must be eliminated. This is done first by isolating all the fasteners from the holders, and second by placing the test specimens in a manner such that they are grouped by their position in the galvanic series, if at all possible. The electrical insulation must be applied intelligently, so that spurious information will not result.

Laboratory Test

The laboratory corrosion test is used for a check or screen of the corrosion rates of materials for a given application. A wide array of test methods, such as the Huey and salt spray tests, fall in this category. The Huey test is a standard test which must conform to specific standards regarding solution concentration, temperature, and length of exposure, whereas other tests might not be run under standard conditions. Care must also be taken in the Huey test to avoid boil-off of the solution. Good design of a condenser system is imperative. There are standard conditions for the solution volume to sample size ratio. This is an important factor in laboratory tests since a relatively large sample will contaminate a solution at a much greater rate than will a smaller sample.

The complexity of laboratory corrosion tests may range from a simple Erlenmeyer flask containing one specimen to elaborately controlled high pressure and temperature installations, or even pilot plants. Where high pressures are involved, the entire test must be conducted in a properly designed pressure bay. The main advantage of the laboratory corrosion test is to have a method or procedure available which provides information on the performance of a material in a given solution or environment in an expedient manner, usually at a low cost. The terms "expedient" and "cheap" imply that caution must be used in judging the obtained results. Frivolous or overly enthusiastic extrapolation of short term laboratory corrosion test results often have produced unpleasant surprises in actual service. However, as long as the laboratory corrosion test is used for its intended purpose, it is one of the major sources of information and enables the investigator to make a short list of candidate materials for more comprehensive testing.

One of the main features of laboratory tests is that, subject to a few necessary restrictions such as not using fluorides in glass equipment, all test conditions can be selected and controlled, and changes can be recorded or observed *in situ*. In the laboratory, all main parameters, such as temperature, velocity, and solution and inhibitor concentrations, can be observed, measured, and changed to find the effectiveness of a given inhibitor under varying conditions. The laboratory conditions also permit: choice of test solution, whether it be laboratory grade or actual process material from the operation, with aeration or inert gas blanketing; and analysis of the test solution after the test. The color change of the test solution can often be a good indication of the degree of corrosion; e.g., a bad sample of stainless steel having poor corrosion resistance in nitric acid in the Huey test will run the nitric acid from colorless to dark green rather quickly due to the dissolution of chromium ions (ASTM-A262-88T). In this test, the ratio of the exposed sample area to the total test solution volume is critical since any build-up of dissolved chromium ions in solution will cause dramatic increases in corrosion rates of both good and bad materials

It is always good practice to carry out laboratory tests in

duplicate, preferably triplicate. This produces more statistically reliable results. A good deal of laboratory corrosion testing involves nonmetallics. The test parameters for these materials are roughly the same as for metals. However, the evaluation of the results differs substantially. Discoloration of the test medium and swelling or shrinkage of the test samples are prominent parameters in the evaluation of nonmetallics.

Equipment has recently become commercially available to employ a new technique in laboratory testing — the coulostatic method. In effect, this measures the double layer capacitance of a sample immersed in a high impedance electrolyte and seeks to correlate this with corrosion behavior. As yet, there is insufficient experience with this method to judge its usefulness.

Laboratory testing can cover a number of other, more specialized, areas. Suppose susceptibility to SCC is suspected. Arrays of samples in precise metallurgical condition and stressed to precisely determined levels can be exposed to the suspected medium at a selected temperature, usually somewhat above the intended for the process. Such tests are clearly more expensive and time-consuming than more straightforward screening tests.

A recent paper seeks to establish correlations between service applications and laboratory tests with rotating probes and flow loops. The corrosion cases considered would be those where fluid flow would be a significant factor in determining the extent of corrosion. There were indications that the greater severity inherent in the rotating probe would overemphasize the extent of flow-induced localized corrosion. However, the more costly and more time-consuming flow loops appeared to give a better correlation with service.

Electrochemical Test Methods

The increasing availability of the potentiostat, along with a generation of corrosion scientists trained in its use, has led to wide employment of instrumental techniques based upon it. More recently, there has been a note of caution injected, and there is a more critical appraisal of the proper role of the potentiostat and results derived from its use. The most important of the electrochemical test methods is the linear polarization (polarization resistance) method, based on the equations outlined in Chapter 1. In essence, this involves making studies of the low overpotential (linear) region of the potential vs current relationship for a corroding sample, and using the values obtained to predict the Tafel slopes in the more practical high overpotential region.

This technique has been reviewed by Mansfield, who analyses limitations of the method and concludes that the following six assumptions are involved: (1) The Butler-Volmer equations of electrochemical kinetics are applicable; (2) ohmic drops in the electrolyte and in surface films are absent; (3) concentration polarization is absent; (4) the corrosion potential does not lie close to the reversible potential of either of the two reactions occurring; (5) the whole metal functions simultaneously as a cathode and anode, rather than being a mosaic of separate cathodic and anodic areas; and (6) there are no secondary electrochemical reactions occurring.[7]

The first assumption naturally implies that the reaction is under activation control, though it may be possible to obtain technically useful results for other corrosion mechanisms, albeit on an empirical basis. An empirical approach to pitting, based on the difference between the anodic and cathodic part of the linear polarization pulse, also is possible. Those who intend to use the linear polarization technique should consult this review. There can be no doubt that, where linear polarization is effective, it is a powerful tool for corrosion study. But it should be used with care.

Given the availability of the potentiostat, it can be used to generate other data in corrosion systems. For example, pitting potentials can be determined, as can differences in potential between high and low scan rates for the same test sample. In general, the measurements are easier to make than they are to interpret, and once again there is a list of limitations. Shibita and Takeyama emphasize the statistical nature of such measurements.[8]

There have been striking advances in the use of electrical transients to analyze what is going on at the reacting interface in a corrosion or other electrochemical system. Macdonald's monograph gives a useful, though advanced, account of many of these.[9] His chapter headings include: potential step chronoamperometry and chronocoulometry; chronopotentiometry; linear potential sweep and cyclic voltammetry; and AC impendance techniques. These techniques help define the electrical events that occur at the reaction sites and allow an interpretation to be made of the reaction kinetics based on ideas stemming from the Butler Volmer equation. Electrical artifacts and the influence of imprecision of electrical measurements inherent in these techniques have not always had the attention they deserve.

All of the methods that depend on the application of a small potential step or ramp can be shown to be mathematically equivalent in terms of ability to determine the corrosion rate and reaction mechanism.[10] Where they are not equivalent is in terms of the precision, convenience, and speed with which this can be done.

Electrochemical impedance spectroscopy (EIS) is a strong candidate for the favored technique. Each scan at a particular frequency yields one of a set of simultaneous equations; greater precision can be achieved by merely increasing the time over which the measurements are taken. The necessary number of equations to define all the kinetic parameters can be achieved by repeating the scans at a sufficient number of frequencies, followed by computer analysis of the data. For results to be valid, all relaxations must have time constants within the frequency range covered by the set of scans. The required experimental time can balloon where very low frequencies have to be included.

EIS data can be displayed as a complex impedance following a Laplace transform operation.[11] Most commonly, Nyquist diagrams are used. Mathematical criteria can be applied to determine whether the impedance data is valid. Both mechanisms and corrosion rates can be determined. Corrosion rates also can be obtained where there is a paint film, for example.

An important lesson seems to be that results obtained from electronic test methods are just as subject to scatter as, for example, weight loss or pit depth data, particularly where the sample size is small. Results from a strip chart recorder can generate a false sense of security.

Table 11.01 summarizes the comparative features of each corrosion test method. The conclusions are not necessarily fixed and are intended only as guidelines. Often, these tests will complement each other, and an intelligent combination of two or three methods in conjunction may increase the confidence with which the conclusions can be applied by an order of magnitude.

Safety in testing is of paramount importance. Many laboratory workers have been injured or even killed while performing rather simple corrosion tests. Adequate personal protection must be worn at all times, and face shields are no luxury. Fumes escaping from

176

corrosion flakes may be extremely corrosive or sometimes lethal. A small drop of water falling into a container of molten acid, e.g., adipic or phosphoric acid, may erupt the hot corrosive content in the worker's face. Care must be taken in mixing the test solutions. Dangerous reactions will occur with a variety of mixtures. The pyrophoric reaction of some metals, e.g., Ti in red fuming HNO_3, may lead to major explosions. Lastly, ensure that the container selected to carry out the test will not corrode faster than the test sample.

Finally, let us look at an example of a test that went wrong. An earnest worker had to conduct some U bend tests for stress corrosion cracking. He stressed the specimens to yield point, removed the stressing bolts, and inserted the samples in the test medium. All

TABLE 11.01

Comparison of Various Test Methods

Type of Test	Reliability	Cost	Remarks
Service	High	High	Cost is high due to shutdown of equipment. Bypass may partly solve this. Watch for compatibility and strength of spool piece.
Field	Moderately	Medium	Many samples tested on one holder. Samples must be isolated and firmly secured. Removal usually requires equipment shutdown.
Laboratory	Usually low; can give good comparative data	Inexpensive	Excellent for preliminary screening. Difficult to reproduce precise process conditions, e.g., impurities and hot wall effect. Short exposure corrosion rates are extrapolated.
Electronic (linear polarization)	Variable	Inexpensive to run — needs costly equipment	High reliability only when proper precautions are taken.

concerned were surprised by the lack of cracking on the outside of the U. What had happened is revealed in Figure 11.02. When the stressing bolt was removed, the U bend sample relaxed, and the inner part of the U was in tension. That is where the cracks were found.

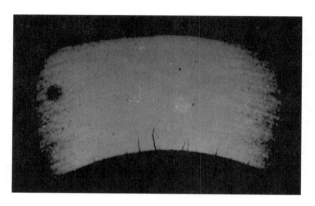

Figure 11.02 *Example of a U bend specimen that went wrong.*

References

1. H.H. Uhlig, *The Corrosion Handbook* (New York, NY: Wiley-Interscience, Inc., 1948).
2. L.L. Shreir, *Corrosion* (Woburn, MA: Butterworths, 1967).
3. B. Lloyd et al., CORROSION/89, paper no. 22. Houston, TX: NACE, 1989.
4. H.P. Godard, *Materials Protection* 2, 6(1963): p. 38.
5. ASTM Standard A-262-88T, *Annual Book of ASTM Standards* (Philadelphia, PA: ASTM).
6. G. Schmitt et al, CORROSION/90, paper no. 23 (Houston, TX: NACE, 1990).
7. F. Mansfield. (Review) *Advances in Corrosion Science and Technology*, Vol. 6 (New York, NY and London, UK: Plenum, 1976).
8. T. Shibita, T. Takeyama, *Corrosion* 33, 7(1977): p. 243.
9. D.D. MacDonald, *Transient Techniques in Electrochemistry* (New York, NY: Plenum, 1977).
10. D.D. MacDonald *Corrosion* 46 3(1990): p. 229.
11. S. Goldman, *Transformation Calculus and Electrical Transients* (New York, NY: Prentice Hall, 1949).

12

Detecting and Monitoring Corrosion

Introduction

The employment of metallurgical engineers (e.g., in the chemical industry), although relatively new, is gaining rapid acceptance. This seems logical, particularly if the total productive output of an industry is considered a team effort: A chemist develops a certain chemical process; the mechanical and/or chemical engineer designs the equipment; and the metallurgical engineer specifies the materials of construction (and fabrication techniques). By virtue of specifying the materials, the metallurgical engineer becomes directly involved in the fabrication of equipment, which requires a good understanding of related fields, such as forming, welding, test methods, and all relevant statutory regulations, including ASME and ANSI codes. Once the equipment has become operable, the engineer automatically assumes the position of corrosion engineer, equipment inspector, and failure analyst, if failure should occur. Although responsibilities are usually indirect, the engineer plays a major part to ensure the proper, and above all, safe operation of equipment. This chapter deals with the inspection function of a metallurgical engineer and/or technologist/technician working as a team to provide guidance and assistance in a total effort to keep manufacturing operations at high utility, but above all, in safe operating condition.

Plant Inspection and Inspection Techniques

Plant inspection techniques generally employ nondestructive evaluation methods. These can be subdivided into two main categories: defect detection NDE and analytical NDE. The former includes penetrant analysis, in place metallography, ultrasonics, eddy currents, radiography, and acoustic emission analysis. The latter includes more indirect analysis, such as thermal analysis, finite element stress analysis, strain gauging, photoelasticity, and brittle coatings.

Inspection of chemical plants must be carried out in an organized and systematic manner, particularly as the size of chemical complexes continues to increase. A number of major chemical industries now have a computerized program dealing with frequency, timing, and recording of equipment condition, specifically for continuous processes. Safety valves require special attention. Their continuing ability to function properly is vital, but not necessarily obvious. Construction of such a program is by no means an easy task. It involves a great deal of know-how in areas of preassessment with regard to specifying how and how often particular pieces of equipment must or should be inspected. Once this is accomplished, a suitable computerized program can be prepared. As a general guide, it is assumed that all equipment must be inspected at least once every five years. Critical equipment operating at high pressure (essential to utility), or operating in severe conditions, is inspected annually. The most probable sites of first failure often can be predicted, especially in situations where fluid flow is a factor, as in cases of erosion by flowing sulphuric acid. The inspector has to have access to the past history of the equipment or of similar units it has replaced.

In today's industry, inspectors, or better, authorized examiners, play a major role in engineering. The inspector's job starts even before the equipment is fabricated by checking shop drawings, welding procedures, capability of vendors, and the acceptance of the finished product.

Inspection groups usually contain a variety of skilled persons: mechanical inspectors; corrosion technicians; technologists; chemists; and metallurgical, mechanical, or chemical engineers. Each person is trained in considerable depth in a specialty. A high degree of proficiency in the particular field is essential since in many situations personnel may be the final authority and exercise judgment which could have great impact on whether the operation is safe and successful. Nowadays, it is becoming even more apparent that a great deal of reliance is placed on the performance of an individual inspector or inspection department. Quality control or assurance programs are being established that involve mandatory professional licensing for inspection personnel. Certification by government or institutions on subjects such as radiographic, ultrasonic, magnetic particle, eddy current, and liquid penetrant inspections is mandatory in many countries, including Canada and the United States. Furthermore, thorough training is required in the pressure vessel and inspection codes published by the American Society of Mechanical Engineers (ASME), the Canadian Standards Board (CSB), and in provincial regulations of the Ministry of Consumer Affairs and Customer Relations. In a nutshell, the inspection effort is the foundation of an all important preventive maintenance programs. Detailed and precise plant condition reports should be part of this. Management must be convinced of the value of such effort. If properly organized and accepted, it will save money in terms of reduced downtime, fewer accidents, and decreased cost of insurance. Equipment inspections can be divided into two parts, scheduled and unscheduled inspections.

Scheduled Inspections

These are periodic equipment inspections, as mentioned previously. They are planned and scheduled with proper priorities and are carried out before or during a scheduled outage. Much of the information is usually obtained prior to a plant shutdown by means of "onstream" inspection where techniques such as ultrasonics and radiography have been utilized to determine, if possible, the equipment condition in advance. Proper action and/or replacement of equipment or equipment components can be readied prior to the outage.

Unscheduled Inspections

Unscheduled inspections usually occur when equipment fails. This often will put the inspection department under high pressure, particularly since most chemical operations are continuous, and the failure of one component can bring the total operation to a grinding halt. This situation mandates a cool head, good judgment, and an intelligent approach to an immediate problem. The inspector's experience and know-how is put to the test, and often the inspector will carry the responsibility of recommending alterations or repair methods, which must be within the rules set forth by codes and laws. Note that repairs to an item such as a pressure vessel, which would originally be subject to the ASME code, must conform in detail to that code. This means that all who work on the repair must be duly qualified and the shop where the repair is done also must meet all code requirements.

It is not within the scope of this presentation to detail responsibilities and job descriptions of all personnel involved in inspection. The spectrum ranges from highly skilled senior metallurgical engineers to junior technicians in training.

Defect Detection NDE Methods

Nearly every form of energy has been utilized at one time or another for nondestructive testing. The most widely used methods for corrosion detection fit into seven distinct categories: (1) visual; (2) radiographic; (3) acoustic or ultrasonic; (4) electromagnetic; (5) liquid penetrant and magnetic particle; (6) in place metallography; (7) acoustic emission; and (8) neutron backscatter inspection.

1. Visual

Visual examination is one of the oldest, simplest, and cheapest nondestructive test methods. Here, the object is examined visually or with the aid of optical devices, often accompanied by discreet probing with a penknife. The experienced inspector can determine much from the appearance of the surfaces. In most cases, corrosion penetration cannot be ascertained, but often an indication of the corrosion can be obtained by measuring pit depth or the thickness of protuberances. The experienced eye can find conditions which would cause premature failures and unscheduled shutdowns, such as weld defects; general corrosion; pitting corrosion; SCC; weld metal or weld heat effected zone attack; liquid/vapor phase interface effects; erosion/corrosion; and chemical degradation of plastics. When physical access to the equipment is impossible, or details are too small to be seen with the unaided eye, visual inspection is accomplished with optical and illuminating aids. For example, borescopes and flexible fiber optic instruments can be used to inspect the interior of small parts, tubes, etc. It should be noted that the end of a borescope is a concentrated source of heat as well as light. It could act as a source of ignition if used carelessly. The use of penetrants to enhance the visibility of small cracks, etc., will be detailed in Section 5.

2. Radiography by X-ray and Isotope Examination

Radiography has five distinct advantages in the assessment of corrosion problems: (1) The inside of complex and small parts such as valves and pipes, which are not accessible, can be evaluated; (2) outer coverings, such as insulation, need not be removed; (3) the radiograph is a permanent record; (4) the attacked area shown on the radiograph can give some indication of the nature and degree of attack; and (5) pit depth can be evaluated by means of density measurements on the radiograph. (Strict control of film processing is required.)

The main limitation to radiography is that both sides of the part must be accessible. Radiography is a useful technique to determine weld quality. Flaws in the weld, lack of penetration, etc., can be identified as initiation sites for crevice corrosion or mechanical failure. Other uses for radiography are: inspection of valves; detection of plugged lines; determination of liquid levels in columns; core pipe location, etc. Radiography is also a useful corrosion trouble-shooting technique, both in establishing the nature of corrosion and evaluating the extent of corrosion damage. Pitting and general corrosion are the types of damage that can be most readily evaluated by radiography. The thickness remaining on the radiograph of a pipe can be measured using proper geometrical correction factors. If the original thickness is known, corrosion rates can be determined. In many cases, it is necessary to take more than one radiograph at different angles to characterize a defect.

The particular advantages of using isotopes to generate gamma rays is that the source is easily portable, explosion-proof, has wide angle capability, and requires no power or process control. Disadvantages are that it is "on" all the time and requires more care in shielding and transporting on a continuing basis, and that the intensity of the source decays with time, albeit predictably. X-ray sources are less easily portable, require power, can be a source of ignition, are usually effective over a narrow angle only, and are limited in thickness capability by the voltage of the source and the nature of the x-ray tube itself. Both require close control of film and film processing, and need to be calibrated with penetrameters. Both require fully trained operators and full radiation safety protocols.

The detection of defects with radiation is based upon differing absorption of the radiation by a full thickness piece and the defective area. The differences in transmitted intensity are recorded photographically. The energy of the incident radiation must be matched to the thickness and density of the item examined so that the fraction absorbed is neither too high nor too low. Because of their low penetration power, low voltage x-ray and low intensity isotope units, such as Yb 169, are most useful for the radiography of thin sections or of material of low density, such as aluminum and plastics. High voltage x-ray equipment, accelerators, and high energy isotopes, such as cobalt 60 and IRIDIUM[192] must be used for thick sections and high density materials. There is a problem with radiography of thick sections where the defect to film distance becomes excessive, resulting in loss of definition. Ultrasonic examination would be the preferred method of examination. Radiation safety standards must be rigorously maintained. It is necessary to follow regulations for the use of x-rays and the use and transport of isotopes in meticulous detail.

3. Ultrasonics

Ultrasonic equipment is widely used now for the nondestructive thickness gauging of in-service equipment subject to corrosion and erosion for the detection of laminar discontinuities and for crack detection. Inherent accuracy, small size, and continuing improvements in operation have made ultrasonic inspection equipment particularly suitable for field inspection.

The three ultrasonic techniques are: (1) the pulse-echo; (2) transmission; and (3) resonance methods. The original units were mostly of the resonance type, but these are being supplanted by the ultrasonic pulse-echo equipment. (Figure 12.01).

Only the transmission method requires access to both sides of the object under examination. The normal technique is that the transducers are acoustically coupled to the test piece. This may involve stripping off insulation and so forth and using a couplant oil film to connect the transducer to the test piece.

In principle, transducers could be electromagnetically rather than acoustically coupled. Such units are currently under development. This would allow for remote ultrasonic inspection of components in nuclear boiler rooms, etc., where access by inspection personnel for more conventional testing is difficult or impossible. The main requirement would be to position the transducers precisely and reproducibly and keep a record of their output over a series of examinations.

Some advantages of ultrasonic testing are: High sensitivity; great penetrating power, which allows for examination of extremely thick sections; and accuracy in the measurement of thickness or flaw

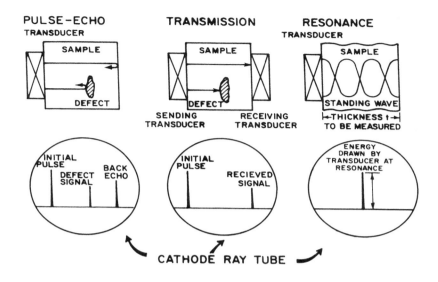

Figure 12.01 Comparison of ultrasonic techniques.

position and size. Present units are capable of an accuracy of plus or minus .005 inches or better; fast response, which permits rapid and automated inspection; access to only one surface is required; high temperature probes are now available for testing on surfaces exceeding 400°C (752°F).   This allows hot line or onstream inspection. It should be noted that ultrasonic inspection makes extreme demands on the experience of the operator.

The test conditions, which may limit the application of ultrasonic methods, usually relate to one of the following: unfavorable sample geometry — size, contour, complexity, and defect orientation; undesirable internal structure — grain size, structure, porosity, inclusion content, or fine dispersed precipitates; temperature; vibration; and stray electric currents, e.g., from welding machines.

Another use of ultrasonics is in air and gas leak detection. In these cases, a detector is used that utilizes the ultrasonic energy generated by molecular collisions as gas escapes or enters a small orifice. Usually, a directional probe is sensitive only in the ultrasonic frequency spectrum.

The scope of ultrasonics has been radically enhanced by the

185

development of a variety of ultrasonic imaging techniques.[1] Acoustic microscopy and scanning acoustic microscopy are both available. Acoustic methods also can be used to monitor internal temperature distribution in metals.

4. Eddy-Current

The eddy-current tester is a comparatively recent nondestructive technique which depends on electromagnetic induction. The principle involved is simple: A coil carrying AC is brought into the vicinity of the test piece, eddy or induced currents are generated in the test piece, and the secondary interacting magnetic field formed by the induced current is monitored for changes (Figure 12.02). The induced eddy currents are affected by electrical conductivity and permeability, as well as workpiece dimensions and homogeneity. In addition to determining the presence of defects, the method can determine internal stresses, structures resulting from heat treatment, and can help to identify particular materials. Coupling is not required.

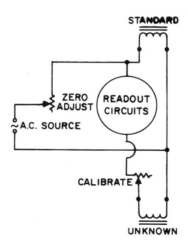

Figure 12.02 Eddy current circuit diagram.

The Probolog, an effective instrument of this type, is used for tubing inspection. This unit will detect general corrosion, pitting, stress corrosion, fatigue cracking, and microstructural changes in nonmagnetic tubing.

186

Eddy currents also can be used for the measurement of the thickness of a nonconducting surface layer; i.e., plastics, paints, or corrosion scale. An example of this type of unit is a Turner-gauge † used in measuring scale thickness in boiler tubes. This unit can be used on magnetic material.

The serious financial and environmental consequences of a sudden failure of oil platforms in the North Sea have led to the development of improved eddy-current methods for detection of cracks in welded structures *in situ* as well as methods for measuring and monitoring crack growth. The ultimate objective is to follow the growth of cracks in large welded tubular structures so repairs can be made before cracks become critical. Accurate stress analysis and accurate NDT assessments are both needed.

At a frequency of about 6 kHz, the induced current will be concentrated in a "skin" of about 0.1 mm; this permits a detailed evaluation of any cracks which come to the surface, even when measurements are made in a conductive medium such as seawater. Improvements in the front end amplifier to virtually eliminate the common mode signal, along with a microprocessor to fit an observed crack to one of a number of possible models, have enabled Dover et al.to meet the intended objectives.[2] Their instrument is portable and can be used either in air or under water with little reduction in performance in the latter case.

5. *Liquid Penetrants and Magnetic Particle Inspection*

In many cases, flaws are open to the surface, though they may be impossible to find visually without aid. These include fine cracks caused by stress corrosion, fatigue, grinding, galling, etc. Flaws of this type usually are found easily by applying a liquid penetrant or a liquid dispersion of magnetic particles on ferromagnetic materials. Where the liquid penetrant is used, it normally contains a dissolved dye, which may be fluorescent. If so, the most effective examination would be in a darkened booth under ultraviolet illumination. The part to be tested must be clean and dry, and at close to ambient temperature for maximum sensitivity. The penetrant is drawn into the crack that is, in effect, a capillary. A chalky film of "developer" is applied, causing

---

† Trademark

187

the penetrant to bleed out of the crack. Examination in normal or ultraviolet light follows, disclosing cracks that would not have been seen without optical enhancement.

For magnetic materials, the test piece may be magnetized and coated with a liquid dispersion of fine magnetic particles. Surface and subsurface flaws will cause irregularities in magnetization and, hence, in the distribution of these particles. In this way, both of these types of flaws can be seen.

The foregoing examination methods will increase the sensitivity of unaided visual examinations and, in some cases, extend the range of detection.

6. In Place Metallography

Local polishing, followed by etching and microscopic examination in place is a possible technique that may be used to follow up a failure examination. Suitable replicas also may be prepared, allowing for examination either by optical or electron microscopy.

7. Acoustic Emission

The audible creaking of wooden structures under load and the "tin cry" emitted when pure tin is deformed are classic examples of acoustic emission. In general, elastic energy is spontaneously released when a material either cracks, undergoes plastic deformation, or disbonds. It follows that when loaded, many structures emit sound which can be monitored with appropriate sensitive pickups and displayed or recorded. There are indications that this technique can be developed to anticipate failure of stressed storage tanks of reinforced plastic construction. Sudden failure of FRP tanks has been found to be a problem in the chemical industry. It now appears that acoustic emission techniques will be useful for anticipating such failures.

In the case of reinforced plastic tanks, etc. under stress, the sound pulses appear to result from local disbondment of the glass reinforcement. When disbonding events become too numerous or too frequent, the storage tank would have to be down rated and eventually withdrawn from service.

8. Neutron Backscatter Inspection

A recent NDT tool is based on the ability of water to absorb high energy neutrons and re-emit them as lower thermal neutrons.[2]   A neutron source is employed at a sufficiently low level so that its hazard is minimal.   The backscattered neutrons are detected and analyzed to detect water, particularly as an unwanted invader of insulation.   This technique has been quite effective for inspection of hot product pipelines in the extreme north.

Analytical NDE Methods

The methods considered under this category are essentially indirect, but promise to become more important in the future.

1.   Finite Element Stress Analysis
With the advent of suitable computer programs, it is now possible to follow both thermal and mechanical stresses by determining a large number of displacements of particular points on complex structures. These displacements can be translated to stresses, and results can be obtained even for some statically indeterminate cases.

2.   Brittle Coatings
The brittle coating method has been available for some 40 years and can be used to give a semi-quantitative determination of the stresses applied to a machine component.   Lines of crazing in the coating will be perpendicular to the stress.   It can locate maximum stress and also show where strain gauges can be usefully applied for a more complete analysis. The method is quantitative when the strain required for the coating to crack is known.

3.   Photoelastic Methods
In this technique, a model of the structure is built using a transparent polymeric material which exhibits stress birefringence. This is then examined under polarized light, usually monochromatic, between crossed polarizers.   In some cases, circularly polarized light techniques have to be used.   Interpretation is difficult, but the fringe pattern can give useful information on the distribution of stresses.

4.   Strain Gauges
This is the most accurate method for determining strain at a particular point.   It is most effective when a preliminary survey by either brittle coatings or photoelastic methods has helped define the

locations of maximum stress and their orientations. Strain gauge elements operate by means of a change in electrical resistance as they are strained.

5. *Thermal Methods*

The increasing use of composite structures in equipment has focused attention on the problem of checking the integrity of bonds between disparate materials. One effective way of attacking this situation is to use heat as a testing medium. The flow of thermal energy through the specimen will be affected by discontinuities. This variation would show as a temperature gradient on the surface. One method for testing is to coat the surface with a heat-sensitive film that melts or changes color at a certain temperature. Monitoring of the surface exposes cool spots, which are indications of lack or loss of bonding. Infrared sensors also may be used to detect defective insulation, hot spots on equipment, etc. at a considerable distance.

General

Finally, leak detection is one method that really is not a nondestructive testing procedure, but it also should be mentioned. There are a number of methods that can be used for leak detection, including that already mentioned — ultrasonic leak detection. Other methods include: the helium mass spectrometer; the halide sensitive electronic detector; color indicator methods, in which a dye is placed on the surface and changes color because of material leaking out; the air-soap solution test; and the hydrostatic test.

The use of hydrostatic testing as a means of detecting corrosion is diminishing in favor of visual and other inspection methods for these reasons: Severely corroded vessels or piping that have been thinned almost to a perforation may still have sufficient sound metal remaining to pass this test, but may fail in service shortly afterwards; and, under certain conditions, a hydrostatic test can actually damage sound piping and equipment beyond repair. Any test that involves an increase in internal pressure is likely to damage expansion joints and must not be used where these are present. Furthermore, air must not be used for proof testing pressure equipment.

190

How to Manage Information Obtained

In the course of their duties, the inspector or inspection unit accumulates a wealth of information regarding the condition of all equipment on the plant site. The point now becomes how to share this information with all interested parties, and the format of this exchange. In modern plants, this is done by a computerized printout of a card system, but if computer facilities are not available or cannot be justified, a written inspection report must be issued. These are some of the essential items of information which need to be shared: (1) Type of report, date and report number; (2) equipment registration, equipment number, and location; (3) service condition, such as media and pressure; (4) materials of construction; (5) date of inspection; (6) the inspector; (7) observations — a factual account of what was observed during the inspection; (8) conclusions — description and discussion of what was observed, its impact on operations, and cause; (9) recommendations — what action must be taken now, or if not now, when — assign responsibility; and (10) remarks — anything that may follow up the inspection to increase understanding.

This report should be distributed to all parties concerned, and an attempt must be made to standardize the distribution list. The reports then must be filed in orderly fashion, and items that need further attention should be deposited in a proper tickler system.

Other types of reports may arise from inspection efforts, particularly if further work is required to analyze or solve a problem. Separate reports on failure analysis, corrosion investigation, ultrasonic information, radiographic inspection reports, or letters dealing with consultation on the subject should be numbered, identified, and properly cross-referenced to the particular installation file. Many good and worthwhile efforts have gone astray by not following up with the paper work.

NDE in the Atomic Power Industry

Because of the drastic consequences of a failure, the atomic industry must pay special attention to nondestructive examination. These tests must trigger appropriate action, regardless of the immediate economic consequences. It is not clear that reporting to the owner of the facility will necessarily achieve this.

The Canadian experience has been that all such test schedules must follow guidelines set up by an independent agency, the Atomic Energy Control Board. Results of all tests are made available to AECB as well as to the owner of the facility, and AECB can issue and enforce orders that it feels are necessary. This appears to be a more effective method of protecting the public interest than requiring the owner to do its own policing.

Operators of NDE Equipment

The various national societies for nondestructive testing have established certification procedures for operators of NDE equipment. Table 12.01 shows the educational requirements that the Canadian Counsel for Nondestructive Examination has set up for the two recognized levels of ultrasonics operators and radiographers. There is a detailed breakdown of the hours of classroom instruction and related work experience. Examinations are required to qualify.

TABLE 12.01

Education and Work Experience Required for
(a) Ultrasonics Operators, (b) Radiographers, Levels 1 & 2[3]

Prior Formal Education	Min. Hours Training		Min. Months Experience	
	Level 1	Level 2	Level 1	Level 2
(a) Ultrasonics, Levels 1 &2				
2 yrs+ post-secondary	24	40	3	9
graduate from secondary school	40	40	3	9
graduate from elem. school or proficiency, or extra training.	40	80	3	9
(b) Radiographers, Levels 1 & 2				
2 yrs+ post-secondary	21	47	3	9
graduate from secondary school	33	47	3	9
graduate from elementary school , etc.	100	123	3	9

Somewhat less extensive training is required of eddy-current operators. A considerably shorter training protocol is required for both magnetic particle and liquid penetrant inspectors. It must be emphasized that, wherever NDE procedures are specified, the operators of the equipment must hold appropriate current certificates.

References

1. E.A. Ash, C.B. Scruby, eds. *Novel Techniques of Non-Destructive Examination* (New York, NY: Cambridge Univ. Press Royal Society Discussion Vol. Series, 1988), p. 220.
2. W.D. Dover, R. Collins, D.H. Michael, *Phil. Trans. Roy. Soc.* A 320 (1554) 1986: pp. 271-283.
3. Canadian Counsel for Nondestructive Examination, Mohawk College (Hamilton, Ontario, Canada: 1990).

Recommended Reading

1. J.M. Galbraith, T.A. Karnowski, CORROSION/89, paper no. 61. Houston, TX: NACE, 1989.
2. Nondestructive Inspection and Quality Control, *ASM Handbook*, Vol. 11 (Metals Park, OH: ASM, 1983).
3. D. Enswinger, *Ultrasonics* (New York, NY: Marcel Dekker, Inc., 1973).
4. *Manual on Industrial Radiography* (Canadian Government specifications Board, Dept. of Supply and Services, Hull, Que., K1A 1C1).
5. W.J. McGonnagle, *Nondestructive Testing*, 2nd ed. (New York, NY: Gordon and Breach, 1971).
6. Anon. *Inspection Techniques and Applications* (Canada Chemical Processing, May 7, 1980), p. 38.
7. L.E. Bryant, P. McIntire, eds. *Radiography & Radiation Testing*, 2nd. ed., Nondestructive Testing Handbook Series (Columbus, OH: American Society for Nondestructive Testing, 1984).
8. B. Hull, V. John, *Nondestructive Testing* (Springer-Verlag, 1988).
9. P. McIntire, M. Mester, eds., *Electromagnetic Testing: Eddy Current, Diverted Flux and Microwave Nondestructive Testing*, 2nd. ed., Nondestructive Testing Handbook Series Columbus, OH: American Society for Nondestructive Testing, 1986).

13

Regulations and Specifications

Many of our industrial operations need to be controlled in particular ways so there can be a balance between the interests of the owners, the workers, and the public. Regulations and specifications are part of this process. A regulation is a principle or law designed to govern behavior in accordance with a rule. Specifications are detailed descriptions of how regulations are to be followed. Procedures contain a series of steps needed to effect this.

Code regulations and specifications are intended primarily to protect the public. These regulations control the everyday and industrial environment to a great extent. Material specifications will ensure proper material for a given job. Code regulations will force the designer to come up with a responsible design. Specifications governing fabrication will ensure adequate fabrication. Once installed on site, specifications, such as operating procedures, maintenance procedure, inspection and control by government, underwriters, and plant rules, dictate performance and safe operation of the particular part. It must be realized that the two principal reasons for all specifications are safety and utility of operation. This holds for such diverse items as cars, airplanes, boats, hot water kettles, life jackets, pipe coatings, electrical protection, and paints.

Most people find specifications dull, and they can be. Too much paper, too many specifications, and too much volume are counterproductive. This brings the discussion to its first point: Keep specifications and standards simple and straightforward. Too many jobs have gone astray because of specifications that were too complicated.

The ASME Code

In 1905, 58 people were killed when a steam boiler in a shoe factory blew up in Massachusetts. During the aftermath of this disaster, state legislators demanded and initiated a code containing rules for fabricating pressure vessels. As already indicated in Chapter 6, the chemical treatment of boiler waters is also necessary. For pressure vessels, generally, procedures are also needed to define and limit the internal chemical environment. A number of other states followed suit and instituted their own codes. Unfortunately, all the codes differed somewhat in detail; hence, it became difficult to fabricate vessels for use in another state under a different code. To resolve this problem, ASME appointed a committee to formulate standard specifications for the construction of steam boilers and other pressure vessels and for their care. The preliminary report was issued in 1913, and the final draft adopted in 1915.

The ASME Boiler and Pressure Vessel Code has been developed to include these 11 headings:[1]

1. Power Boilers
2. Material Specifications
3. Nuclear Vessels
4. Low Pressure Heating Boilers
5. Nondestructive examination
6. Recommended Rules for Care and Operation of Heating Boilers
7. Recommended Rules for Care of Power Boilers
8. Division 1. Pressure Vessels
   Division 2. Pressure Vessels, Alternative Rules
9. Welding and Brazing Qualifications
10. Fiberglass-Reinforced Plastic Pressure Vessels
11. Rules for In-Service Inspection of Nuclear Power Plant Components

Note that item 8 Division 2 allows for pressure vessels where there are environments that call for particular and unusual materials. These call for detailed stress analysis. Note also that item 9 covers both the welder and the welding procedure.

The main requirements and rules for the fabrication of pressure vessels contained in this draft have the following four effects: (1) To certify and control manufacturers of pressure vessels and components to ensure proper design, fabrication method, and inspection techniques; (2) to fabricate all pressure equipment within accepted safety standards; (3) to institute an approved quality control system in each fabricating shop; and (4) to register each shop with the National Board of Boiler and Pressure Vessel Inspectors (1919), the enforcing agency of the ASME. When a shop fabricates pressure equipment and is in compliance with all the described rules, it will be supplied with a registration and a stamp (R). All equipment must be identified with this "R" stamp; this certifies that the standards have been followed.

The enforcing agency in Ontario is the Provincial Ministry of Consumers Affairs and Customer Relations (MCCR), Pressure Vessel Branch. All applications for registration are dealt with by this agency. Prior to final approval, a quality assurance or control manual is mandatory. This manual attests to the manufacturer's integrity and ability to fabricate pressure vessels to be used in industries with high utility and safety requirements. If weld repairs or alterations are performed on pressure vessels or components, the same rules apply as in fabrication.

Quality Assurance Requirements

An appendix to the regulations of the Nuclear Regulatory Commission contains a convenient and helpful definition of "quality assurance." This comprises all those planned and systematic actions necessary to provide adequate confidence that a structure, system, or component will perform satisfactorily in service. Quality assurance includes quality control, which comprises those quality assurance actions related to the physical characteristics of a material, structure, component, or system which provide a means to control the quality of the material, structure, component, or system to predetermined requirements.

Quality assurance and control programs in Canada must be in accordance with Canadian Standards Association (CSA) standard Z299, 1979, parts 1 to 4[2], and section 8 of the *ASME Boiler and Pressure Vessel Code*.[1] The current trend in industry is to supplement the concept of final acceptance inspection with an ongoing and more preventive quality assurance approach. Rather than relying on inspection after the fact when final rejection is the only remedy, quality assurance proposes action at an early stage of fabrication to preclude eventual rejection. Quality assurance programs call for a planned sequence of actions necessary to provide adequate confidence that the structure, system, or component will perform satisfactorily and safely in service. The standard Z299 gives details of the necessary specifics. Part 1 covers quality assurance, part 2 is quality control, part 3 is quality verification, and part 4 embodies quality inspection.

Guideline B of the above standard offers a non-mandatory set of criteria for selecting a quality program category for manufacturing. Basically, the intent is to set up the minimum quality assurance program that will assure the product will be acceptable to the user. Economic considerations should dictate an optimum quality program category in terms of both benefit and minimal incremental cost. Cost must, of course, include, in the words of the standard, "rework, repair, replacement, loss of production, consequential damage, loss of reputation, claims and other related costs."

Safety considerations can, of course, call for more stringent standards than would be suggested by mere economics. Both the potential consequences of failure and the probability of its occurrence are germane. Within this overall framework, four additional evaluation factors are used to determine the proper quality program level. These are: design process complexity; design maturity; manufacturing process complexity; item or service characteristics, along with safety and economics. The six scores associated with the six factors are summed, and the sum is used to select the required quality program standard from the set of four that are available. A fifth (unstated) standard is also available — to have no quality assurance program.

Any quality assurance program must include a number of elements, as detailed in the following:

Organization. Senior management ordinarily delegates approval and authority to the quality control manager. There should be an organizational chart showing the relationships and responsibilities of all involved parties. Impartiality is essential, along with the willingness to back up the decisions of the quality control manager.

Design Specifications. Specifications and design calculations must have approval by the authorized inspector (MCCR).

Control of Material and its Procurement. Control and identification of all materials of construction for pressure vessels must be in compliance with the appropriate code regulations. Mill test certificates showing heat numbers, analysis, and strength data must be checked and verified. Components that do not conform to the code requirements must not be used for code pressure vessels or components.

Process Control. Flow charts indicating the process must be prepared, and during the course of the project each operation can be examined and approved by the authorized inspector.

Correction of Nonconformities. A nonconformity is the condition of the finished product which does not comply with the code or the approved specifications and/or design parameters. Any deviation from the code must be either corrected or not used for code vessels. Weld flaws furnish an example of what has to be corrected. Novel equipment that involves features beyond the existing code calls for negotiation in advance with the inspecting authority.

Welding Quality. This is an important requirement, including three major parameters: (1) Welder capability and certification or recertification; (2) proper design for welding or weldment, with both design and technique following the code; and (3) the inspection of welds by methods ranging from visual observation through radiographic or ultrasonic examination to see that welds conform to established standards. The welder should be encouraged to see the inspectors as allies, rather than as adversaries, in ensuring production of the best possible product.

Heat Treatment. Heat treatment of pressure vessels, if so specified, must include parameters such as temperature, support, type of furnace, time to heat and cool, and how these are, or must be, controlled. Distortion can be a complication of heat treatment for stress relief.

Measuring and Test Equipment. The measuring equipment available in the shop and how it is identified, calibrated, and administered must be specified. Measurement includes the whole spectrum, ranging from calipers to hydrostatic test equipment.

Program Documentation. Careful and accurate control of documentation must be maintained at all times. Documentation should include welding procedures, design calculation, welder qualification, welder log, traveller sheets, material specifications, inspection by the authorized examiner, and test results.

Record Retention and Audits. The manufacturer is responsible for the record retention of all pertinent data of the project. From time to time, audits of the quality control manual may be carried out by the authorized inspector. The inspector will report findings and revisions, if required, to top management. An appendix should include a table of revisions and all standard forms.

Engineering Specifications and Standards

When a pressure vessel is to be constructed, it is the responsibility of the user to inform the manufacturer of all pertinent information regarding the use of the equipment. Such information should include a line sketch giving dimensions, material of construction including corrosion allowance, and relevant process information regarding temperature and pressure. The user is not obligated to divulge certain information, such as the details of process media, to the manufacturer. It follows that the user must develop procedures to protect the pressure vessel from inappropriate chemical exposure. Extensive corrosion testing may be involved.

It is the manufacturer's responsibility to produce shop drawings that must be duly authorized by a registered professional engineer. The design and all other relevant data must be agreed upon by the user and approved by the MCCR, Pressure Vessel Branch (or other appropriate government agency, outside of Canada).

Most major industries have developed and maintain an engineering standards program. The purpose of engineering standards is to have ready access to a number of repetitive designs and to include the policies of safety and integrity of that particular organization (which, of course, may differ somewhat from the one company to the other). Engineering standards have become an integral part of the engineering department, and a great deal of expense and effort is spent by many companies to continually develop new standards and revise existing ones.

Summary

Code regulations, specifications, and standards contribute greatly to efficient operation, but mostly reflect concern about safety. True, the code is a form of enforcement, but history has shown that this policing is necessary in our industrial endeavors. In addition to the authorized inspection agency, most major companies have their own inspection departments. Once appointed, these inspectors are the only authorized examiners on behalf of the company. These inspectors, of course, must bear the responsibility for their decisions. Again, this illustrates industry awareness of the critical nature of pressure operations and the progress that has been made in the enlightenment of attitudes dealing with the protection of society.

Role of the User

In the preceding treatment, user responsibilities have been indicated from time to time. All major chemical and other companies develop detailed company procedures which go beyond the scope of the codes. For the corrosion-conscious employee, it is necessary to help develop, account for, and implement all of these procedures. Many incidents outlined in the following chapter on safety can be traced to noncompliance with, or perhaps even ignorance of, established company procedures. Such procedures definitely are not frills. Those who ignore them invite prompt termination.

Standard Engineering Specification

Most major corporations reinforce their purchase orders of corrosion-resistant materials, such as stainless steels, by detailed specifications. The object is to assure that, regardless of the particular supplier, all intentions of the purchasing company regarding material quality are both evident and enforceable. Primary producers are not deterred, but those who have imported a boat load of material of unknown processing history may not be able to submit tenders.

The standard purchase specifications normally contain headings such as: Scope — to indicate the range of coverage intended. Acceptance — definition of what is acceptable and what is not. Test Samples — to indicate precisely what the purchaser requires for test purposes, how they are to be identified, what manufacturers' test data is required, and how samples are to be selected. Where welding is to be used, particular care is necessary to obtain proper samples for use in weld tests. Test Procedures — these spell out in detail appropriate tests for whatever condition is of concern; e.g., sensitization of stainless steel if welding is involved, or low-temperature characteristics for materials for outside storage tanks. In most cases, ASTM tests will be specified, and numerical limits will define what is acceptable and what is not.

The intent of purchase specifications is to ensure that the material purchased is suitable for its intended use. Chemical composition and mechanical properties must be defined, but they are merely the point of departure. Optimum corrosion resistance may call for particular processing steps in manufacture, or for the selection of particularly suitable lots of material. Cost is an ever present factor; ultimately, a choice has to be made that any cost premium is or is not justifiable in terms of expected performance.

References

1. *ASME Boiler and Pressure Vessel Code* (New York, NY: American Society of Mechanical Engineers, 1992).
2. CSA Standard Z299 (Ontario, Canada: Canadian Standard Association, 1979).

14

Safety and
the Corrosion Engineer

Introduction

Safety in corrosion engineering is not restricted to the regulatory aspects of safety and the adherence to such standards by all concerned in the course of their duties. We must realize that the safety standards and philosophy in corrosion engineering, and for that matter engineering in general, are not well appreciated; the aspect of self-discipline is too often neglected. It is not inferred that the safety attitude and standards are different for people working in the corrosion field, be it in the laboratory, or in the field, than for the other engineering disciplines. One must state categorically, however, that corrosion engineers and support staff routinely receive more exposure to hazards than workers in most other engineering disciplines.

The extent of the hazards can be quantified with a fatal accident frequency rate. The ideal would be to have a zero rate, but this is not achievable. Some major companies have accepted the concept of an average interval between such incidents (IBI) as 10,000 years (about 100,000,000 hours). The failure rates for people and for mechanical components can be combined in a form of fault-tree analysis.

Central to this concept is the determination of an individual hazard index (IHI), defined as the number of fatal injuries per hundred million hours of a particular activity. From the point of view of management, the difference between individual and group exposure to a hazard needs to be quantified. This requires a process hazard index (PHI), defined as the years per fatal injury associated with the operation of the process. A difficulty in this approach is that very few processes have been in operation long enough to generate statistically valid data. This leads to the grouping of processes considered to involve similar risks.

Table 14.01 shows a small sample of data on comparative risks.

The industrial entries were developed by a major corporation for its North American operations. This company has safety and plant inspections which are both highly effective and have full backing from management.

TABLE 14.01

Comparative Individual Risks[1]

Activity	Person Hours per Year Exposure	Individual Hazard Index IHI	Process Hazard Index PHI
Disease Age 60-65	8,766	180	60
General Aviation	35	2,500	1,500
Auto Driving	350	100	3,000
Accidents at Home	8,766	2.5	4,500
Exposure to Process Hazards	2,200	1.5	30,000
Operators and Mechanics in Light Industry	2,200	0.2	230,000
Natural Disasters	8,766	0.04	300,000

The IHI and PHI terms in the table need to be discussed briefly. An individual hazard index that exceeds 100 is to be avoided in the workplace; a hazard of this severity cannot be tolerated for the entire working day, but may be marginally acceptable for a task performed infrequently. It is instructive to note that the hinge point corresponds to driving the family vehicle, but we do not spend as much time behind the wheel as we do at work. Professional drivers, of course, require a more exacting approach to safety on the road. Growing old is clearly, but unavoidably hazardous, while flying a private plane is risky business. The process hazard index, on the other hand, represents the years between fatalities and should be kept as high as possible. One major company feels that corrective action is needed when the PHI dips below 10,000. This index is intended to allow for both the severity of the hazard and the accumulated time of exposure.

However, data, such as that in the table, do not tell the whole story. If there is an industrial accident, the employer ultimately bears the cost of compensation and of procuring and training a replacement worker. Accidents or illness outside the plant sites still costs the company the same replacement costs. And the public sector normally bears the lion's share of the medical costs.

This implies that it is strongly in the company's pecuniary interest to promote safety and health off the job, and address the issues of substance abuse, including tobacco and alcohol, likely to lead to lost time or poorer performance levels. There are, of course, other costs such as grief and suffering that cannot be evaluated in monetary terms. But how far should the company go?

The risks of incurring major disasters need to be evaluated in advance rather than after the fact. Commuter train crashes may say something about the relative merits of safety and the "bottom line" for a quasi-public railroad. In developing countries, chemical plants for hazardous products, operation of supertankers in environmentally sensitive areas, and adequately protecting large passenger aircraft should all have called for detailed advance planning and action before there was a drift into an unthinkable accident. A whole range of other operations needs hard-nosed scrutiny with disaster potential in mind. So far, engineers have not always been able to protect the public adequately. A more radical approach to safety is needed, including teaching it at the university level.

In more than 30 years of industrial experience in the metallurgical corrosion field, one of the authors knows that, despite all the safety training received, there have been instances where he could have been injured or caused injury to others. One instance occurred when two corrosion engineers went up a water tower ladder at a corporate site. After 30 minutes they reported back, obviously quite upset. What had happened? The man leading up the steps became uncomfortable halfway up and froze, hanging on for dear life, hand and foot. At that instant, the second man, an experienced inspector, froze, too. Eventually, they guided each other downward, very slowly, encouraging each other on the way down. The painful realization dawned that one of the most important rules in safety had been overlooked. One must ask the question, "Is what my people were asked to do safe, and can they physically do it?"

Since then, the water towers have been inspected by specialists who have received proper training in high structure work and have been approved to carry out such assignments. Skills such as the ability to steer, propel a collapsible boat, and the ability to swim could be part of the qualifications. It is not the intent of this chapter to preach doom, but rather to discuss past experiences frankly and without hesitation so that this may reflect upon a particular employee's or supervisor's beliefs, attitudes, and safety performance. The intention is to instill a greater safety awareness in everyone, but above all, to set the stage for an extensive dialogue through exchange by all concerned.

This chapter will deal with the safety aspects of three areas of corrosion engineering: (1) safety in the corrosion laboratory; (2) safety in the design function; and (3) safety in plant inspection.

Safety in the Corrosion Laboratory

The importance of safe practices in the corrosion laboratory is often taken lightly and considered routine. At least this may be the case until an accident shocks the corrosion laboratory worker into the brutal reality of being part of an incident that could have led to maiming or scarring for life. Most laboratory safety incidents are not of the order of total destruction, but rather the kind that involves small mishaps exposing only one worker. Another criterion is that safety awareness in the laboratory seems unrelated to academic training. All too often, the workers with degrees or advanced degrees start with the poorest safety awareness, and, hence, have a higher risk factor, at least in the early part of their careers. This may be related to being overconfident, wishing to demonstrate laboratory competence, and not wanting to ask advice. Since there are so many different backgrounds among those who work in a given department, it should be regarded as normal for a mechanical engineer to seek the advice of a chemist regarding the nature of a chemical hazard, for example. The questions directed to our learned institutions may be whether sufficient efforts are being made to instruct students in the elements of safe laboratory practices, or whether safety is being crowded out by more intellectual priorities. The previous statement is not intended to be derogatory to engineers and scientists, but rather to point out that safety awareness is not necessarily guaranteed by scholastic competence.

Consider a small incident that involved a bright young engineer. In the laboratory, 2% and 5% nital etching solutions are prepared once a week on Monday mornings. These solutions are a mixture of ethyl alcohol and concentrated nitric acid, which can cause an explosion if not handled properly. The laboratory procedure states that the required amount of nitric acid must be added slowly to the alcohol. That particular morning, the engineer reversed the mixing procedure and added the alcohol to the concentrated nitric acid, which promptly exploded in his face. He had prepared this solution many times in the past, but on this blue Monday morning, his mind obviously went blank. Luckily, he was wearing gloves and safety spectacles, and was thrust immediately under a safety shower. That time, he got away with some minor burns on his face. In conclusion, this man was lucky; he violated two procedures — not wearing his face shield and improper addition of alcohol to acid. Only instantaneous action by his co-workers saved him from a permanent injury. The moral of this story may well be not to prepare etching solutions on Monday mornings.

It is essential for a corrosion laboratory to institute safety procedures and safe practices that are well-defined and descriptive. Bear in mind that corrosion workers are from many different engineering disciplines and may initially have little feel for handling chemicals. Therefore, the safety manual should spell out, in detail, the safe handling of chemicals and compounds. This manual must encompass all facets of laboratory procedures — handling molten acids, hydrocarbons, highly corrosive acids, corrosive and toxic fumes, electrical hazards, etc. It also should serve as a training manual to improve techniques and create proper safety awareness. It should emphasize again and again that if a person is not completely cognizant of handling certain corrosive media, they should ask advice or confirmation from a specialist or more experienced individual.

The previously described incident involved a young engineer, but consider now a few examples of incidents involving well-trained and experienced laboratory workers. There is the well-publicized case of the titanium sample exposed to a concentrated nitric acid explosion in which one worker was fatally injured. Here, the pyrophoric reaction of titanium metal with the acid led to an explosion during the removal of a test sample.

In the laboratory of one of the authors, a worker removed the lid of a glass condenser kettle containing phosphoric acid at 300°C

(572°F); some small drops of condensate had settled on the lid. When the lid accidentally slipped out of his hand, the water drops fell into the molten acid, which immediately erupted, propelling the hot acid contents toward the worker. Fortunately, he was well-protected (wearing gloves, safety glasses, and face shield), and received only minor burns. Another case involved one of the authors who had developed a method of removing process tar from small screened ejector nozzles by an electrolytic process. The nozzles were put in a small open tank containing 10% sulfuric acid and connected to a 10 amp circuit. This process cleaned the nozzles immaculately; however, a considerable amount of hydrogen evolved. When a poor electrical connection produced a spark, the hydrogen-rich gas detonated with a tremendous bang, splashing all the contents through the laboratory. Because of adequate protective equipment, the only damage suffered was to personal pride. What went wrong? Despite many successful cleaning operations in the past, "familiarity bred contempt." To forget or ignore the consequences of a spark in a hydrogen oxygen environment is to invite such an incident or worse.

To operate a corrosion laboratory or other operation in an efficient and safe manner, good housekeeping is essential. Laboratory personnel should be trained in good housekeeping, and their compliance with the rules should be part of their overall performance. Good housekeeping encompasses all facets of laboratory work, including cleaning glassware, cleaning work areas, properly storing chemicals and etching solutions (oxidizing etching solutions must be stored in a separate area), legibly identifying labels on etching solutions and containers at all times, etc. A well-defined housekeeping audit system is mandatory and will contribute greatly to safe and pleasant working conditions in the corrosion laboratory.

Good housekeeping can only succeed where the original laboratory design was adequate. In one major corrosion laboratory, there were teakwood topped benches in an area where electrolytic polishing was done with perchlorate containing solutions. Needless to say, the bench top was kept clean. Despite this, after a couple of decades, there was some accumulation of unwanted perchlorates. When a plumber inadvertently laid a pipe wrench none too gently on the bench, the bench promptly exploded. The replacement bench top was impervious.

Safety requires a detailed knowledge of the specific hazards of all materials to be used in an industrial site. The chemical aspects of these hazards receive treatment in many works, two of which are *Dangerous Properties of Industries Materials* by N.I. Sax,[2] and the more recent *Handbook of Reactive Chemical Hazards* by L. Bretherick.[3] These sources should be consulted when new materials or chemicals come into practical use. Strict protocol has to be observed to prevent the unintentional introduction of high hazard items. The elimination of asbestos or urea-formaldehyde foam insulation after the fact are classic examples of what not to do.

Safety in the Design Function

In the design function, the corrosion worker can probably make the greatest contribution to the safe operation of plants. After all, one of the foremost objectives of the corrosion engineer, along with other disciplines, is to provide a safe working environment for all. To reach this goal, a prime prerequisite is that the engineer be knowledgeable and capable of making contributions, and that this is recognized by others.

To be effective, these contributions must start at the beginning of a project, when the engineer recommends the materials of construction, dictates the mode of fabrication to ensure maximum systems integrity, and incorporates the principles of quality assurance. Many companies will have all drawings, procedures, and specifications pertaining to a specific project checked and verified by a corrosion specialist.

The corrosion specialist must have a thorough knowledge of code regulations and must be able to apply corrosion allowance principles intelligently. Through well-planned efforts, the specialist then makes substantial contributions toward ensuring the high integrity required of equipment operating under often potentially hazardous conditions.

Detailed responsibilities fall outside the scope of this chapter, but this may present a challenge for future publication. One suspects that safety receives more consideration where a more or less major hazard is seen to exist. Perhaps the residual risk will become greater in other areas regarded as intrinsically safe because little design effort is directed to safety matters.

Safety in Plant Inspection

From the safety standpoint, the corrosion worker engaged in plant inspection work probably has the highest overall exposure factor to hazard of all the personnel employed in the chemical industry. The specialist works on pipe bridges, climbs distillation towers, and inspects storage facilities, often while physically carrying inspection equipment. (Equipment loosely termed portable by the manufacturer may get to feel pretty heavy as one nears the top of a long ladder.) This task calls for a special person that must not only be a good technician and a good observer, but also must be able to physically do the job without endangering health. If alone in a storage vessel or boiler firebox, obviously he/she should not suffer from claustrophobia and must be able to climb ladders (sometimes rope ladders) and manipulate from a scaffold 200 feet up in the air in a calculated, responsible, levelheaded manner. Therefore, it is one of the prime responsibilities of management and supervision to ensure that the person carrying out this job not only is technically capable, but also has and continues to have the physical and mental attributes to accomplish these assignments. Noncompliance with this philosophy often has led to serious consequences for the worker, who may well be too proud to admit inability to perform such assignments. Annual medical examinations are mandatory, and conclusions and recommendations assessing the physical capabilities of a particular inspector should be forwarded to management and (if necessary) acted upon.

As mentioned before, the corrosion worker or inspector has a high safety hazard exposure which automatically mandates that the safety attitude and awareness of this person must be without question. To assist in the safe execution of responsibilities the specialist must also rely on the judgment and experience of others, such as plant engineering and operating personnel. Most industries have combined all the know-how and experience into written procedures for any given situation. Consider vessel entry as an example.

Safe Entry into a Confined Space

Valving off equipment prior to entry is not sufficient; all associated piping must be physically disconnected and blanked as close to the vessel as possible. In one case some years ago, it was discovered just prior to vessel entry that a large quantity of corrosive process material had plugged the 12 inch line between the vessel and a valve 40 feet away. If, during the entry of the vessel, this plug of process material had become dislodged a certain fatality would have resulted.

Consider, for a moment, how to devise a document to include all aspects that should be in a procedure for tank and vessel entry. Every year, fatalities are reported of people engaged in working in or inspecting vessels ranging from process vessels, storage and trailer tanks to farm silos. In every subsequent inquest, it has been reported that the incident could have been avoided if only proper safety procedures were followed. There is not sufficient space in this chapter to discuss such procedures in detail, but the following are some of the salient points to consider when work is carried out in a confined space.

1. Definition. Definition of what a confined space is and is not usually refers to all tanks and bins entered through a manhole and where the structure is sufficiently deep to require special means of entry and/or exit. It is essential that, where a special ruling is required, responsibility for this definition be assigned to a senior member of management.

2. Responsibility. The responsibility rests primarily on the owner/landlord, although a direct responsibility also must be assumed by the inspector's supervision to ensure that all safety precautions have been taken.

3. The Entry Permit and Preparation to Enter. The hazards of working in confined spaces must be eliminated before the job starts, and a possible rescue must be planned in advance. Tests to be carried out must be specified and the area inspected. When all requirements are met, the vessel entry permit must be signed by both the supervisor(s) and (immediately prior to entry) the employees involved. Minimum requirements for entry involve a long list of items, such as: allowable residues present; ventilation; locking and tagging procedures; blanks; deenergization, etc. The entry permit must state explicitly how many people may enter at the same time, and requirements for the rescue of one or more people. The standby or rescue group must be specified, along with its organization, so it is prepared to deal with an emergency. A 140-pound person cannot be expected to lift a 240-pound person out of a confined space, for example. The permit must also state what hazard monitoring is necessary and sufficient, and what protective equipment and type of harness should be worn by the entry personnel and by the rescue group.

4. General. There must be continuous communication between the personnel inside the confined space and the standby group. Ensure adequate air supply, especially when torch operations are being performed, since a flame will consume oxygen at a rapid rate. Explosiveness tests and hot work permits are required when hot work is carried out in confined spaces. Particular caution must be exercised in eliminating dust, residues, and combustibles. Continuous ventilation must be supplied and oxygen levels checked. Protective equipment such as harnesses, life lines, respirators, clothing, ladders, and hoist equipment must be of good quality and inspected prior to use. Electrical lights and tools shall be of low voltage or protected by ground fault interrupter devices, and be explosion-proof where appropriate. All test equipment, such as explosimeters, oxygen analyzers, etc. should be of approved quality and checked prior to use. The rescue team must be trained in cardiopulmonary resuscitation (CPR). Finally, the procedure also must be followed by outside contractors working in the plant area.

The preceding material is an abbreviated description of confined area entry considerations, and it may be used by the reader as a guide. It should be realized that this description is by no means complete. It does indicate, however, the meticulous planning necessary to ensure that all work in confined spaces is carried out in a safe and efficient manner.

Mention also should be made of the practice in the aircraft industry for internal inspection of such items as wing assemblies. In this case, the hazard to the inspector is low, but the space is particularly cramped. The solution is to recruit and train a team of dwarfs for the inspection function.

Miscellaneous Safety Matters

Hazards are not always easy to recognize, as a dockyard safety inspector discovered when he was immobilized by a set of coveralls. The laundry system had delivered him a set of coveralls at least a couple of sizes too small. He received an urgent call to determine that repair welding would not create an explosion hazard in the bilge space of an engine room where there might be fuel residues. He grabbed the coveralls and set off to a distant dock. Getting into the coveralls was a challenge, but he managed it, completed the safety check, and drove back to his home base without trying to get out of the coveralls, preferring to leave that chore for the privacy of his home office. It turned out to be quite a struggle, and in the process he wrenched his back and had to miss a week's work. The worker's compensation authorities were incredulous.

No account of safety hazards would be complete without some reference to radiation hazards, particularly where energetic isotopes and portable x-ray sets are used in plant inspection procedures. Film badges and dosimeters must be used as required, and when tests are in progress the spherical zone of radiation exposure must be cordoned off and marked with warning labels. The radiation hazard on other floors should be of particular concern since there would be no obvious indications of unusual conditions. Regulations concerning radiation safety must be followed to the letter. Laboratory work using radioisotopes as tracers usually involves low-level radiation of little penetrating power. Toxicity on ingestion would be the principal hazard in most such cases. Rigid enforcement of safety procedures is mandatory.

Despite all procedures, accidents still happen. In the majority of cases, it has been revealed that someone did not do their job, or else misinterpreted or overlooked a procedure. Procedures are effective only when they are adhered to, and the corrosion worker/inspector can never afford to take a short cut or gamble. Conscientious adherence to procedures, then, is also an important attribute of the corrosion worker, particularly since there is often pressure from line organization to carry out the work as quickly as possible and reduce downtime to a minimum.

In the author's experience, unsafe practice and resulting incidents are seldom obvious before the fact. Subsequent investigation after the fact always finds a logical reason for the incident. It is also true that once an accident has taken place, the probability that it will repeat itself is imminent. Those are the prime parameters to consider and resolve.

To illustrate the point, consider a few mishaps that have occurred, and may well happen again. A welder began to cut a two-inch, 20-foot long process line out of a sulfuric acid plant which had been transported to his construction shop. The moment he started to cut, an explosion occurred, lifting the line 10 feet in the air. What happened? The line had not been flushed properly and still contained a small quantity of concentrated sulfuric acid. During transport on a rainy day, the sulfuric acid became diluted and corroded the carbon steel line, thus evolving hydrogen. The heat of the cutting torch triggered the explosion.

A scaffold plank gave way, and a worker almost fell 40 feet to the ground. Investigation revealed that the plank was made from an inferior wood having a coarse grain. At that time, an inspection of the steel scaffold material showed a number of welds to be cracked, surely indicating a dangerous situation. Examination of the scaffold steel revealed the carbon level to be in excess of 0.6% carbon. The badly cracked welds did not then come as a big surprise, but only good fortune had prevented a more serious incident. The plank and the steel scaffold illustrate the fact that rigid rules must be enforced to inspect the quality of such materials prior to use. Relaxation of these rules would certainly create unsafe conditions.

Timely and alert action of an inspector avoided a certain disaster when a process technician had borrowed a Borescope to inspect a water line. After his observation, he decided to have a quick look at a distillation tray contaminated with hydrocarbon inside a distillation tower. The high temperature of the glass envelope of the light source most certainly could have caused a major explosion. Fortunately, his venture was aborted by the alertness of the inspector.

Without any doubt, the most dangerous exposure condition is created for the inspector and corrosion engineer when they are asked to inspect equipment thought to be failing in service. The usual question is, "How bad is it, and how long can we continue to operate with this marginal situation?" It is here the inspector must use optimum care and judgment to avoid exposure to equipment that is about to fail catastrophically. Two workers were scalded to death a few years ago in the United States by removing insulation from a leaking condensate storage tank still under pressure. While removing the insulating material, the tank wall erupted, resulting in a tragedy. Another example occurred when a steam turbine driving a coal pulverizer was not running properly, according to a maintenance mechanic. He shut down the turbine and asked a co-worker to confirm his suspicion, and he restarted the 5,300 rpm turbine. His friend agreed that the turbine did not run properly. A few others were asked for an opinion, including the foreman. When five people were observing the obviously malfunctioning turbine, it disintegrated into hundreds of pieces of shrapnel. To this day, the fact that no one was hurt remains incredible.

The golden rule is, when not sure, shut down and/or depressurize the equipment and then observe. This is doing the job in a safe and responsible manner.

Storage and Transportation of Hazardous Materials

The realities of modern industrial society dictate that hazardous materials be used as chemical intermediates, and, hence, that they be stored and transported. The storage containers are adequate for the temperatures and service conditions for which they were designed, but in an accident situation they may fail rapidly, particularly where fire is involved. Engineers employed in the chemical industry must develop strategies for neutralizing tank car spills of hazardous chemicals in advance of the crisis situation. For example, the concentration of aqueous NaOH appropriate for addition to liquid chlorine in a ruptured container should be known in advance.

The role of fire in disaster control needs more study. Fire has been proposed, and to some extent used, as a fog dispersal technique. It is known to assist in toxic hazard control by sucking up hazardous material in an updraft. But we do not yet have the basic data that would allow for the use of a controlled fire as an alternative to a massive evacuation.

Loss Prevention

Loss prevention is a topic which bridges the gap between corrosion economics and safety. An important two-volume book, *Loss Prevention in the Process Industries*, has been written by F.P. Lees.[4] While the book is written for those in the United Kingdom, the principles delineated are of wider application. The engineering content is important for those who must justify expenditures to anticipate and prevent losses of various kinds. Not surprisingly, little emphasis was given to serious incidents in rail transport since all of the action has been in North America. Since this book was written, there have been two disasters involving chlorine tank car leaks: (1) the Mississauga incident that established the free world record for a peacetime evacuation without casualties; and (2) an incident in Mexico that involved multiple fatalities.

Major chemical industries are responding to the problems of transportation hazards by organizing emergency response teams. Specially equipped trucks are used to transport the equipment needed to cope with chemical spills. For longer distances, most equipment is readily transportable by air.

Example of a Process Risk Calculation[1]

A chemical process involves a high pressure reactor containing dangerous chemicals. This is located next to a department office. The most severe incident in this case would be a reactor explosion with an IBI of 10,000 years. The hazards review team has judged that all persons in the reactor area and the adjacent office would be fatally injured if the reactor should explode.

Number of Persons	Duties	Average No. Exposed
2	Operators (4 shifts)	2
8	Office Workers (days only)	2
1	Maintenance Worker (days)	0.25
Total		**4.25**

PHI = IBI/No. Exposed = 10,000/4.25 = 2,353

Since the PHI in this case is below the target minimum of 10,000 it must be increased. The obvious first option is to relocate the office. This would increase the PHI to 10,000/2.25 or 4,444. By itself, this would not be enough.

The most obvious solution would be to barricade the reactor and prohibit entry while it is in operation. This could reduce the exposure to rule violations.

If this is not done, measures must be found to increase the IBI for process by a factor of at least three if the office is to be relocated or by a factor of at least 5 if the office is to stay. This would involve scrutinizing the fault tree analysis which led to the original IBI estimate for ways to increase it.

Adhering to a safety standard costs money. Ultimately, there can be no meaningful safety program unless top management is willing to pay for it.

216

Epilogue

Safety is, to many of us, a dull, uninteresting subject. Safety training is, to say the least, uninspiring probably because of its repetitious nature. Over and over again, one is exposed (some say indoctrinated) to the same rules and regulations, and it is easy to subconsciously develop a mental barrier for further conception. One of the authors sometimes compares this with his time in the military service. There was a corporal as Bren machine gun instructor. Day after day, the Bren was dismantled and assembled. This was a hated drill, particularly when blindfolded and with a time limit set at 15 seconds. This exercise was considered a total waste of time and effort. However, during the war on a rainy night in action, the Bren gun jammed and was cleared in a time that would have made the old instructor proud. A difficult situation was routinely handled without panic because of the tedious training. When an incident occurs, unfamiliar conditions tend to agitate one, and actions or reactions lack a normal rationale. Unless proper adjustment to a new situation has become a part of the person through training and instruction, a hazardous situation exists. How many drivers still try to get back on the road immediately after swerving off the road, instead of slowing down? Hundreds of people lose their lives each year by rolling their car. A policeman drowned in the river after attempting to rescue another person. Why? The policeman never learned to swim.

In conclusion, it is hoped that this chapter has convinced the student of corrosion that safety training and instruction has an overwhelming impact on the quality of the job. It not only makes one more knowledgeable, but even more important, it prepares one to deal with unusual events in a rational and calculated manner.

References

1. DuPont Safety and Fire Protection Guideline, January 1981.
2. N.I. Sax, *Dangerous Properties of Industrial Materials*, 5th ed. (New York, NY: Van Nostrand Reinhold, 1979).
3. L. Bretherick, *Handbook of Reactive Chemical Hazards*, second ed. (Woburn, MA: Butterworth, 1979).
4. F.P. Lees, *Loss Prevention in the Process Industries*, Vol. 2, second ed. (Woburn, MA: Butterworth, 1980).

15

Engineering Materials

This chapter deals with specific practical points of material selection and will stress the avoidance of potential pitfalls at the design and fabrication stage. The wealth of specific information on strength and corrosion properties, as found in other handbooks and texts, will not be duplicated here. Unfortunately, the ideal material that has good mechanical properties, good corrosion resistance, and a modest cost cannot always be found. The *Metal Progress Data Book* and the latest issue of *Advanced Materials and Processes*[1] are useful sources of information on the composition and properties of metallic materials while the *NACE Corrosion Data Survey*[2] gives a collection of data on specifics of corrosion resistance, and the *NACE Corrosion Engineer's Reference Book*[3] gives a convenient pocket-size mix of data.

Metallic Materials

Cast Irons

ASTM A48-92 classifies cast irons (3% C and 1½% Si) by strength and hardness.[4] The strength range is from 20,000 to 65,000 psi. There are three different types of cast iron: (1) white, which is brittle and glass hard; (2) gray, soft but still brittle; and (3) the more ductile nodular and malleable irons.

1. White Cast Iron. This has practically all its carbon in the form of cementite, Fe_3C, which is hard and devoid of ductility. This is formed by the rapid cooling of iron from the melt. This, in turn, prevents the precipitation of carbon as graphite, a process that requires more time. Items such as streetcar wheels and bulldozer tracks are typical uses of white cast iron. White cast iron is difficult to machine and is best finished by casting. A limited amount of grinding also is possible.

2. Gray Cast Iron. This is produced at a slower cooling rate than that used for white cast iron. This results in an iron in which much of the carbon is found as graphite flakes in a matrix of either ferrite or ferrite plus pearlite. Because of the silicon content, the fluidity of the liquid metal is good, and intricate shapes such as machine frames, etc. can be produced. This form of cast iron is brittle, but it has excellent damping characteristics for noise and vibration and also has good machining characteristics. Gray cast iron is often used for bases for machines and items such as engine blocks, particularly where noise or vibration would otherwise be a problem.

3. Nodular and Malleable Cast Irons. These are high carbon irons that maintain good ductility. Nodular iron contains some nickel, along with a nucleating agent that allows the graphite to separate as compact nodules rather than flakes. Malleable iron achieves the same objective by prolonged heating which causes the graphite flakes to come together into compact rosettes. These types of cast iron are more or less equivalent to a steel diluted with innocuous small spheres of graphite.

High Silicon Cast Irons. Additions of up to 14% silicon to cast iron create an iron with excellent corrosion resistance to a number of media. However, it is hard, brittle, unmachinable, and subject to damage by mechanical and thermal shock. Prior to the development of stainless steels, this material (known as Duriron†) was widely used. It is available only in cast form.

Nickel Cast Irons. The addition of nickel to cast iron in amounts of up to 30% improves the corrosion and erosion resistance of the material. Other additional alloying elements, such as Mo, Cu, and Cr, can be added to improve specific properties. Nickel cast irons retain good properties to low temperatures and may be used in cryogenic applications.

Carbon and Low Alloy Steels

This is by far the most widely used of the metal groups. Versatility and low cost are notable characteristics. While pure iron is too soft to be particularly useful, alloying iron with a little carbon improves strength and hardness without sacrificing ductility. It also yields a material that is easy to fabricate, machine, weld, and has reasonably good corrosion resistance. Steels for pressure vessels contain carbon from 0.1 to 0.35%. Higher carbon additions lead to problems with weldability and also call for care in design to avoid the

---

†Trademark

brittle behavior associated with formation of martensite.

There are two main groupings of steel. The so-called flange grades specify strength only and do not call for any particular chemical analysis. As long as the required values for tensile and yield strength and elongation are met, there are no further constraints. On the other hand, the so-called firebox quality steels require both strength levels and particular chemical compositions. The code mandates that steels for pressure vessels should have both composition and mechanical properties specified.

1.   Ductility is more readily achieved in steels of small grain size; absence of interstitial impurities is also desirable. Steel that is to be used in thick sections must follow these principles. For low temperature applications, as in northern pipelines, open pit mining operations, etc., it is absolutely essential to use steels with a low brittle to ductile transition temperature. Of the steels that can be readily procured, the lowest transition temperatures are found in some of the weathering steels. For 75,000 psi yield pipeline steels, the carbon content has to be kept below 0.03%, and strength is achieved by adding about 1% Mn. For much lower (cryogenic) temperatures, face-centered cubic (fcc) materials, such as austenitic stainless steels, should be used, or there should be fairly large amounts of nickel added. These materials do not show a transition to brittle behavior at low temperatures.

2.   In the case of pipe, the specification of welded or seamless pipe is significant. In larger sizes, only welded pipe is available. With adequate modern quality control this is not a problem. However, both grades are available in smaller sizes, and seamless grade is preferred for all but the most readily weldable steels.

3.   For thick plate (2.0 inches), the effect of triaxiality on fracture toughness must be considered carefully. Stress relief is necessary for thick steels.

4.   When high strength steels are used and lead to use of a thinner material, caution is appropriate at the design stage to ensure mechanical stability of the structure.

5.   Proper quality control is essential for all steels, but particularly for forgings. These are often thick and may contain flaws. Ultrasonic or radiographic inspection should be mandatory, but is only effective if strict acceptance/rejection standards are invoked. Metallurgical forgings also may suffer from "banding." These are distinct parallel layers of ferrite and pearlite. This leads to

transverse strength problems and also may lead to all the MnS inclusions settling preferentially in the ferrite bands. This is of special consequence if the steel is being overlaid with nickel or stainless steel weld metal, as shown in Figure 15.01.

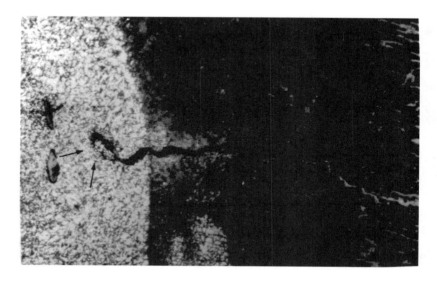

FIGURE 15.01   *Large MnS inclusion responsible for cracking the nickel cladding layer on a forged carbon steel plate. Arrows indicate inclusion.*

6. Chemical composition of candidate steels, and particularly carbon content, must be considered carefully. At high carbon levels, pre- and post-heat treatments are mandatory along with welding. These are costly at best, and it may even be impossible to achieve the desired level of structural integrity. Other elements, such as Cr, V, Ni, Cu, and P, may be added to steels to enhance strength and ability to harden. Such alloy steels may call for particular heat treatment and welding procedures. Specialists should be consulted.

Nickel and Nickel Alloys

Nickel is established as the prime material for use in alkaline media. In high temperature applications, nickel is used in stainless steels and in super alloys. For chemical resistance, nickel is found in monel [for hydrogen fluoride (HF) service] and in many alloys of wide applicability, such as Hastelloys, Chlorimets, and Inconels. Most Ni alloys have good weldability, though some alloys need special precautions in welding. Ventilation of welding fumes is of paramount importance when welding nickel and nickel alloys since the welding fumes will contain deadly nickel carbonyl $[Ni(Co)_4]$ released due to the heat of the welding process. The permissable exposure limit for $[Ni(Co)_4]$ is only 0.001 ppm.

Lead and sulfur must be strictly excluded when welding nickel alloys as they can cause serious cracking. Nickel is sometimes applied as a coating by electrodeposition, etc. on carbon steel. Such nickel-cladded steels are cheaper than the equivalent all-nickel structure, but call for particular care in welding. Nickel alloys in general are suitable for cryogenic applications.

Copper and Copper Alloys

Copper is the ideal heat transfer metal because of its high heat and electrical conductivity. It can be used in water service at low flow rate as pure copper and also may be alloyed, mainly with zinc, tin, and nickel. The Cu-Zn alloy is called brass while the Cu-Sn alloy is bronze. Improved mechanical properties can be obtained by alloying copper with silicon or beryllium. Beryllium copper can be age-hardened to around 200,000 psi UTS and is used for nonsparking tools in areas of explosion hazard. Silicon bronze is a good engineering material of moderately high strength that is readily weldable.

Copper alloys are prone to SCC in amines or ammonia (season cracking). Dezincification in waters is a problem for brasses unless they are inhibited with a group V metal, as shown in Figure 15.02. Impingement attack also can be a problem.

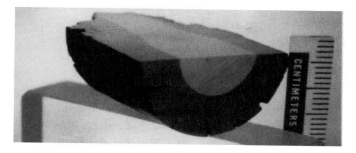

Figure 15.02   *Brass valve stem, showing extreme example of dezincification.*

223

Aluminum and Aluminum Alloys

Aluminum's corrosion resistance depends on the everpresent oxide film on its surface. This film is impervious and a good insulator, and may be enhanced by anodizing. The passive nature of the film explains its ability to neutralize aluminum's energetic tendency to react with the environment.

Aluminum has good electrical and thermal conductivity, and it can attain a high strength-to-weight ratio when alloyed. Pure aluminum is rather weak while its stronger alloys are prone to stress corrosion cracking and exfoliation attack. They have to be protected with a thin skin of pure aluminum Alclad. A more general solution is to avoid the use of alloys of highest strength. There are a number of alloys strengthened with Mg and Si, etc., that can be corrosion reliable up to 65,000 or 70,000 psi UTS.

Aluminum has excellent resistance to waters, organic acids, and certain oxidizing acids. Its resistance to nitric acid is shown in Figure 15.03. It can be used as a shipping container for acetic acid. On the other hand, it can sometimes react with organic halides with considerable violence following a quiescent induction period.

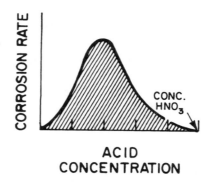

ACID CONCENTRATION

FIGURE 15.03 Schematic corrosion of aluminum in nitric acid.

Aluminum and its alloys corrode rapidly in alkaline environments. When used in waters, the pH level should not exceed 9.5 to 10. If aluminum is to be cathodically protected, there is a danger that cathodic alkali can be generated by overprotection. Expert design is mandatory.

Stainless Steels

These will be discussed in detail in Chapter 16. Without a doubt, stainless steel has become the workhorse in the chemical industry. But it is not a universal material. If wrongly applied, it offers little advantage over much cheaper materials, and misjudgment in its use may lead to a false sense of security.

Titanium and Titanium Alloys

Titanium is one of the newer metals available to the chemical and aerospace industries. Like aluminum, it is a potentially reactive metal that owes its exceptional corrosion resistance to its excellent protective oxide TiO_2. Because of its low specific gravity (~4.5), the volume obtained per unit weight of metal purchased is some 80% more than for stainless steel. Also, the excellent strength properties of some of the Ti alloys mean that it can be used in tubing of reduced wall thickness relative to some of its competition. But, the use of thin-walled tubing of a material of relatively low elastic modulus (16.8 x 106 psi) invites excessive deflection and instability under load and can cause problems, particularly where vibration can lead to excessive mechanical wear. It offers an interesting challenge to designers. Its high cost can be justified only by long life and, hence, in applications where the vehicle or process will remain profitable for many years.

Titanium may be specified in four grades (ASTM B265-93, Grades 1 through 4) according to purity.[5] Considerable strength advantages, without much decline in corrosion resistance, can be realized from the lower purity grades. A general limitation is that titanium is highly sensitive to interstitial oxygen and nitrogen. At higher temperatures, this can lead to catastrophic embrittlement. All heat operations with Ti, including welding, call for particular care to ensure that inert gas shielding is fully effective. With proper technique, it can be successfully welded, except in the overhead position.

Titanium offers excellent corrosion resistance to seawater, wet chlorine, $CuCl_2$, and $FeCl_3$ salts. Mercury, dry chlorine, and fuming nitric acid can lead to explosively violent reactions following an induction period in which the Ti appears to be tolerating the chemical assault.

Magnesium and Magnesium Alloys

As a structural material, magnesium is not used widely despite its low specific gravity (~1.74). The oxide film is somewhat protective, but it is still vulnerable to chlorides and all acids. It requires careful protection with surface conversion coatings (fluoride-phosphate-chromate, etc.) followed by painting. It is used to some extent in aircraft and automobile applications, though all of its stronger alloys are prone to SCC in the presence of chlorides. An interesting metallurgical sidelight is that additions of about 10 atomic % of lithium will cause it to change its structure from close-packed hexagonal to cubic. The Li-Mg alloys are much more workable than any others, and they show no deterioration in corrosion properties. Magnesium alloys are used as sacrificial anodes in small cathodic protection systems and in specialized battery applications.

Lead and Lead Alloys

Lead in its pure form (chemical lead) has long been used with great success to resist many chemicals, notably in the sulfuric acid industry. However, its combination of high specific gravity (~11.3) and negligible mechanical properties means that it creeps readily and must be mechanically supported with great care. Its strength may be increased by alloying with antimoy, tin, tellurium, or calcium, often with some improvement in corrosion resistance.

As in the case for other metals, working with lead, particularly welding (lead burning), does present a health problem. Adequate ventilation must be used. Lead corrosion products are also toxic. Since lead is anodic to copper, lead-based solder must not be used, for instance, in electric kettles. Lead-based solder to join copper pipe in domestic water service is also suspect. The latest Scandinavian specifications for joining copper water pipe call for tin with 3% Ag as a solder to avoid toxicity problems while maintaining excellent solderability.

The maximum contaminant level (MCL) for lead was set by the U.S. EPA at 50 ppb in 1985. It is likely this will be further reduced to perhaps 10 ppb as information comes in. (By comparison, the levelfor copper is likely to remain at 1.3 mg/L.) Perhaps the gravest concern arises from the possibility of long-term neurological damage to infants – the most sensitive group to low level chronic lead intoxication.

Three CORROSION/90 papers identify the source of lead in

drinking water as corrosion of lead water pipe and the corrosion of lead-based solders used to join copper pipes.[6-8] The problem is most severe where the water is both soft and somewhat acidic. Typically, the problem is most significant in stagnant water, rising to a maximum lead content after about 5-12 hours. Flowing water furnishes dilution to below MCL. It is recommended that pipes be flushed before taking water for drinking. Perhaps a rule of thumb would be that the toilet should be flushed before the kettle or coffee maker is filled. Delicate pH adjustment with NaOH and the addition of small amounts of zinc orthophosphate inhibitor also are proposed.

Precious and Refractory Metals
    The precious metal grouping includes silver, gold, platinum, palladium, rhodium, and the three other metals in the Pt group. Tantalum, zirconium, columbium, and molybdenum, along with ceramics, glasses, and graphite, are materials which are also sufficiently expensive; they are employed only when uniquely required (e.g., Zr alloys in the nuclear industry). The value of precious metal equipment as a part of a corporate investment portfolio should not, however, be overlooked. Few other items are able to appreciate in value with use.

Nonmetallic Engineering Materials

Natural and Synthetic Rubbers
    The two main classes of rubber are natural and synthetic rubber.
    Natural rubber can react with sulfur to increase its cross-linking and hardness in the vulcanizing process. It has great elasticity, the modulus of which can vary from ~800 to 450,000 psi. Its resistance to many aqueous chemicals is good, but it has poor resistance to oil and gasoline.
    Synthetic rubbers, such as neoprene, have much better resistance to organic chemicals. Silicone rubbers, usually called silastics, have good high temperature properties and can be used up to ~500°F (260°C). Many materials depend on rubber gaskets and O-rings for successful use. Flexible tube and hose is another important application.
    Rubber-lined equipment is used in a variety of services: e.g., hydrochloric acid, regenerating feed water service, and in electroplating tanks, etc. The specification of a particular rubber for

a given lining application calls for expert judgment.

Engineering Plastics

These are polymeric materials which may be divided into two classes, the thermoplastic and thermosetting types. Thermoplastics become and remain pliable whenever they are heated, whereas the thermosetting resins harden and remain hard after one exposure to heat. Both classes can be subdivided into groups based on common or closely related chemical building blocks. Within each group, there can be wide variations depending on modifications of these building blocks. The modifications may include the way in which they are combined structurally, and the compounding of polymeric resin with other materials. Important structural effects include molecular weight, cross-linking, degree of crystallinity, presence of hydrogen bonding, presence of bulky substituents, etc. For details, refer to any good materials science textbook.

Typical thermoplastics are polyvinyls, polyolefins, nylons (polyamides), polyfluorocarbons, polycarbonates, polyacetals, acrylics (polyacrylates), and silicones (polysiloxanes). Each group can be subdivided. For example, polyvinyls include subgroups: polyvinyl chlorides (PVC); polyvinylidene chlorides (e.g., saran); polyvinyl acetates; and polyvinyl butyls. Each subgroup contains particular types and subtypes of materials with a relatively narrow range of properties often tailor-made for particular uses. The thermosetting class can be subdivided similarly. Typical groups of thermosets are phenol-, urea-, and melamine-formaldehydes, polyesters, and epoxies. The chemical resistance of plastics is reasonably well-documented, particularly in manufacturers' literature.

Plastics have extended the choice of materials of construction by an order of magnitude. All show useful physical properties. However, many show limited tolerance to temperatures in excess of ambient. Only a few can be continuously exposed to temperatures over 100°C (212°F), and few maintain much strength above that temperature. Supported films of polyfluorocarbons, for example, can show useful corrosion resistance to much higher temperatures than the maximum temperature at which they could be used for self-supporting structures. The main drawback in their use in the chemical industry is a lack of understanding of their mechanical characteristics by many who use them. Their behavior is significantly different from that of metals at ambient temperatures. It more closely resembles the

228

behavior of metals at much higher temperatures in the creep regime.
For metals, all design calculations are determined by the
properties of the material, such as modules of elasticity, tensile
strength, yield strength, hardness, etc. For metals at room
temperature, all these properties are stable and time-independent.
Plastics, however, are quite different, with properties being load and
time-dependent. Realization of this fact and of the nature of the
dependence is of the utmost importance to avoid mistakes in their use.
Without going into great detail, the following discusses some of the
differences between metals and plastics, and serves to introduce
appropriate terminology.

Plastics have a number of characteristics that have an important
bearing on mechanical properties. First, their molecular weight is
large, typically from 1,000 to 1,000,000. It is important to know
whether the molecule is straight chain or branched, and how the
molecules are organized with respect to each other. The aggregate
could be amorphous, or at least partly crystalline. It should be
recognized that the molecular arrangement also can change in
response to deformation or in response to a stress applied for some
time. This complicates the measurement and specification of physical
properties.

A good example to start with is a simple ASTM hardness test
using a .5 mm ball. For metals, this is done simply by a set period,
application of the load, release, and direct reading of the final
hardness value. For plastics, however, all readings from the dial must
be recorded at exactly set (15 second) intervals. Slight errors in
timing will cause differences in hardness readings.

This time-dependent phenomenon is caused by molecular
movements in response to the strain and opposed by frictional
resistance due to the close proximity of neighboring molecules. The
molecular segments vibrate continuously in a random fashion by
reason of their thermal energy, but when an external stress is applied,
some movements become more likely than others. The net result can
be that long chain molecules align in the direction of the applied
stress. Particularly if there are possibilities for secondary Van der
Waal's or hydrogen bonding, the alignment will be maintained to
some extent even after the stress is removed. Secondary bonding also
can facilitate an increase in crystallinity with time, even in the
absence of stress. It is also possible that the molecular weight of the
polymer can change with time. Condensation reactions can be

activated with ultraviolet light, and there are also possibilities for chain scission. Such changes lead to the observed time dependence.

The question then arises, "How does one judge this time dependency phenomenon and apply it intelligently to establishing design procedures?" There is no definitive answer to this question. One reasonable design strategy is outlined in the following paragraphs. It is presented as a possible answer which may not be the ultimate solution. In any event, the phenomenology of the mechanical behavior of plastics must be taken into account. In the tensile testing of plastics, three distinct types of stress strain curves may be observed (Figure 15.04).

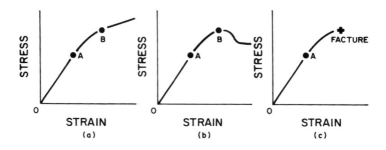

FIGURE 15.04   *Stress strain curves for plastic materials: (a) displays gradual yielding (polyethylene, acetyl); (b) displays abrupt yielding (nylon); and (c) displays failure without yielding (phenolic, acrylic).*

The designer is concerned with two distinct portions of the stress strain curve: (1) In the first region (OA), elastic design principles may be applied; and (2) in the second region (AB), point B will be referred to as the yield point and can be used when fracture or failure due to large deformation is of primary concern.

Proportional limit and elastic limit are two terms used to describe the point of termination of the linear portion of the stress strain curve. However, in thermoplastics there is a deviation from a straight line. At low 0.5% strain, most published figures of the elastic modules E_o are on the low strain portion of the curve.

Yield Point. The actual calculation of a yield point is fairly simple as long as it is remembered that for large strains one must use the logarithmic stress and strain. As long as the strain remains low,

230

the conventional strain can be applied, but to develop stress strain curves over a wide range it is convenient to use logarithmic stress and strain.

Creep and Relaxation. The phenomena of creep and relaxation are of prime concern to the designer. For metals, creep and relaxation are usually encountered only at high temperature, but creep will take place even at low loads and temperatures for plastics. When this occurs, the load carrying capacity decreases with time (Figure 15.05).

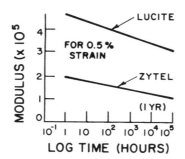

FIGURE 15.05 *Reduction of elastic modulus and, hence, load-bearing capacity with time.*

With thermoplastics there is no "limit;" rather, it is a matter of degree of increasing deviation with increasing strain and a concept of "modulus accuracy" is introduced. As an arbitrary choice, a modulus accuracy limit of 15% is chosen as an allowable error. Design calculations are then based on a secant modulus, which is 85% of the original modulus (Figure 15.06).

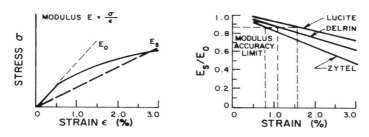

FIGURE 15.06 *Illustration of modulus accuracy limit (= secant modulus/ original modulus).*

It is possible that beyond a limiting strain value marked inaccuracies in calculations for creep deflection and stress relaxation may occur. This emphasizes the importance of using the modulus accuracy limit concept as a checkpoint and using this limit to restrict allowable strain.

There is one more problem, however, concerning the structural stability of most plastics. While the creep recorded in early stages of exposure is ductile, there seems to be a transition to brittle behavior after prolonged exposure.

There is another parallel between ambient temperature behavior of plastics and the creep of metals at high temperature. In that case, simplified rupture tests and the use of Larson-Miller parameters avoid costly and expensive creep tests. For plastic materials, a plot of the elastic modulus vs log time exposes a Larson-Miller-like transition from ductile to brittle behavior for elastically stressed samples (Figure 15.07). From a practical point of view, this emphasizes that creep in plastics eventually progresses from ductile to brittle in nature at any given temperature.

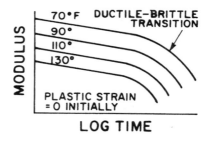

FIGURE 15.07 Typical Larson-Miller tendency of polyethylene.

As can be seen from the diagram, the "knee" (transition) is caused by stress, but temperature also has considerable influence. A designer of plastic systems must bear this ductile to brittle transition in mind, estimating beforehand how long the structure must last and managing the applied stresses/strains accordingly.

From the foregoing, it follows that the use of plastics dictates a different design rationale right from the start. However, there are other factors which still have to be considered. Notched impact strength is generally poor, there is rapid loss of strength as temperature rises [e.g., from 21 to 71°C (70 to 160°F)], loss of

232

strength due to moisture adsorption, and low impact strength values at subfreezing temperatures.

Joining of Plastics

The construction of plant or underground piping systems from plastics calls for joining operations. While cementing operations with adhesives or solvents has some value, the most satisfactory method will be hot air welding, at least for thermoplastic materials.

For underground piping systems there has been a marked increase in the past few decades in both pipe size and in the total number installed. For the larger sizes, 50 to 60 in., welding is, of course, necessary. The procedure is as follows: The two pipe ends are machined and carefully aligned. They are then pressed into a TFE-fluorocarbon coated disc heated to about 153 to 175°C (300 to 350°F) until the pipe ends start to flow. The disc is then rapidly removed and the pipe ends are pressed together. The resulting welds are strong and flexible and need no further work. An example of a cross-section of such a weld in a polyethylene pipe is shown in Figure 15.08.

Outside wall

Inside wall

FIGURE 15.08 *Cross section of a weld in a large polyethylene pipe, polished and treated with hot air. Note the protrusions on both the inside and outside formed solidification.*

How Polymers Deteriorate

To place polymeric materials in perspective relative to other materials choices, it is necessary to develop a more detailed understanding of their deterioration processes. Let us start from a familiar example — the automobile tire. Tires on high mileage vehicles do not lead to surprises or disappointments. The tread wears more or less on schedule, and the tire is replaced. On lower mileage vehicles, there tends to be failure of the sidewalls while there is still adequate tread remaining. This will be in the form of radial cracks in the side-wall.

The mechanism of cracking appears to be a combination of tensile stress with a change in elastic properties of the rubber brought about by long exposure to ultraviolet light and oxygen or ozone. UV light tends to promote continuing polymerization of the rubber; the higher average molecular weight makes the rubber more rigid and helps to promote cracking when the tire flexes as it rotates. The effects of oxidation are complex, but may lead to an increase in cross linking that also increases the cracking tendency. The use of carbon black filler serves to reduce these effects. This allows nondamaging absorption of UV, and the carbon particles set up a designed amount of what serves as cross linking but is not readily enhanced by oxidation. The overall result is a reasonable compromise in properties which leads to an acceptable, though not indefinite, sidewall life.

Polymeric materials other than rubbers are also subject to oxidation. The oxidation process is typically a chain reaction and often involves peroxides and free radicals as intermediates. Any carbon-hydrogen bond might be attacked, but particular kinds are especially vulnerable. These include sites adjacent to a double bond or either linkage, as well as at a tertiary carbon.[9]

Oxidation reactions can be considered in two groups, backbone effects and side group changes. The former classification can be further broken down into scission, depolymerization, cross linking, and bond changes. It is possible to slow down the process of these reactions with suitable inhibitors, but it is not possible to stop the reactions entirely.

As a matter of interest, it is possible to use similar inhibitors chosen for low toxicity in foodstuffs and in sun tan preparation. In addition, some of these additives are particularly effective in

234

preserving vitamin content. This is probable because the vitamins are the component of the food most subject to oxidation.

All amorphous or partially amorphous polymeric materials exhibit glass transition temperatures. Below this temperature, the amorphous portion is glassy and brittle. If it is useful at all in the glassy range, it must be treated as a glass for design purposes, and allowances will have to be made for its essentially brittle behavior. The earliest remedy for this was to incorporate a suitable plasticizer, such as castor oil or an alkyl or aryl phthalate, in the compounding step. Unfortunately, these plasticizers gradually exude from the plastic component. This causes an increase in its glass transition temperature and its brittleness, and may lead to contamination of the surroundings by traces of plasticizer. The more acceptable technique for avoiding glassy behavior is to co-polymerize the potentially glassy polymer with a second species that has a much lower glass transition temperature. This form of plasticization is permanent.

The effect of stress on polymeric materials is twofold. Firstly, there is the general effect of tensile stress in tending to open up cracks and allow the process of crack formation to accelerate. Secondly, there is a tendency for stress of any kind to align or partially align those parts of the polymer structure that were amorphous. This causes an increase in crystallinity which, in turn, causes an increase in glass transition temperature and also helps to promote crack growth.

Another important cause of deterioration of polymers is solvents, of which water is the most common example. In this case both liquid water and water vapor can be implicated. The effect is complicated because water can act as a plasticizer, in addition to its other effects. Liquid water can be much more aggressive in the presence of wetting agents. Warm solutions of detergents can be used as an accelerated test. Paint solvents also can cause polymer deterioration. Cracking of hard hats used by painting crews is a typical example of this phenomenon.

In such cases, the solvent will initially cause some degree of swelling, which in turn leads to tensile stresses. The cracking which results is akin to stress corrosion cracking. If there is already a tensile stress in the polymer, the process will, of course, proceed more rapidly.

Fiberglass Reinforced Plastics (FRP)
Plastic materials reinforced with fiberglass and other fibers have

gained rapid acceptance during the past decade as a material of construction, particularly for housings (e.g., car bodies), storage tanks, and piping. The polymeric material used in FRP structures is one of three resin types: epoxy, polyester, or vinyl ester. These are formulated and cured to give optimum chemical resistance. The reinforcing material is woven or nonwoven cloth or fiber, either in strands or chopped. The reinforcement is applied in successive intermediate layers saturated with uncured resin to build up to the required thickness.

Most equipment is constructed either by filament winding or by hand lay-up of mat and/or cloth. For maximum strength, the hand lay-up is normally recommended because of the poor transverse properties associated with filament winding. Note that the orientation of the fibers in different ways to achieve strength also can be done mechanically, e.g., by transverse winding or braiding. Usually, a final layer of resin gel, low in fiber content, is applied to the surface that will be exposed to the corrosive medium.

Reinforcement with strong fibers is also a typical means of extending the range of usefulness of polymers such as nylons. Reinforcements such as glass, Kevlar and graphite might be appropriate. In general, the properties of reinforced polymers can be determined with reasonable certainty when they are new. However, such materials gradually deteriorate in response to such factors as UV light, oxygen or ozone, humidity, presence of water and wetting agents, and applied stress. The presence of particular structural features can cause sharp increases in these effects.

Piping, along with valves and fittings, is now produced in a prefabricated condition, and it may be purchased off the shelf. The purchase price of FRP equipment is competitive with steels, and may often have an advantage in its lightness, ease of fabrication, and absence of expensive outside painting. Lack of fire resistance can be a negative factor. Fire retardants for polymers generally need to be carefully considered. Where the polymeric materials are being used in applications such as aircraft cabins, the toxicity of breakdown products can be at least as important as the inhibiting effect on combustion. The best compromise may be a highly hydrated salt which absorbs latent heat as water of crystallization is driven off.

A more serious problem has emerged recently. There have been catastrophic failures of a number of tanks, and some industrial concerns have discontinued their use. The failures are due to separation of the glass layers and aging or creep of the resin; the problems are enhanced by poor fabrication procedures.

Standards are being formulated to control the design and construction of FRP pressure vessels. These can be expected to prevent failures resulting from bad manufacturing practice. However, the basic responses of the resins to time and to stress cannot be changed. Fortunately, inspection techniques are being improved; acoustic emission offers promise of being developed into a reliable test for anticipating major failures of FRP tanks.

Degradation of Reinforced Plastics

The degradation of reinforced plastics, of course, includes all of the considerations relating to polymeric materials. There are important considerations relating to disbonding of the reinforcement. In the case of glass reinforcement, which is the type most commonly encountered, anything that can disturb the glass-polymer adhesion will have a negative effect. The influences which can degrade the polymeric component have to be added to the factors which can attack glass. Notable among the latter is moisture; solutions of wetting agents can be particularly damaging.

Any difference in elastic modulus between the glass reinforcement and the polymeric matrix guarantees that, if there is any disbondment at all in a stressed composite, there is a ready mechanism for the disbondment to grow. The fact that atmospheric moisture, almost always present, can attack both the glass and the polymeric matrix exacerbates the problem.

Fabrication and Related Considerations

Forms Available

When selecting materials of construction, it often does not suffice to recommend a material suitable for a given condition. Although the choice of material may be correct, its availability also must be considered. Is the selected material available in strip, sheet, plate, forgings, castings, etc.? Would the corrosion behavior differ between one form and another? The corrosion resistance of a specific material in sheet condition may be superior to that in forged or vice versa. For instance, the maximum allowable carbon content in 304L stainless steel is 0.03% C, but in thin sheet or small thin walled tubing, the carbon content is increased to 0.035%. Is this tolerable for the particular condition? Often, a mistake is made by selecting a material next to impossible to obtain in a suitable period of time. Time of delivery and availability is of utmost consideration, particularly when new projects are involved.

Fabrication

Once we have selected the material of construction, a major consideration becomes whether and how it is to be put together to make a piece of equipment that will perform as intended. It is obvious that the material must undergo a series of manipulations in fabricating a vessel or component into a certain shape. The following discusses some of the major considerations:

1. **Corrosion Resistance vs Mechanical Properties.** A prime example of how corrosion is influenced by the mechanical property of a metal occurs when austenitic stainless steel is used in a severely work-hardened condition. Assume, for instance, that the steel should be resistant to 30% HNO_3 at 80°C (176°F). Its corrosion resistance to the acid will not be impaired substantially, but high stress levels have been introduced in the metal; hence, external stress corrosion cracking will become a distinct danger since the equipment is exposed to an industrial atmosphere containing a trace of chloride. Another example is the case where high strength bolting is used in chemical buildings. At low stress levels, alloy steel bolts will perform satisfactorily, whereas at high stress levels in a heat-treated high-strength condition they may fail rapidly when exposed to a low concentration of chlorides or nitrates. Welded plain carbon steel equipment, exposed to anhydrous ammonia, hydrogen fluoride, or sodium hydroxide (caustic), must be stress relieved to avoid cracking in the weld stressed areas.

2. **Shop vs Field Fabrication.** Most equipment, with the exception of storage tanks, is usually fabricated in construction shops, generally considered to offer ideal conditions. However, somewhere in the fabrication process, this equipment and/or piping has to be installed and tied in with other equipment. Sometimes, this may present problems, for instance, with titanium piping or equipment. Titanium is readily weldable, but certain precautions must be taken into account, such as cleanliness and shielding with inert gas. This

238

can be done easily in the shop, and all welds can be made in flat or horizontal positions. In the field, however, cleanliness and inert gas blanketing become more difficult. Above all, it is virtually impossible to weld titanium in the overhead position. The logical conclusion is to use flanged, instead of welded, connections in the field.

3. Weldability. Welding of all fabricated equipment is probably the single most important part of fabrication. Too often rigid material specifications to ensure optimum performance of equipment are voided by mistakes in welding. One must start with the conviction that no short cut can be taken on the weld integrity and quality. Strict adherence to fabrication codes regarding the welding method to be used, joint preparation, welder qualification, selection of compatible welding technique and electrodes, and thermal pre- or post-treatment is mandatory. Welding has become a field of considerable specialization. Techniques may range from gas welding to electron beam welding with a whole array of possibilities between. The appropriate technique of selection of joining methods is a must in modern fabrication if optimum performance is expected. This basic checklist may be used as a guide in selecting the proper sequence and approach to ensure high weld quality and integrity:

1. Keep the weld design simple.
2. Insist on approved shop drawings.
3. Conform to code regulations.
4. Specify whether radiographic or ultrasonic examination is required, and set appropriate standards to show what is acceptable and what is not.
5. Specify welding procedures in detail along with detail on the care of coated electrodes prior to use.
6. Specify proper weld filler metal.
7. Make an inspection agreement with the fabricator.
8. Ensure the vendor's capability to fabricate the equipment. (Does the vendor have adequate shop facilities? Is his shop ASME approved for fabricating pressure equipment?)
9. Know whether the fabricator employs qualified inspection personnel.
10. Know whether thermal treatment is required after fabrication. (Specifications with regard to temperature, time at temperature, and type of treatment

facilities should be considered carefully. What are the chances of distortion? Make sure that no further welding is done after the final stress relief.)

11. Consider how the equipment will be shipped. (Does it require special precautions, etc.?)

4. Heat Treatment and Stress Relief. The purpose of heat treatment is to improve the quality of the end product. This may have the form of annealing, stress relieving, or hardening. Annealing is commonly carried out to homogenize a cast structure by heating close to the solidus or eutectic temperature for nonferrous metals, and above the α–γ transition for steels. Annealing is a three stage phenomenon, and both time and temperature are significant variables. The first stage is recovery or stress relief; the second is recrystallization where new grains are formed; and the third is grain growth which further increases ductility — but this grain growth has to be controlled carefully since it reduces the strength of a metal. In fabricating equipment, the stress relief treatment is normally applied when required by the code, or for reasons of improving corrosion-resistant properties, e.g., stress corrosion. Note that for stainless steels stress relief also may sensitize the metal (Chapter 16). When required, steels are stress relieved at a temperature of 615°C (1150°F) at a soaking time of 1 h/in. thickness (Figure 15.09).

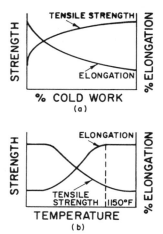

FIGURE 15.09 *Response of mechanical properties to: (a) cold work; and (b) stress relieving temperature.*

Depending on the steel and other special conditions, this temperature may be reduced somewhat provided soaking time is increased.

Hardening treatments usually are employed to improve the hardness and wear resistance of a metal. Steels are exposed at a temperature in the gamma range and quenched in water, oil, air, or brine. They will then have maximum hardness because of the martensitic transformation; however, because of brittleness, they must be tempered to become more ductile.

Another heat treatment is age or precipitation hardening. Here, strengthening is produced by a two-stage treatment: putting into solution at high temperature followed by a lower temperature treatment to give finely dispersed precipitates (blocking).

Overview of Fabrication

In summary, a particular metallurgical structure is desired for the finished product. This is not necessarily guaranteed by an unsophisticated specification that calls for the use of a particular material. A great deal of painstaking detail in the specification may be required to assure that the finished product will be able to live up to the expectations of the original designer.

A Closer Look at Temperature

A number of questions need to be asked about temperature. For example, what are the operating temperatures of all of the components? If high temperature, would oxidation of steel be a problem? A distillation column on a wintry night in the northern U.S. or Canada can cool off quickly after an emergency shutdown. If the column is made from a carbon steel having a poor low temperature transition point, catastrophic failure may well result.

Equipment containing sharp notched flaws made from large grain carbon steel may fail at moderately low temperatures. Table 15.01 gives some of these temperatures and grain sizes of steels used in actual equipment.

TABLE 15.01

Low Temperature
Transition of A201 and A285 Pressure Vessel Steels

Spec. Number	Charpy V15 Transition Temperature (°F)	Plate Thickness (Inches)	ASTM Grain Size (Actual)
A-201 Steel			
Exceptionally Good Transition Temperatures			
305	-20	1	5 to 6
About Average Transition Temperatures			
306	15	1	4 to 6
438	45	1.25	5 to 7
439	45	1.25	4 to 7
440	55	1.25	4 to 7
A-285 Steel			
Better Transition Temperatures			
304	ɔɔ	1.125	5 to 6
329	50	1	5 to 7
333	50	1.25	4 to 6
348	30	1	6 to 7
351	50	1.25	4 to 6
408	45	1.25	4 to 6
Poorer Transition Temperatures			
332	70	1.25	4 to 6
334	80	1.25	2 to 7
359	95	1.25	3 to 6
403	115	1.25	4 to 6
441	90	1.25	3 to 7
442	90	1.125	3 to 7
461	120	1.25	4

In contrast to low temperature consideration, we also must assess the maximum operating temperature the equipment will be exposed to in service. Often, a materials engineer must consider the maximum temperature operating equipment may be exposed to in cases of malfunction. A car radiator operates at temperatures of 80 to 90°C

(175 to 195°F), but in the event some fluid is lost, the temperature may go well in excess of 100°C (212°F) and the radiator or coupling hoses will blow out. In the same sense, if a large steam boiler loses its water or steam content (starvation), the boiler tubes are no longer cooled by the steam, and the steel tubes will oxidize catastrophically due to the flame impingement in the fire box. It must be emphasized that under all circumstances, the true temperature must be considered, which is not always the process operating temperature. If a tubular steam calandria carries a process liquid inside the tubes and is heated from the shell side (Figure 15.10), the actual tube wall would be hotter. This hot wall temperature must be taken as representative in assessing the materials of construction for that particular service.

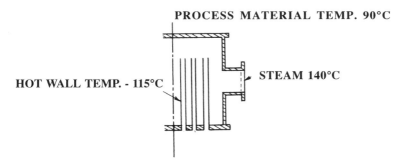

FIGURE 15.10 *Hot wall effect in a tubular heat exchanger.*

With regard to the medium, it can be generally stated that the higher the temperature, the more aggressive the corrosive environment. However, there are exceptions to this rule.

There is one more important temperature-related factor, and that is the coefficient of expansion. If metals are heated, they increase in length, hence needing more space. This does not too often present a problem, as long as the metals are not restrained. When restraint occurs, however, the differential expansion coefficient plays an important role, and it may produce undesirable stresses in a system. A long pipe system that carries a heated fluid will expand considerably; for example:

1,000 steel pipe:

Δ temperature 200°F = 200 × .0000064 × 12,000 ~15 inches

1,000 stainless pipe:

Δ temperature 200°F = 200 × .000009 × 12,000 ~22 inches

1,000 polyolefin pipe:

Δ temperature 200°F = 200 × .00009 × 12,000 ~220 inches

Note that the lengthening of the pipe is considerable, but also that there is a difference in expansion length for differing materials. This is called differential expansion. In practice, the process lines described will be protected from excessive expansion stresses by either expansion loops or flexible expansion bellows (Figure 15.11).

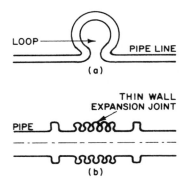

FIGURE 15.11   *Parts of an expansion system: (a) expansion loop; and (b) expansion bellows.*

Consider a heat exchanger with stainless steel tubes and a carbon steel shell. When this is heated, the tubes will expand more than the shell, and tend to buckle the tubes or the tube sheet. A flexible expansion joint in the shell will remedy this situation.

A Closer Look at Pressure

Equipment designed to operate at pressures in excess of 15 psig are considered pressure vessels, and must be registered and constructed under ASME regulations (Chapter 14). The main concern about pressure is that the larger the volume involved, the higher its

244

potential energy and, hence, the kinetic energy it can deploy in case of failure. Pressure is poorly understood by engineers and scientists. Perhaps "poorly understood" should be "poorly appreciated" or "recognized." It is important that air or any other gas not be used for the hydraulic testing of equipment because of the danger of the sudden release of large amounts of PV energy.

A car tire contains only 25 to 40 psig pressure. But many accidents have occurred to people in close proximity to a blowout. In the industry, the vessel size may range from a few gallons to hundreds of thousands of gallons; obviously, the greater the volume, the greater the consequences of a sudden pressure release will be. An example of a burst tube is shown in Figure 15.12. Modern industry employs thin wall (0.250 to 0.750 inch) vessels, but also vessels having wall thickness up to 10 inches. Thick wall vessels present a real challenge to materials engineers due to their increasing susceptibility to brittle fracture as the thickness increases.

Failure to contain the pressurized contents may exhibit three failure modes.

FIGURE 15.12 Burst tube in preheater coil.

Liquid Spill

Here, most often, corrosive liquid is spilled and presents a danger to personnel or destruction of adjacent equipment, particularly flooring and structural steel. Particular attention must be given to small, almost undetectable leaks gnawing away vessel supports, etc., and rendering the structure unstable.

Much attention has been focused lately on the storage and transportation of lethal liquid and gases (e.g., 1979 Mississauga chlorine incident). Strict laws and regulations are enforced for the storage and transport of such substances, but alas, their interpretation often leaves something to be desired. A precise strategy needs to be developed to deal with a leaking tank car of chlorine, or hydrofluoric acid, or whatever. In most cases, emergency response teams have been set up cooperatively by the major chemical manufacturers, but the local authorities do not necessarily know what to do until the emergency response team arrives. The use of propane burners to create a ring of fire is a palliative for toxic spills that should receive more consideration. Local fire departments, on the other hand, are well-trained in dealing with flammable spills.

Vapor Cloud

Here, the process medium released under pressure does not escape through a defect as a liquid, but as a gaseous cloud. This cloud may often be toxic, but if it contains, e.g., hydrocarbons, it also may be explosive. A tragic disaster occurred in Flixborough, UK, a few years ago, where a large rupture of a process line caused the formation of a large vapor cloud which was eventually detonated, destroying the plant with the loss of 29 lives. Today, industry is well aware of such possibilities, and strict materials engineering practices and standards are mandatory. An occurrence of this kind is the Three Mile Island radioactive gas release.

Auto Ignition

Here, the temperature and pressure of the escaping medium is such that when released, it automatically burns. Leaks of this order often have been the cause of many major fires leading to plant destruction.

246

Other Design Considerations Relating to Materials

Compatibility

Compatibility means that, within a system, no metal is installed that could adversely affect other metals galvanically. For instance, if we install a copper or brass valve in a plain carbon steel system, copper has a more noble potential in contact with steel; hence, the adjacent steel portion of the line will corrode more rapidly. Often, this is the case with the water system in homes, but it can be avoided by either selecting compatible materials or electrically insulating the system. The area effect in this type of corrosion is quite pronounced. Less corrosion is suffered if the noble (cathodic) part is comparatively small and the less noble (anodic) part is large. Often, galvanic effects are difficult to judge; therefore, when in doubt, consultation by experts in the field may not be a luxury. For instance, consider the combination of two cast iron flanges with a copper gasket between (Figure 15.13). A joint failure occurred, and upon investigation, it was revealed that the actual leak resulted from corrosion of the copper.

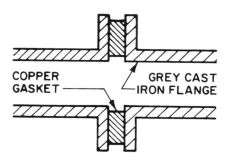

COPPER
GASKET

GREY CAST
IRON FLANGE

FIGURE 15.13 *Corrosion of flange to gasket combination.*

At first glance, and with uncritical application of galvanic principles, it may be assumed that the leak must have been caused by corrosion of the iron flanges. Initially, and as expected, the galvanic process began with their dissolution. Once the corrosion process had started to dissolve the iron, the surface of the flanges changed potential slowly because of increasing exposure of graphitic flakes. Eventually, the copper gasket was corroded by contact with the more noble graphite.

Mechanical compatibility also can be significant. The load-bearing characteristics of any element in a system must be compatible with all of its components. This will be particularly important when plastic materials, thin-walled expansion joints, or metals with a lower modulus of elasticity are used.

The Weakest Link (How Critical?)

A precise and thorough analysis assesses the strategic function of a particular piece of equipment in a given process. A systematic approach along the line of a fault tree analysis of every piece of equipment is required. Questions, such as how the failure or malfunction of the component would affect safety and utility of operations, must be answered. Some operating equipment may fail but not cause a safety hazard or disruption. Upon failure, however, others may produce either an unsafe condition, or, being a critical link in a continuous process, cause a total disruption and process shutdown. The awareness of these consequences tends to cause overdesign. It must be remembered that economical design is the first duty of an engineer.

Corrosion Allowance

All pressure vessels and components are designed to comply with the ASME code. They also should be designed in the most efficient and economical way. Now that higher strength materials are used, thinner wall thicknesses are adequate; hence, lighter equipment and easier fabrication are possible. When equipment operates in a corrosive service, even at low corrosion rates, there will be some reduction of wall thickness. Unless provision is made for this, it will soon render the equipment inadequate for the designed pressure rating. All that can be done is to reinforce the vessel or reduce its pressure rating. To overcome this problem, a corrosion allowance has to be specified, the thickness depending on the type of service and expected corrosion rates. A typical allowance is from 1/8 to 1/4 inch extra wall thickness for a vessel shell. One bit of caution is needed, however. If a corrosion allowance is specified for a distillation column shell based on a known corrosion rate, it must be realized that the internals, such as trays and down comers, will corrode at twice the

248

rate of the shell (Figure 15.14).

It is mandatory to obtain baseline wall thickness on all equipment prior to commissioning. For instance, if the shell of a vessel has a design thickness of 0.500 inch, the plate tolerance may allow the thickness to be 0.520 inch. If the vessel has been in service for three months, and ultrasonic readings indicate a loss of wall thickness to 0.495 inch, it would be assumed that, if no baseline readings were obtained, the loss was 0.005 inch. In fact, the loss is 0.025 inch, which is unacceptably high for most vessels.

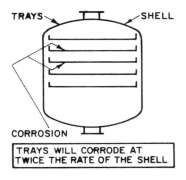

FIGURE 15.14 *Corrosion in a distillation column.*

Maintenance

Consideration must be given to how the specified equipment can be maintained or repaired. Glass-lined equipment, for example, is not repairable. Can the need for repairs be predicted, and repair procedures worked out in advance to minimize disruption, or would it be better to carry a spare unit, which can sometimes be preinstalled (duplex system)? How long would it take to repair a certain component? The repairs per se are seldom costly, but the outage of the plant is. If, for instance, titanium or tantalum equipment is used, there may be problems making repairs in place because of the high affinity of these metals for oxygen during welding. Furthermore, it is almost impossible to weld these metals in the overhead position. If nonmetallic systems, such as polyethylene and FRP, are specified, are persons on the site capable of making repairs? Will the intended repairs meet all of the code requirements? Is there a means of inspecting such systems and making intelligent deductions from whatever information can be obtained?

A problem that often dictates whether repairs are possible is the type and amount of surface contamination. Weld repairs are often extremely difficult, if not impossible, when equipment is contaminated. Would equipment have to be removed from the process building to carry out repairs because of high risks of explosion, for instance, in hydrocarbon service? Before making weld repairs, the safety aspects must always be considered carefully. Many accidents have been caused by repairing corroded equipment where hydrogen was still present and could cause a major explosion.

Scaling

In almost all instances of designing chemical process equipment, heat transfer plays an important role. All calculations dealing with heat transfer from one medium to another are made assuming a temperature differential across the wall thickness of a component. Once this is known, the capacity and, hence, size of the equipment can be determined readily. An impressive case is presented later in this chapter, where the equipment became inoperative because of excessive tar deposits, but often loss of heat transfer is not as imminent or fragrant. Thin calcium carbonate deposits on tubes of a tubular heat exchanger can alter the operating characteristics or performance considerably.

The type of scale that is deposited is of utmost importance. A tightly adherent ferrous scale may have little effect on heat transfer, whereas a silicate scale is an excellent insulator and has an adverse effect. Therefore, it seems logical that not only the thickness of the scale deposits, but also the composition must always be considered. This can be done simply by carefully removing some scale and subjecting it to analysis. Once scale has formed to such an extent that it adversely affects operations, it must be removed. In some cases, it may simply be brushed off, but almost always turbining or chemical cleaning is involved. Acids such as inhibited hydrochloric, sulfuric, or sulfamic are used.

One must make sure that the correct amount of inhibitor is mixed with the cleaning acids. If one is not sure, a simple test can be performed to establish the corrosivity of the solution using different amounts of additives. The best test for inhibition efficiency is the NACE standard test TM0172-93.[10]

An example of the magnitude of problems that may be encountered with excessive scaling is a case where scaling led to failure of a steam boiler. This boiler had a flame out caused by the rupture of a boiler tube. In a steam boiler, the steam is on the inside of the tubes, which are flame heated in a fire box which may either be gas, coal, or oil-fired. The fire box temperature may be approximately 1,082°C (2,000°F), at which steel would oxidize rapidly. The steel tubes, however, resist oxidation by virtue of the cooling effect of the steam or water on their inside walls. As scale slowly builds up on the water side, the heat transfer from the flame to the steam through the tube wall is reduced, resulting in a slow increase in temperature of the tube wall. For instance, the tube wall temperature may be between 395 to 422°C (750 to 800°F) on clean tubes. The temperature will rise gradually as the scale builds up and will eventually damage the tubes by overheating.

Figure 15.15 shows a boiler tube which bulged due to overheating. Metallurgical investigation of this particular tube (Figures 15.15 and 15.16) showed: sample (1) to contain a normal ferritic pearlitic structure; sample (2) a spheroidized (divorced pearlite) structure; and sample (3) a recrystallized structure. If we consider that spheroidization occurs on carbon steel at somewhere around 670°C (1,250°F), and recrystallization at 635°C (1,550°F), we now easily reconstruct the failure. Slow overheating led to spheroidizing the steel and reduced its strength. Eventually, the weakened steel failed by yielding.

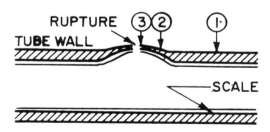

FIGURE 15.15 *Boiler tube that bulged due to overheating.*

Velocity

All materials of construction for pipe or tubing have a definite resistance to velocity. Strictly, this should be expressed in terms of

Reynolds numbers. In practice, however, the limiting velocity for a given pipe material, rather than a limiting Reynolds number, is usually specified. Turbulent flow is much more damaging than laminar flow and can cause excessive erosion (see Chapter 6).

Differential velocities are encountered in process lines at pipe elbows, etc. The outside stream in contact with the large bend radius of the elbow will have a considerably higher velocity than at the inside bend. This effect becomes more pronounced if there are suspended particles, or if the particular solution has a high specific gravity, such as concentrated sulfuric acid. When these lines are inspected for thinning, it suffices to check the loss of metal at the outside bend only. Erosion caused by high velocity should not be confused with impingement attack or cavitation. Impingement is a localized attack caused by turbulence or impinging flow often accompanied by entrapped air. Cavitation is the sudden collapse of bubbles in a liquid due to differential pressure areas. In the extreme case, such bubbles actually may remove protective films or even metal mechanically.

As a practical matter, flow velocities that are too low also can cause problems. Particulate matter can deposit in low-velocity locations and eventually plug tubes or cause serious local pitting.

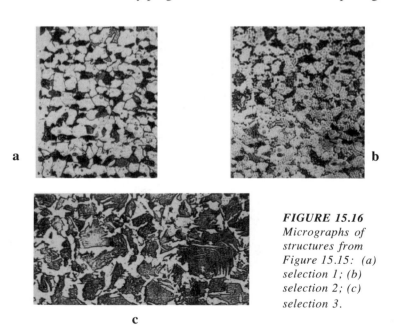

a

b

c

FIGURE 15.16
Micrographs of
structures from
Figure 15.15: (a)
selection 1; (b)
selection 2; (c)
selection 3.

The Materials Selection Process

The trend in materials of construction in the chemical industry has partly retreated from the old concrete and steel philosophy. Today, there is a great deal of refinement in the availability of materials of construction, varying from metallics to nonmetallics. It is obvious that a large number of factors have to be taken into consideration when selecting a material for a given application. These factors can be put into three major groups: (1) materials of construction; (2) environment; and (3) economics.

Materials of Construction

In an industry such as the chemical industry, the normal delegation of duties for a project or plant is: The chemist develops a process; the chemical/mechanical engineer designs the equipment; and the materials/metallurgical engineer selects the materials of construction. At the onset, five criteria must be considered by the materials engineer.

1. Appearance. This can be expressed as the need to reach and maintain an acceptable appearance. A material could be specified for the facing of a building, together with finishes such as paint. The main criteria obviously are that the facing will not rust or discolor. (Note: The weathering steels and copper are an exception. Here, the patina has a pleasant aesthetic appearance.) The cost of painting structures, pipe bridges, water towers, etc., and of chromium plating and paint on cars is substantial.

2. Permeation. This can be expressed as the time required to penetrate a material, liner, or coating due to corrosive action of the media. The worst offenders in destructive permeability are corrosion, cracking, and pitting.

3. Efficiency of Operation. How long would it take to impair the heat transfer of a heat exchanger tube on the surface of which a thin layer of calcium carbonate is being deposited? This question calls to mind an example of good corrosion. A large carbon steel steam coil installed in a tar vessel normally lasted about three years. To improve its service life, a new coil was made from stainless steel. After five days of operation, the process came to a sudden stop. The subsequent investigation revealed that the outside of the coil had completely coked up and no heat was transferred. The difference was that the carbon steel coil would slowly corrode; by doing so, it kept the surface clean from tarry deposits.

4. Contamination. This can be expressed as the time limit where contamination becomes excessive, from either a products or corrosion point of view. A brief story concerns the fall of the Roman Empire. According to some corrosion engineers, the fall was caused by affluent Romans poisoning themselves by eating and drinking from lead based water pipe, utensils, goblets, and plates. Ironically, in 1946, all patients in a European hospital were poisoned by lead because a contractor solved a water corrosion problem by replacing all the carbon steel water feed lines with lead lines. Contamination can become a problem in corrosion, particularly if closed systems are used and the concentration of heavy metal ions may increase, enhancing the corrosivity of the medium.

5. Unsafe Operation. This can be expressed as the time limit in which a structure becomes unstable due to the effects of corrosion. Good examples of this are available, such as road salt on bridges, corrosion of car structures, and corrosive thinning of equipment in general.

If the development of an engineering project is pursued further, it is evident that the materials engineer of the team must obtain the necessary design information in detail. Too many mistakes have been made in the past due merely to a lack of information that was readily available.

Environment

The influence of the environment has been discussed from time to time in this textbook. Prior to material selection, a check should be made of whether any deviations from a standard chemical medium may have to be considered. The following describes 10 such environmental factors.

1. Purity. Chemicals in process streams are seldom in pure form. Impurities may be inhibitive, corrosive, or synergistic. For instance, corrosivity of nitric acid is greatly accelerated by the presence of minute quantities of vanadium or chromous ions.

2. Solution Concentrations. It is not always true that the lower the concentration of the medium, the lower the corrosion rate. Ten percent H_2SO_4 is much more corrosive to steel than is 93% H_2SO_4.

3. Temperature. As a general rule, as the temperature

increases, so does the corrosion rate. There are, however, exceptions.

4. Aeration. The presence, or lack, of air in solution may be of considerable importance. Air-free 2% H_2SO_4 will corrode an austenitic stainless steel considerably while copious amounts of air will reduce this corrosion due to passivation. The reverse is true if a copper/nickel alloy is exposed to this solution.

5. Agitation. Dead spots in design should be avoided. Agitation will prevent oxygen concentration cells by ensuring the presence of oxygen, and also will prevent deposition of sediment.

6. Reaction with Environment. Titanium will react violently (pyrophoric) with dry sodium and fuming nitric acid. All metals are hazardous when finely divided.

7. Velocity. The engineering data of a material of construction with regard to its erosion, turbulent flow, heavy particles, and stagnation should be checked.

8. Contaminants. Some metals will, when corroding, contaminate the process solution with species harmful to the product. Copper in yarn spinning solution is a major cause of yarn breakage; lead in water lines can cause poisoning, etc.

9. Stray Electrical Currents. Many premature failures have been caused by electrical currents in soil. If in doubt, ask a qualified cathodic protection expert since this field requires a great deal of expertise.

10. Atmospheric Corrosion. Too often, expensive materials of construction have been used successfully to contain corrosive media only to fail from the outside surface due to the corrosive action of the extended environment, particularly where there is a mechanism available for concentrating chlorides, etc.

Economics

Much has been written lately about the aspects of economics in materials engineering. The economic conditions are actually quite simple. Materials must be applied or selected that are the cheapest solutions to a given problem. This also implies that a set standard of values must be applied to justify reasoning. What may be most economical for one industry may not be in another. Apart from many details, the main consideration must be utility and safety.

Utility of Operation

Today's chemical and petrochemical industries are finely tuned precision installations designed to operate in a continuous fashion. The old batch type system is still used in particular processes, but more and more industries aim to operate continuously, which is usually desirable from the productivity standpoint. This philosophy dictates that all equipment must be operable at all times: if one component fails and is taken out of service, the whole production, or at least a good part of it, comes to a grinding halt. Therefore, it becomes obvious that considerable emphasis must be placed on the fact that the performance of all equipment must be at the same level. If this were not so the weakest link principle would come into play. The overriding concern then becomes a matter of the longevity, corrosion resistance, required maintenance, etc., of the selected materials of construction. All equipment must be of the same quality, dependability, and durability. It is also fair to state that, in a given process, some equipment may be exposed to more severely corroding conditions than other equipment. This situation would require the application of a range of materials of construction varying from plain carbon steel to expensive inert materials. Other factors, such as preservation, maintenance, mode of operation, etc., are important aspects of utility, but they fall outside the scope of this chapter.

One fallacy of the utility game is the assumption that if the equipment must last longer, the materials of construction should be thicker. This is sometimes a necessity, but basically there is something wrong with this kind of reasoning. If extra thickness is specified in excess of the normal corrosion allowance, it should automatically be assumed that something is being done wrong. Often, this philosophy may aid in a reevaluation of goals. In most cases, proper analysis will produce a cheaper and more technically acceptable solution to a choice of construction materials.

Also, it must be remembered that by increasing the wall thickness of major piping and vessels, the materials resistance to catastrophic failure is impaired by introducing triaxial stresses, thereby lowering fracture toughness. Of course, in almost all instances, the cost of the equipment increases. This cost factor is of utmost importance. Engineers are paid to design equipment as economically as possible without sacrificing reliability. The materials engineer has a unique role to play in judging the economic choice of equipment. Most companies operate a design and a maintenance division or department. If ailing equipment is simply replaced and capitalized, the cost is charged to the design budget. If, with considerable effort, the equipment is maintained in an operable condition and made to last, the charges will accrue to the maintenance budget. It is obvious that both groups aim to have a balanced budget at the end of the year. Hence, the design group prefers maintenance, and the maintenance group prefers the purchase of new equipment.

This principle also holds true for the choice of materials of construction. An actual example: In part of an operation, where the medium consisted of nitric acid and other impurities, the equipment was fabricated of 304L stainless steel. The process lines corroded in about six or seven years, although more maintenance on flanges and welds was required earlier. To solve this corrosion problem, the maintenance department planned to replace all the piping with titanium pipe. This material is inert to the conditions quoted, and the maintenance budget could then be reduced substantially. However, the purchase price of the new material tripled the investment — which was no problem to the maintenance group because the charges would go to design. Predictably, the design group objected to this plan. The author, being the referee on this argument, considered all aspects, such as personnel, utility, and safety, and finally recommended that they remain with the choice of stainless steel, with the overriding justification being the obsolescence factor. This obsolescence factor dictated the most economical solution based on a six to seven year basis. The reasoning behind obsolescence is that, with ever increasing production rates, etc., today's equipment will be obsolete within the six to seven year period, mostly due to increased pipe diameters (scaling-up). If obsolescence does not occur within that period, someone is probably out of the business. The decision for this particular case proved to be correct and resulted in a large savings.

Utility may mean a lot of things to different people, but the prime consideration must be the awareness and dedication of materials engineers to recommend those construction materials that result in the best and most economical overall operation.

Selection of Materials for Specific Corrodents

A substantial body of information on the selection of appropriate materials is available in the literature. The most convenient collection is found in the *NACE Corrosion Data Survey*.[2] This collection is also available on disc for computer use. It is more valuable in this form because complete tables of data are given, including footnotes, rather than having data compressed on a small chart. Figures 15.17 through 15.19 show three sample pages from this publication. The first two pages show the corrosion behavior of aqueous solutions of some salts, and the last page gives information on hydrochloric acid solutions.

References

1. *Metal Progress Data Book* and *Advanced Materials and Processes* (Metals Park, OH: American Society for Metals).
2. N.E. Hamner, ed., *NACE Corrosion Data Survey* (Houston, TX: NACE, 1974).
3. R.S. Treseder, ed., *NACE Corrosion Engineer's Reference Book* (Houston, TX: NACE, 1980).
4. ASTM Standard A48-92, "Standard Specifications for Gray Iron Castings," *Annual Book of ASTM Standards* (Philadelphia, PA: ASTM, 1992).
5. ASTM Standard B265-93, "Standard Specification for Titanium and Titanium Alloy Strip, Sheet and Plate," *ASTM Annual Book of Standards* (Philadelphia, PA: ASTM, 1993)
6. C.H. Neff, M.R. Schock, "Monitoring Lead Concentrations and Treatment Effects in Public Water Supplies," CORROSION/90, paper no. 169 (Houston, TX: NACE, 1990)
7. B.P. Boffardi, "Minimization of Lead Corrosion in Drinking Water," CORROSION/90, paper no. 171 (Houston, TX: NACE, 1990).
8. P.M. Temkar et al., "Lead Reduction Strategies in Drinking Water Systems Using the CERL Pipe Loop System," CORROSION/90, paper no. 168 (Houston, TX: NACE, 1990).
9. F. Rodriguez, *Principles of Polymer Systems*, 2nd ed. (New York, NY: Hemisphere Publishing, 1982).
10. NACE Standard TMO172-93, "Antirust Properties of Cargoes in Petroleum Product Pipeline" (Houston, TX: NACE, 1993).

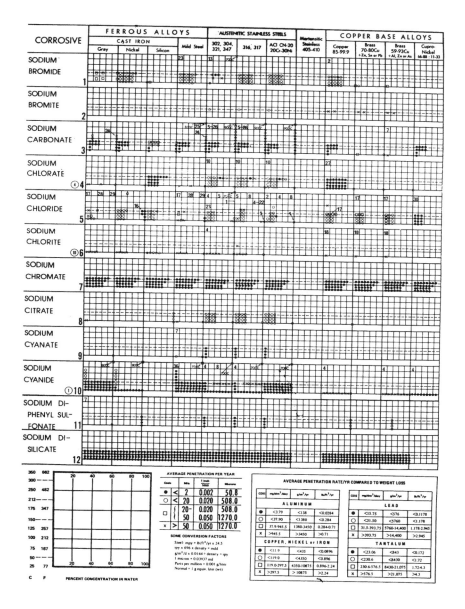

Figure 15.17 — *Sample page from NACE* Corrosion Data Survey.[2]

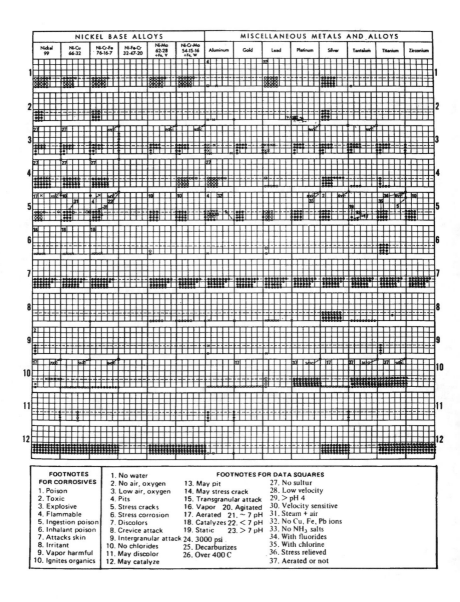

Figure 15.18 — *Sample page from NACE* Corrosion Data Survey.[2]

CODE FOR HYDROCHLORIC ACID GRAPH

Materials for shaded zones have reported corrosion rates of <20 mpy.

ZONE 1
20Cr 30Ni[1]
66Ni 32Cu
62Ni 28Mo
Copper
Nickel
Platinum
Silicon bronze
Silicon cast iron
Silver
Tantalum
Titanium
Tungsten
Zirconium

ZONE 2
62Ni 32Cu
Molybdenum
Platinum
Silicon bronze
Silicon cast iron
Silver
Tantalum
Zirconium

ZONE 3
62Ni 28Mo[5]
Molybdenum
Platinum
Silver
Tantalum
Zirconium

ZONE 4
66Ni 32Cu
62Ni 28Mo
Platinum
Silver
Tantalum
Tungsten
Zirconium

ZONE 5
62Ni 82Mo
Platinum
Silver
Tantalum
Zirconium

1. <2% at 25°C
2. No air
3. No FeCl$_3$
4. <10% at 25°C
5. No chlorine
6. <0.05% concentration

Figure 15.19 — Sample pages from NACE Corrosion Data Survey[2]

261

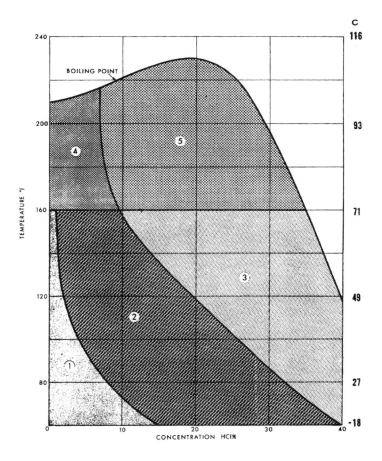

Figure 15.19 *(continued)*

262

16

Stainless Steels

Introduction

Stainless steels are not a recent development. Faraday worked with chromium additives to iron in 1822 and noted remarkable improvement in resistance to atmospheric oxidation, but found only a marginal improvement in corrosion resistance to hot sulfuric acid.[1] In 1838, Mallet discovered that additions of chromium to steels would improve corrosion resistance only in certain media.[2] It was not until the end of the 19th Century that improvement of the chromium additives for media other than hot sulfuric acid was appreciated. Soon after (1904), Guillet made useful observations with regard to chromium composition ranges in steels.[3] In 1908, Monnartz discovered the real virtues of chromium additions with respect to corrosion in oxidizing media.[4] He recognized that the improved corrosion resistance was due to a passive surface layer, and he experimented with the electrode potentials of the different alloy additives. Today, there is a wide range of stainless alloys available, most designed for a specific goal or application. Selecting the correct stainless steel for a particular use is by no means easy.

Metallurgy of Stainless Steels

To better appreciate the passivation phenomenon that led to the use of the term "stainless", a cursory understanding of the effect of additives other than chromium to stainless steels may be instructive. It must be remembered that stainless steels are basically an iron alloy, and in many instances, if the passive film is not developed, they will corrode at rates similar to those found for other alloys of iron.

The first stainless steels contained from 10 to 18% chromium to facilitate passivation. However, early steel makers did not have the technique of the austenite-ferrite and austenite-martensite transformations. Steels of this type have substantial martensite content at all

263

cooling rates likely to be achieved in practice. These martensitic stainless steels are difficult to form, machine, or weld.

Later, stainless steels at the same chromium level, but with carbon 0.1% or less, tend to follow the ferritizing influence of chromium and give rise to ferritic stainless steels. Both ferritic and martensitic steels are magnetic, and both are in the 400 series. Ferritic steels are body centered cubic (bcc) in structure while martensitic steels are heat treated to a distorted tetragonal martensite structure. The carbon content is the primary identifying characteristic between the two classes. More recent techniques in steelmaking are leading to lower attainable carbon contents. Argon oxygen decarburization (AOD) and vacuum oxygen decarburization (VOD) can be practiced routinely, and carbon or carbon plus nitrogen contents of 150 ppm or even less can be specified and attained. The resulting ferritic stainless steels are often termed superferrites. The technology of these materials is still in a state of flux; some, however, have now been assigned AISI designations.

The third main class of stainless steels is the austenitic type. In this class, there has to be a fairly high proportion of an austenite stabilizer. Nickel is the most common of these and needs to be present to a minimum of about 8%. This amount will make the austenite to ferrite transformation sluggish so that it persists while larger amounts — about 25% — will render the austenite completely stable.

The metallurgy of stainless steels can be understood most readily from a study of the various types of phase diagrams, as shown in Figure 16.01, that can result from the addition of various alloying elements. The effect of the specific additions, alone and in combination, can then be related to these phase diagrams.

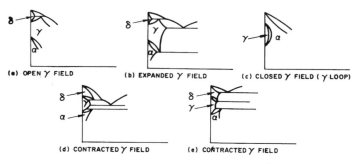

FIGURE 16.01 Types of iron alloy phase diagrams.

Structural Effect of Carbon

Figure 16.01 shows a form of the Fe-C phase diagram in which the range of stability of the δ ferrite phase has been overemphasized. This diagram is typical of an expanded γ field, as would occur with C and N as alloying additions for Fe. As can be seen in Figure 16.02, the A_3 transformation temperature is lowered while the A_4 transition temperature is raised by adding carbon. Carbon is thus an austenite stabilizer. Carbon also lowers the melting point and reduces the δ ferrite range. The role of carbon in martensite formation also must be remembered. If the carbon level is below 0.1%, martensite cannot form and the steel remains ferritic. For carbon at higher levels, there is potential for hardening via martensite formation on quenching, even at modest rates. Such stainless steels are termed martensitic.

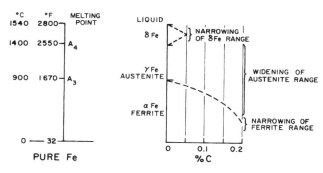

FIGURE 16.02   *A_3 to A_4 transformation in steel at different carbon additions.*

Another technique for reduction of carbon activity in a stainless steel is to add an alloying element which is an energetic carbide former but which does not form an energetic intermetallic compound with iron. The addition of such an element will thus serve to overcome the interaction between carbon and iron as well as to show a specific effect of the new element on the starting iron.

Structural Effect of Chromium

For additions of chromium, both the effective elimination of carbon as $Cr_{23}C_6$ and the specific effects of chromium tend to reduce the stability of the austenite phase to the closed γ loop shown in

265

Figures 16.01(c) and 16.03. Chromium thus extends the α ferrite range and unites it with δ ferrite: chromium is thus a ferritizer. Mo, W, V, Ti, Cb, and Si behave more or less similarly.

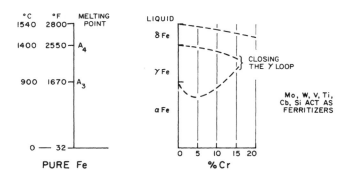

FIGURE 16.03 A_3 to A_4 transformations in steel at different chromium concentrations.

Structural Effect of Nickel

The addition of nickel will markedly increase the range of stability of γ-Fe and will lead to an open γ field, as shown in Figure 16.01(a). Addition of Mn, Cu, and of the other group VIII elements will have a similar effect. Increasing additions of nickel change this alloy substantially.

Just as with carbon, nickel has a strong effect on the so-called gamma range by widening the austenitic range at lower temperatures to such a degree that, if sufficient nickel is added and the material is cooled reasonably quickly through its transformation range, the metal will remain austenitic face-centered cubic (fcc) and be nonmagnetic. This constitutes a 300 series stainless steel. The effect of nickel and other austenizers on the A_3 and A_4 transformations is indicated in Figure 16.04.

Structural Effect of Boron, etc.

Boron and other elements such as Nb, Ta, and Re also will lead to a restricted range of γ-Fe stability, as shown in Figures 16.01(d) and (e) as a restricted γ field.

266

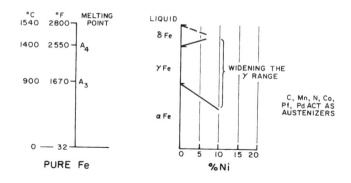

°C   °F   MELTING
1540 2800─┐ POINT   LIQUID

                            δ Fe
1400 2550─ A₄

                            γ Fe   WIDENING THE
 900 1670─ A₃   │ γ RANGE

                                              C, Mn, N, Co,
                                              Pt, Pd ACT AS
                            α Fe   AUSTENIZERS

   0 ── 32─┘
                            0   5 10 15 20
     PURE Fe   %Ni

FIGURE 16.04 *A₃ to A₄ transformation in steel at different nickel additions.*

Effect of Composition on Physical, Mechanical and Corrosion Properties

Alloying is a well-developed empirical procedure designed to improve the properties of a metal, often for a certain application. Not all alloying will improve metal quality, and if wrongly applied, metal quality may be greatly reduced or the metal may be rendered useless.

Effect of Carbon

As in plain carbon steel, the addition of carbon may enable attainment of a wide range of mechanical properties. As seen previously, small differences in carbon content change the stainless steels from a soft ferritic to a hard martensitic steel. Carbon additions will give a stainless which is somewhat harder without heat treatment and can be heat treated to give a hard martensitic stainless steel. It should be noted that the martensitic stainless steels harden as a result of hot processing followed by normal cooling.

Carbon also will increase strength level, and moderate additions of carbon will highly increase the strength of ferritic steels (Figure 16.05). Unfortunately, there is a consequent loss of ductility, and often of corrosion resistance. The role of carbon in austenitic stainless steels is also critical for corrosion resistance. This will be discussed later.

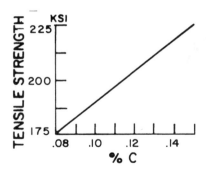

FIGURE 16.05 *The effect of carbon tensile strength of 410 ferritic stainless steel.*

Effect of Chromium

Almost without exception, the effect of chromium additives to steel has major consequences. Even a small addition of 0.5 to 1% will alter mechanical properties of steel substantially (Figure 16.06).

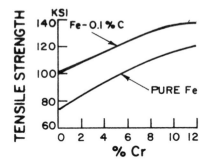

FIGURE 16.06 *Increased tensile strength vs % chromium.*

Chromium also improves resistance to high temperature oxidation (Figure 16.07) and provides better wear resistance, but above all, for stainless steels, it will increase the corrosion resistance of a steel in a wide spectrum of corrosive media. The effect of chromium additions vs corrosion resistance has been studied extensively. Small additions of chromium will readily improve corrosion resistance of a steel exposed to industrial atmospheres.

268

Further chromium additives will produce an alloy that is inert and will not corrode unless exposed to particular destructive chemicals. Hence, chromium is able to render steel stainless.

If we expose steel to an atmospheric industrial environment, it will rust readily. As we increase the chromium content, the steel will stain less and less until we reach 12% chromium, at which composition no rusting is observed. This is well-illustrated in Figure 16.08 in which we can observe the beneficial effect of small chromium additions and the complete lack of corrosion at the 12% Cr level. The resistant passive behavior is obtained through a layer containing chromium oxide as the trivalent part of a spinel coating which is impervious and self-healing.

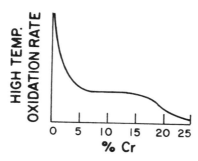

FIGURE 16.07 *Effect of chromium on high temperature oxidation.*

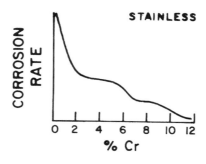

FIGURE 16.08   *Effect of chromium additions to steel exposed to an industrial atmosphere.*

It must be realized, however, that if the properties of a stable and protective spinel film that is characteristic of a 12% Cr alloy are needed, the 12% Cr must be kept in solid solution. Unfortunately, there are a number of ways in which this solid solution concentration can be lowered. Formation of chromium rich carbide ($Cr_{23}C_6$) precipitate will lower the Cr concentration remaining in solution nearby; accordingly, the corrosion resistance of the part of the alloy which is depleted in Cr is lowered. Also, the chromium steels will depend on the mentioned thin layer of iron and chromium oxide, which is stable under oxidizing conditions but not in reducing environments. Reducing acids, e.g., hydrochloric acid, will strip the protective layer, which is then unable to repair itself in a reducing environment; hence, corrosion will proceed at a rapid rate.

It is necessary to recall that stainless steels occupy two positions in the electromotive series; when in a passive condition, it is at the passive end while in active form it changes position to the less noble or active end occupied by ordinary steels. This implies that, if a small portion of a passive stainless steel surface is destroyed and has become active, a galvanic cell has been created in which the current flows from the large passive surface (cathode) to the small active surface (anode) with an attendant increase of corrosion. Figure 16.09 shows this effect.

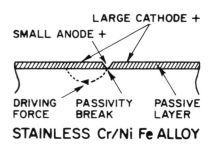

FIGURE 16.09   *Mechanism of an active break in a large passive surface.*

Effect of Nickel

Nickel added to iron will not form a complex compound like carbon will but dissolves in both bcc iron (ferrite) and fcc iron (austenite). Both nickel and carbon lower the A_3 transformation temperature and have a tendency to form austenite. If additions of nickel are increased to over 8%, the $\gamma \rightarrow \alpha$ transformation of the Fe-Cr alloy becomes rather sluggish. If quenched more or less rapidly, the steel remains austenitic (fcc). At this 8% Ni addition, the austenitic is called "metastable"; higher additions of up to 25% are required to obtain a fully stable alloy. This alloy, termed austenite, will enhance corrosion properties in a variety of environments, but also will produce a steel that has desirable strength properties in work-hardened conditions, as shown in Figure 16.10, without suffering significant loss of corrosion resistance.

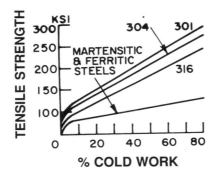

FIGURE 16.10 *Increased tensile strength vs rate of work hardening of 300 austenitic steels.*

Minor Additions

Molybdenum is classified as a ferritizer, and the usual addition to an austenitic stainless steel is around 2 to 3%. Molybdenum enhances the alloy's resistance to pitting in chloride-containing environments. Additions of molybdenum, however, will definitely lower the corrosion resistance of 18 Cr-10 Ni stainless steel in hot boiling nitric acid. Titanium in type 321 and niobium in type 347 can be added to an austenitic stainless steel in an attempt to avoid sensitization (to be discussed later). Copper is beneficial when stainless steels are used in slightly reducing acid conditions, and it improves resistance to chloride stress cracking. Substantial copper additions, however, impair corrosion resistance to oxidizing acids. Selenium and sulfur are added to stainless steels to improve machinability, but again, these elements lower the corrosion resistance of the steel. Silicon additions improve the high temperature oxidation resistance of the alloy. The various classes of stainless steels now available can be summarized below. Each calls for its own metallurgical and welding strategy.

   1.   Martensitic Stainless Steels. These steels, with 12 to 18% Cr and high C, are hard with moderate corrosion resistance, rather difficult to weld, and have a magnetic tetragonal structure. Their main uses are for mandrels, shear blades, and surgical instruments. (440 A, B, and C.)

   2.   Ferritic Stainless Steels. These steels, with 12 to 18% Cr and low C, are soft, of good work hardening qualities, can be drawn without annealing, are magnetic (bcc), and have excellent corrosion resistance but poor weldability. Their main uses are in chemical equipment and automotive trim where there is good drainage. (430)

   3.   Austenitic Stainless Steels. These steels, sometimes called 18/8, have low carbon, excellent mechanical properties in most hardened conditions, and an austenitic (fcc) structure which is nonmagnetic and of excellent weldability. Stress relief can be dangerous. High strength aircraft steels and chemical equipment are typical applications for types 304 and 316. The extra low carbon grades will be discussed in more detail later.

   4.   Precipitation Hardening Stainless Steels.   The chief advantage of this group stems from high mechanical properties along with good, but not outstanding, corrosion resistance. They are usually heat treated to their final properties by the fabricator. There are two general classes of precipitation hardening stainless steels: those which require a single thermal treatment and those which require a dual treatment. In both cases, there is formation of martensite, which is supersaturated with respect to the eventual precipitant, and final hardening is tied to a precipitation reaction.

   5.   Higher Alloys and Maraging Steels. As the alloy content of stainless steels is increased, the corrosion resistance improves and leads to super stainless steels. Still higher alloying additions lead to alloys, such as Hastelloys,[†] which have very good corrosion properties but can no longer be classified as a stainless steel. Maraging steels are noteworthy for their mechanical properties; their corrosion resistance is good but not exceptional. Their main virtue is that their final strengthening step occurs at a relatively low

---

† Trademark

272

temperature and enables strengthening to be achieved in thick sections with zero chance of distortion or cracking.

6. Duplex Stainless Steels. Duplex stainless steels have compositions which, in the wrought condition, show a fairly even balance in their microstructure between austenite and ferrite. The modern compositions tend to be low in carbon content, though they may contain appreciable nitrogen. Welding is often possible, particularly with high alloy fillers. However, in all instances the welding of duplex alloys requires strict adherence to welding procedures provided by the steel manufacturers. In some environments, the duplex steels are usefully resistant to stress corrosion cracking. This appears to stem from the presence of the two differing microstructures.

Intergranular Corrosion of Austenitic Stainless Steels

Introduction

When stainless steels are cooled slowly through a temperature range of about 500 to 850°C (932 to 1,562°F), or are otherwise maintained for some time in that range, they may become susceptible to intergranular attack when subjected to a number of specific corrodents. The grain boundaries are said to be "sensitized."

The concern of industry is best illustrated by an example. Figure 16.11 shows a 50 mm stainless steel line which lasted only three months in service. Fortunately, this potential disaster was revealed by radiographic inspection. If it had remained in service for one more month, the line would have separated, spilled thousands of gallons of hot nitric acid, and probably led to major injuries to personnel. This form of attack, called weld decay, occurs in the heat affected zone about 6 mm from the actual weld and parallel to it. Weld decay results in uniform thinning where grains of metal have fallen out because of intergranular attack.

FIGURE 16.11

Weld decay on an austenitic stainless steel process line (actual case).

273

There is no need to further dramatize the importance that must be placed by the chemical industry on avoiding such failures. Defensive steps taken to eliminate these occurrences are discussed later.

The Cause of Intergranular Corrosion

The cause of intergranular corrosion of stainless steels is found in the precipitation of carbides of the type $Cr_{23}C_6$ in the intergranular region. As the precipitates form, local depletion of both Cr and C occurs in the part of the grain close to the boundary. The chromium-depleted zone near the grain boundary becomes anodic to both carbide particles and to the unaffected grain bodies. This sets up a destructive corrosion cell with a large cathode of about 18% Cr and a small anode of about <12% Cr. Rapid intergranular corrosion in aggressive environments results, and the stainless steel is said to be sensitized.

Observations on Sensitization

The sensitization process is characterized by the following seven observations: (1) Sensitization occurs when the alloys are slowly heated or cooled through the range of approximately 500 to 850°C (932 to 1,562°F); (2) fast cooling or heating though this temperature does not result in sensitization; (3) quenching from elevated temperatures followed by reheating in the 500 to 800°C (932 to 1,562°F) range causes the steel to become sensitized; (4) the degree of sensitization increases markedly with increasing carbon content, and to a lesser degree with decreasing chromium content; (5) the degree of sensitization varies within the sensitization temperature range; (6) the degree of sensitization also increases with time at the sensitization temperature; and (7) the prominent feature of sensitized austenitic stainless steels is the presence of precipitates of chromium carbides at the grain boundaries.

Any general or unified theory of intergranular corrosion of stainless steels must be able to account explicitly for these observations. As stated in observation 4, the role of carbon is of utmost importance in determining the ultimate susceptibility of an alloy to intergranular attack. Binder et al. were among the first to utilize time-temperature curves to demonstrate the effect of heat treatment in the sensitizing range of steels of varying carbon content.[5] This is well illustrated in Figure 16.12 for an alloy nominally

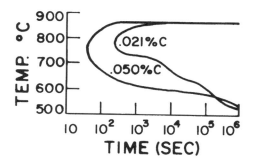

FIGURE 16.12   *The effect of carbon content on sensitization of AISI Type 304 steel tested in acid-copper sulfate solution.*[6]

containing 18.5 Cr-11 Ni-0.05% N and carbon levels of 0.021 and 0.050%.

It is generally assumed that the resistance of a stainless steel to sensitization increases with increasing chromium content because of the increasing tolerance of the alloy for carbon and nitrogen. Depletion of chromium near carbide precipitates is less significant when the starting Cr level is higher. Increasing the chromium to higher levels, however, will also increase the formation of sigma phase and the formation of undesirable delta ferrite.

More recently, there have been indications that the sensitization phenomenon is more complicated than is generally appreciated. The two steps involved are the nucleation of $Cr_{23}C_6$ particles and their subsequent growth. Early studies of the problem have been based on isothermal transformations with no distinction between the nucleation and growth components. Their conclusions were that sensitization at below about 500°C (932°F) was usually too slow to be of practical concern. Povich and Rao have shown that fine carbide particles, visible under the electron microscope, are formed in a few minutes at sensitization temperatures.[7] These nuclei will grow to sizes that confer full sensitization in 10 days at 400°C (752°F) or in an estimated 10 years at 300°C (572°F). The conclusion that should be drawn from this work is that no standard grades of austenitic stainless steel should be used at temperatures in excess of 300°C (572°F) if processing (including welding) has led to precipitation of intergranular carbide nuclei. More detailed studies of the phenomenon will be necessary to demonstrate how this criterion can be met in practice. It should be noted that if sensitized austenitic stainless steel shows adequate corrosion resistance in a particular medium, something cheaper than austenitic steel also would suffice.

Stabilized and Low Carbon Stainless Steels

Once the concept that sensitization could be linked to chromium depletion was accepted, it was reasoned that the addition of elements that would form insoluble carbides having a more negative free energy of formation than chromium carbides should cure the problem. Thus arose the concept of stabilized stainless steels which form an important class of stainless steels today. Some unforeseen pitfalls of the stabilized grades with regard to sigma formation and knife line attack during welding operations have reduced the practical effectiveness of these grades substantially.

Knifeline attacks occur in a narrow zone at the interface of the weld pool and the base metal. It is caused by the fast cooling rate at the interface, thus restricting nucleation of niobium/titanium carbides. Chromium carbides can then be formed at the normal sensitization temperature, which results in intergranular corrosion at a narrow region adjacent to the base metal, as shown in Figure 16.13. The mechanism of the process is indicated in Table 16.01.

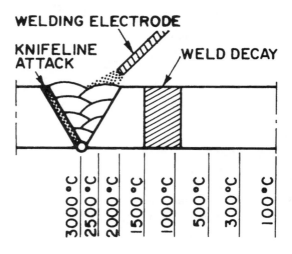

FIGURE 16.13 Problems caused by welding.

TABLE 16.01
Solution and Precipitation
Reactions in Type 304 and 347 Stainless Steel

347		304
Niobium Carbide Dissolves Chromium Carbide Dissolves	MP Temp (C) 1,240	Chromium Carbide Dissolves
Niobium Carbide Precipitates Chromium Carbide Dissolves	800	
Chromium Carbide Precipitates *Only if Niobium Carbide has not Tied up Carbon First*	500	Chromium Carbide Precipitates
No Reactions	25	No Reactions

The authors have observed cases of knifeline attack where the weld metal had lifted completely out of the plate while little corrosion was apparent on the weld metal or the plate. The sensitivity to knifeline attack can be relieved by post heat treatment at 1,065°C (1,949°F) followed by holding at 900°C (1,652°F) for half an hour and quenching to room temperature.

Welding and Intergranular Attack

As the molten weld puddle is moved through the austenitic stainless steel base metal in the welding operation, the resultant heat produced during the process will, at some distance from the weld, lead to temperatures in the sensitization range of 500 to 800°C (932 to 1,472°F). The time necessary for sensitization is shown in Figure 16.14.

The degree of sensitization produced in austenitic stainless steel during the welding operation depends largely on the welding technique used, the time at temperature, and the thickness of the material to be welded. The thicker material will remain in the critical sensitization range longer during welding than will the thinner

277

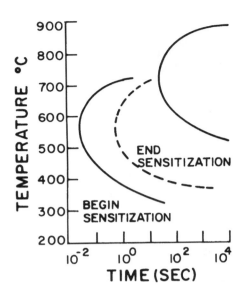

FIGURE 16.14 *Differences in location of time, temperature, and sensitization curves of austenitic and ferritic stainless steels of equivalent chromium content.*[8]

material. To reduce the time at temperature, techniques such as forced cooling of the areas adjacent to the weld or direct contact with a highly heat conductive metal, such as copper, are frequently employed in practice.

If stainless steel structures containing carbon in excess of 0.03% are welded, a remedial treatment consisting of heating between 980 to 1,150°C (1,796 to 2,102°F), followed by a quench must be employed to avoid susceptibility to the form of intergranular corrosion known as weld decay. If this is impractical, either low carbon stainless or one of the stabilized grades must be specified. The main advantage of using low carbon grades is their reduced allowable fiber stress limit, whereas the stabilized grades are susceptible to knifeline attacks as described previously.

The solution to both sensitization and knifeline attack is the use of an extra low carbon grade of stainless steel, such as 304L or 316L, in which the carbon content is held below 0.03%. This was established as the lowest carbon content that could be readily manufactured when the weld decay phenomenon was first understood. Even lower carbon contents, such as 0.02%, have been recommended by some manufacturers of specialty steels. Argon oxygen and vacuum oxygen decarburization processes are both used. The drawback to the L grade steels is that their strength levels are somewhat lower than the standard grades.

It must be remembered that the 304 grade can be welded easily to give mechanically sound welds. However, if type 304 does not suffer weld decay in a particular environment, it follows that a cheaper and lower alloy steel, as in fact exists in the grain boundaries in the sensitized zones, also could resist the environment.

Aside from the potential problem of creating intergranular corrosion susceptibility, austenitic stainless steels such as type 304 are readily weldable in sharp contrast to other stainlesses such as martensitic (type 440), ferritic (type 430), and precipitation hardening types and super alloys.

As an example, Figure 16.15 shows a photograph of two pieces of a ferritic type 430 stainless that have been welded. This shows the initial fine grain size of the parent metal along with the enormous grain growth in the heat affected zone (HAZ). This condition produces brittle behavior which, unfortunately, cannot be remedied. The as-welded appearance gives no indication of the mechanical problem.

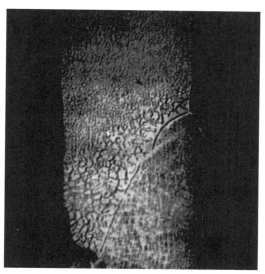

FIGURE 16.15 *Two welded pieces of a ferritic type 430 stainless, showing excessive grain growth in the heat-affected zone (HAZ).*

Problems with Austenitic Stainless Steels

Choice of the term "stainless" to characterize stainless steels as having better corrosion properties in many common environments than carbon steels was historically appropriate. It can, however, give users of stainless steels a false sense of security. We must bear in mind that the good corrosion properties of stainless steels depend on an intact passive film which is essentially $FeO.Cr_2O_3$. Any factor which can damage the oxide film can lead to problems. Some of the causes have been discussed earlier, but it may be instructive to summarize all the pitfalls.

    1. Sensitization. If the carbon content is too high, the steel is subjected for some time to the sensitization temperature, and the metal will corrode intergranularly in a variety of media.

    2. Carburization. Carburization often is observed in thin wall tubing where the inside tube wall may be carburized. Normally, this is caused by using a carbonaceous drawing compound with a subsequent anneal before the compound is completely removed.

    3. Weld Decay. The small identifiable area about 6 mm from the weld where the material remained for sufficient time in the sensitization range [500 to 800°C (932 to 1,472°F)] and where rapid intergranular corrosion occurs upon exposure to many corrodents.

    4. Improper Anneal. If the material is delivered in the as-annealed condition, an inappropriate holding time at the sensitization temperature and/or an inadequate quenching speed would cause complete or partial sensitization.

    5. δ Ferrite. The corrosion rate of austenitic stainless steels containing δ ferrite is increased due to preferential attack of δ ferrite by an oxidizing agent. The ferritizing effect of molybdenum in stainless steels (type 316) produces considerable quantities of δ ferrite; hence, type 316 corrodes substantially in, for instance, boiling nitric acid.

    6. Differential Stress. Small stressed portions in a system, such as from a hammer blow, may set up a differential cell and cause corrosion under some conditions.

    7. Fatigue. Where a small work-hardened portion is embedded in a large annealed structure (for instance, support post reinforcements in distillation column sieve trays), there can be problems. Vibration of the trays may, and usually will, cause failure due to fatigue at the transition from the hard or stressed to the annealed or soft condition.

8. Crevice Corrosion. Austenitic stainless steel is one of the many metals susceptible to crevice attack. Breakdown of passivity at the junction of the crevice will produce an active-passive cell and result in accelerated corrosion. Furthermore, this attack is usually accelerated by the buildup of chloride and/or polyvalent heavy metal ions inside the crevice.

9. Pitting. Since the corrosion resistance of materials like stainless steel is based on a thin passive layer, these metals are susceptible to pitting attack. Once small portions have become active and pitting has started, repassivation of the active area within the pit is not likely to occur, and pitting will progress at a steady rate. Laboratory investigation of pitting attack calls for great care, particularly in the interpretation of results. It is not possible to express meaningful results as a function of weight loss.

10. End Face Attack. This attack of inclusions aligned in the rolling direction of the plate will occur at the transverse face. This is caused by dissolving needle-like inclusions, and thus creating pits or crevices. This type of corrosion can be catastrophic and progress with great speed. Free machining grades of stainless steels are great candidates for this sort of corrosion because of the high amount of selenium and/or sulfur type of inclusion. In actual service, seal welding the surface of the end face can be a remedy for this problem.

11. Presence of Sigma Phase. This hard intermetallic compound (tetragonal FeCr) is occasionally found in stainless steels, particularly those with high molybdenum content. This may substantially reduce the corrosion resistance of the steel.

12. Liquid Metal Attack. If stainless steel is welded in the presence of any amount of zinc, lead, cadmium, aluminum, or copper, wetting and intergranular penetration produces severe cracking.

13. Effects of Carbon to Stainless Steel. If plain carbon steel is welded to a thin stainless steel structure, carbon dissolved from the plain carbon steel may penetrate the stainless. Experience dictates that carbon steel should not be welded directly to stainless steel if the stainless steel is ¼-inch thick or less. In this case, "poison pads" made from stainless steel should be used.

14. Chloride Stress Cracking. This is a particular case of stress corrosion in which chloride ions are the main contributors. Stainless steels may crack spontaneously in waters containing even a few ppm of chlorides at temperatures of around 70°C (158°F). An enormous amount of research has been carried out in this field, but before selecting stainless steel for any application, one must always be aware of chloride stress cracking (Figure 16.16).

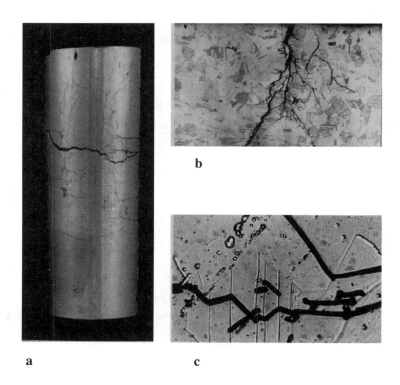

FIGURE 16.16   *Stress chloride cracking of austenitic stainless steel: (a) cracking of pipe under insulation; (b) micrograph; and (c) TEM micrograph, 3,000X.*

The classic example of chloride stress cracking is on warm process piping [70°C (158°F)] under insulation, even where the insulation is nominally chloride free and can be exposed only to minor amounts of rainwater. Chlorides from the water and/or insulation are leached in toward the warm pipe and concentrated there by evaporation. Drip onto warm pipes is also potentially dangerous. In general, insulation should be used only on stainless steel pipes maintained above 100°C (212°F) so that evaporative concentration is kept away from the pipe surface.

Types of Stainless Steels

During the past 40 years, the development of new types of stainless steels has made continuing progress. Most efforts were directed toward searching for a suitable metal for a particular application, e.g., emphasizing mechanical properties or corrosion resistance. Table 16.02 contains many of the so-called environmental stainless steels and contains a brief note on their use and application. Some newer types of stainless steels and related materials are summarized in Table 16.03.

The superferrites merit special mention. These have been made possible by the AOD and VOD processes for decarburization, and are generally directed toward achieving real resistance to stress corrosion cracking by chlorides. These materials are late comers on the scene and have not yet established specific roles for themselves.

TABLE 16.02
Types of Stainless Steel

AISI Type	Composition	Application
301	0.15 C, 2 Mn max., 1 Si max., 0.045, P max., 0.03 S max., 16-18 Cr, 6-8 Ni, etc.	High strength and ductility used in railroad cars, trailer bodies, aircraft structurals,
302	0.15 C, 2 Mn max., 1 Si max., 0.045 P max., 0.03 S max., 17-19 Cr, 8-10 Ni	General purpose austenitic stainless steel.
302B	0.15 C max., 2 Mn max., 0.045 P max., 0.030 S max., 2-3 Si, 17-19 Cr, 8-10 Ni	More resistant to scaling than type 302. Used in furnace parts, etc.
303, 303 Se	0.15 C max., 2 Mn max., 0.020 P max., 1 Si max., 0.60 Mo max., 0.15 S or Se min., 17-19 Cr, 8-10 Ni	Free machining modifications of type 302.
304	0.08 C max., 2 Mn max., 1 Si max., 0.045 P max., 0.030 S max., 18-20 Cr, 8-12 Ni	Low carbon modification of type 302. Chemical uses.

TABLE 16.02 (Continued)

304L	0.030 C max., 2 Mn max., 0.045 P max., 0.030 S max., 1 Si max., 18-20 Cr, 8-12 Ni	Extra low carbon modification of type 302. For welded structures in aggressive chemical environments.
305	0.12 C max., 2 Mn max., 0.045 P max., 0.030 S max., 1 Si max., 17-19 Cr, 10-13 Ni	Austenitic stainless steel with low work hardening rate. For spin forming, severe drawing, etc.
308	0.08 C max., 2 Mn max., 0.045 P max., 0.030 S max., 1 Si max., 19-21 Cr, 10-12 Ni	Higher alloy steel for high corrosion and heat resistance. Weld filler metal to allow for alloy loss in welding.
309	0.20 C max. (309)	For high temperature strength and scaling resistance.
309S	0.08 C max. (309S) 2 Mn max., 0.045 P max., 0.03 S max., 1 Si max., 22-24 Cr, 12-15 Ni	Welded assemblies.
310	0.25 C max. (310)	As type 309 stainless steel but for more extreme service.
310S	0.08 C max. (310S) 2 Mn max., 0.045 P max., 0.03 S max., 1.5 Si max., 24-26 Cr, 19-22 Ni	Jet engines, etc.
316	0.08 C max., 2 Mn max., 1 Si max., 0.045 P max., 0.03 S max., 16-18 Cr, 10-14 Ni, 2-3 Mo	Higher corrosion resistance than type 302, 304. High creep strength.
316L	0.030 C max., 2 Mn max., 0.045 P max., 0.030 S max., 1.00 Si max., 16-18 Cr, 10-14 Ni, 2-3 Mo, balance Fe	As type 316 for welded constructions.

TABLE 16.02 (Continued)

317	0.08 C max., 2 Mn max., 0.045 P max., 0.030 S max., 1.00 Si max., 18-20 Cr, 11-15 Ni, 3-4 Mo, balance Fe	Higher corrosion resistance than type 316.
317L	0.03 C max.	Type 317L for welded constructions.
321	0.08 C max., 2 Mn max., 1 Si max., 0.04 P max., 0.03 S max., 17-19 Cr, 9-12 Ni, 5 Ti x C, balance Fe	Stabilized for weldments in severely corrosive conditions and in high temperature service.
347, 348	0.08 C max., 2 Mn max., 0.045 P max., 0.030 S max., 1.00 Si max., 0.20 Co max., 0.010 Ta max. (348), 10 Cb-Ta x C min., 17-19 Cr, 9-13 Ni, balance Fe	Similar to type 321, but with higher creep strength.
403	0.15 C max., 1.00 Mn max., 0.040 P max., 0.030 S max., 0.50 Si max., 11.5-13 Cr	Martensitic stainless steel steam turbine blading, etc.
409	0.08 C max., 1.00 Mn max., 0.045 PO max., 0.045 S max., 1.00 Si max., 10.5-11.75 Cr, 6 Ti x (0.75 max) C	General purpose and automotive exhaust systems. Readily formed and welded.
410	0.15 C max., 11.5-13.5 Cr, 1.00 Mn max., 1 Si max., 0.040 P max., 0.030 S max.	General purpose heat treatable stainless steel.
414	0.15 C max., 1.00 Mn max., 1 Si max., 0.040 P max., 0.030 S max., 11.5-13.5 Cr, 1.25-2.5 Ni	High hardenability stainless steel springs, scissors, etc.
420	0.15 C max., 1.00 Mn max., 0.040 P max., 0.030 S max., 1.00 Si max., 12-14 Cr, balance Fe	Higher carbon modification of type 410. Cutlery, surgical instruments, and wear resisting parts.
420F	0.15 C max., 1.25 Mn max., 1.00 Si max., 0.060 P max., 0.60 Mo (optional), 0.15 S min., 12-14 Cr	Free machining version of type 420.

TABLE 16.02 (Continued)

430	0.12 C max., 1.00 Mn max., 0.030 S min., 0.030 S max., 1.00 Si max., 16.0-18.0 Cr, balance Fe	General purpose ferritic stainless steel. Decorative trim, furnace chambers, and kitchen equipment.
430F, 430FSe	0.12 C max., 1.25 Mn max., 0.060 P max., 1.00 Si max., 0.60 Mo max., 0.15 S (430 F), 0.06 S max., 0.15 Se min. (430FSe)	Free machining modifications of type 430.
431	0.20 C max., 1.00 Mn max., 0.040 P max., 0.030 S max., 1.00 Si max., 15-17 Cr, 1.25-2.50 Ni, balance Fe	Martensitic stainless steel for very high mechanical properties.
440A	0.60-0.75 C, 0.75 Mo max., 1.00 Mn max., 0.040 P max., 0.030 S max., 1.00 Si max., 16-18 Cr, balance Fe	Hardenable to higher hardness than type 320. Cutlery, surgical instruments, etc.
440B	0.75-0.95 C, 0.75 Mo max., 1.00 Mn max., 0.040 P max., 1.00 Si max., 16-18 Cr, balance Fe	Cutlery grade.
440C	0.95-1.20 C, 0.75 Mo max., 1.00 Mn max., 0.040 P max., 0.030 S max., 1.00 Si max., 16-18 Cr, balance Fe	Highest hardness of hardenable stainless steel.
446	0.20 C max., 1.50 Mn max., 0.040 P max., 0.030 S max., 1.00 Si max., 0.25 N max., 23.0-27.0 Cr, balance Fe	High resistance to corrosion and scaling especially where S is involved.

TABLE 16.03
Recently Developed
Stainless Steels and Related Materials

Type	Approximate Composition	Remarks
17-7 PH 17-4 PH	18% Cr, 7% Ni, 1.5% Al 17% Cr, 4% Ni, 4% Cu	Precipitation hardening: quite good in chlorides. High strength and hardness. Difficult to weld, poor corrosion resistance in nitric acid.
202	18% Cr, 5% Ni 10% Mn	Substitute for type 304; low nickel, high manganese. More economical, not quite as corrosion-resistant as types 304/316.
329 3RE60	25% Cr, 5% Ni, 1.5% Mo 18% Cr, 5% Ni, 27% Mo	Duplex alloys, quite resistant to SCC; not as good in nitric acid.
Jessop JS-777	20% Cr, 25% Ni, 5% Mo, 3% Cu	Resistant to pitting corrosion.
Alloy 600 Alloy 800	15% Cr, 8% Fe, balance Ni 21% Cr, 32% Ni, balance Fe	Developed for superior stress chloride cracking resistance and high temperature properties.
Alloy C276	16% Cr, 16% Mo, 5% Fe, 4% W, balance Ni	
Alloy B, (Cabot)	28% Mo, 5% Fe, balance Ni	Immune to SCC, good corrosion in hot phosphate acid and HCl.
Alloy 18-18-2	18% Cr, 18% Ni, 2% Si	Resistance to stress chloride cracking.
E-Brite	26% Cr, 1% Mo	General corrosion resistance, similar to type 316. Good stress corrosion resistance.

TABLE 16.03 (Continued)

	29% Cr, 4% Mo	Good resistance to chloride induced crevice corrosion and stress corrosion.
	29% Cr, 4% Mo, 2% Ni	Similar to above.
Fecralloy	0.001% C-16% Cr 5% Al, 0.5% Y 0.001% C-18% Cr 5% Al-1% Hf-1% Mo	Excellent high temperature oxidation resistance. For coal gasification plant.
444	18% Cr, 2% Mo	Good stress corrosion resistance, general corrosion resistance as for types 304/316.
904L	20% Cr, 1.5% Cu, 4.5% Mo	Good resistance to pitting and crevice corrosion. Better than types 304/316 for stress corrosion. Good resistance to H_2SO_4, H_3PO_4.

The superferrites were developed to show good resistance to stress corrosion cracking in a variety of media. Research goals are to improve their toughness and high temperature strength.

References

1. J. Stodard, M. Faraday, *Phil. Trans. Royal Soc.*, 112 (1822).
2. R. Mallet, *B.A.A.S.*, 7 (1838).
3. L. Guillet, *Rev. de Met.* 1 (1904): p. 156.
4. P. Monnartz, *Metallurgie* 8 (1911): pp. 161-76, 193-201.
5. W.O. Binder, et al., *ASM Trans. Quarterly*, 41 (1949).
6. W.O. Binder, C.M. Brown, *ASM Trans. Quarterly*, 41 (1949): p. 1,301.
7. M.J. Povich, P. Rao, *Corrosion* 34, 8(1978): pp. 269-275.
8. C.S. Tedmon Jr., et al., *J. Electrochem. Soc.*, 118 (1971): p. 192.

17

Failure Analysis

Failure may be said to have occurred when there is an evident performance deficiency. It may vary from such effects as product contamination to a total catastrophe. There may be unscheduled shutdowns with production losses, release of toxic or flammable vapor clouds, or a call for increased maintenance expense and little else. The severity of the problem and the frequency of occurrences caused by the failure will determine an appropriate response.

From one point of view, failure analysis is the logical outcome of a course in corrosion. From another point of view, it merits extended study as a subject in its own right. But, for the young engineer, some guidance may be needed to help determine whether a failure is the result of normal wear and tear of the system or something that needs to be corrected. It is normal for management to be insistent on a prompt return to full production with little prospect of an unpredictable repeated failure; therefore, analysis of a typical failure tends to be hurried and subject to a firm deadline for a return to production. A strategy must be developed to determine the correct longer range response to each significant failure.

Figures 17.01 and 17.02 show two catastrophic failures, taken from a paper by Shank.[1] The former, which shows a Liberty ship which broke in two, has been used in numerous materials science texts, typically with less than an adequate story. This ship was just being fitted out and had not yet been in service; this was the first such incident. During 1942-1952, there were about 250 reports of major cracking. In 19 of these cases the ships broke in two or had sufficiently extensive cracking that they had to be abandoned. Riveted crack arrestors and better control of grain size and steel composition were the remedial measures adopted. This did not stop the cracking, but controlled its consequences. In all, only a few percent of the Liberty ships were seriously affected, with tankers being the most vulnerable. Ships less than 350 ft in length had very few failures.

Figure 17.01 *T-2 tanker that broke in half at dockside.*

Figure 17.02 *Failed gas line, 30 in. diameter, showing sinusoidal nature of fracture. Note longitudinal welded seam, which appears to be intact. This failure occurred while installation was being tested.*

Figure 17.02 shows a spectacular failure of a high pressure natural gas pipeline. Statistics on such failures are not easy to obtain, but failures with crack lengths from 180 to 10,000 ft have been reported. In most cases, these occurred on test, after installation, but prior to actual use. Laboratory determinations of the velocity of crack propagation have ranged from 2,750 to 6,600 ft/s, whereas the gas pressure could only be relieved at the speed of sound — some 1,300 ft/s; thus, the available energy contained in the pipeline steel remained sufficiently high to maintain instability and further propagation of the running crack.

Both classes of failures, though appearing very different, have very similar causes. Crack susceptible steel, particularly associated with welds, is the culprit. Too coarse a grain size in the steel is definitely implicated as is improper welding technique. Remedies are discussed in "Designing to Avoid Brittle Fracture" (page 300).

Failure analysis must determine why a failure occurred; industry is or should be intensely interested in the answer. Failure analysis is a technique by which facts are gathered and studied to determine the cause of failure of a part of an item of equipment. The experience and training of the analyst plays an important part in this study. Much literature is available on this subject, but the ability to research the answer requires an applied science background as well as experience in the field. Failure analysis includes the study of both metallics and nonmetallics.

A number of questions can be asked. Is failure analysis really necessary? Why not just replace an item of equipment each time it fails? Why spend a lot of time and money analyzing failures? The answer to these questions is profit. The basic reason for studying failures is to reduce costs and to have a safer work place, thereby increasing profits.

It is necessary to recognize that flaws are an intrinsic part of real materials and structures. Since imperfect materials must be used, one must learn to live with and appreciate the consequences of flaws. Perfect materials do not exist; this is one reason for safety factors.

Design-Related Failures. One of the most common causes of premature failure is an inadequate design process. The designer may have taken inappropriate shortcuts or may have insufficient background on the subject of failures. When a failure of this nature occurs, it is obvious that it stems from a particular inadequacy. Examples might be too small a radius at a fillet, or failure to require stress relief of a weld, etc.

Material-Related Failures. These include materials that are wrongly specified as well as materials that have inherent mechanical or metallurgical flaws. The use of welded type 304 stainless steel in corrosive service where type 304L should have been specified would be an example.

Fabrication-Related Failures. These stem from imprecise control of fabrication, manufacture, or assembly. An example would be a burned-on strongly cathodic carbonaceous deposit on the inside of a drawn copper alloy tube that had been annealed without first removing all traces of the drawing lubricant. Small items such as failure to remove weld spatters often have led to severe corrosion problems.

Corrosion-Related Failures. Most often these result from an inappropriate combination of materials in galvanic contact that would have given satisfactory service alone. Problems also can result from using materials that have been corroded to some extent before assembly. Failure to recognize that particular forms of corrosion such as fretting or crevice corrosion can occur is also likely to lead to trouble. Sometimes the failure can result from contamination. Both authors recall that as children they received stern parental injunctions to run the cold water tap for at least 20 seconds so that what came out of the lead piping would be fit to drink. The same protocol should be followed for copper pipes soldered with a lead base solder. Similar problems occur when electric kettles are of soldered copper construction.

Negligence-Related Failures. Poor maintenance is the primary item under this heading. It may be a nut that has worked loose, or failure to lubricate a particular point on a machine. Outdoor applications in northern winters are particularly prone to the latter. Poor maintenance can be more dangerous than no maintenance at all because it can lead to a false sense of security.

Failure from Human Error. Even where a material has been correctly specified, the pipefitter or other tradesperson may pick up a wrong material that looks similar to what should have been used. Monel 400 may have been used instead of type 304L stainless steel, or a brass that is subject to dezincification could have been used in place of one that is immune.

Failure from an Act of God. If lightning strikes, or there is an earthquake or a tornado, considerable damage can result. The design has to be able to accommodate stresses from such sources, or at least ensure that damage will be held in check. It should be noted that, for earthquakes, the effects can be quantified for design purposes. Any building design must make allowances for the severity of possible earthquakes that are predictable for the region.

Failure Analysis in a Broader Context

An engineering material usually fails as a result of excessive mechanical load, corrosion, or a combination of the two. There are only three basic ways to solve corrosion problems: (1) Change the material; (2) change the process; or (3) isolate the material from the environment. However, there are many ways to prevent mechanical abuse.

Before proceeding with a discussion of engineering material failures, it is imperative to establish a proper perspective. It is well-established that material failures occur, and the diagnosis of their cause is an essential step in prescribing a remedy. However, the record clearly shows that the number of items out of service because of material deficiencies is minute in comparison with the total amount in use. Furthermore, the experience of innumerable service investigations shows that most failures are caused by improper application or inadequate design, rather than by defective material.

From the outset, two different kinds of materials and corrosion failures must be identified: (1) The failure, which is merely a nuisance; and (2) that which is highly dangerous or excessively costly. The former can be treated quite casually, but the latter calls for a precise strategy. For example, if a high speed turbine is creating unusual noise or vibration, it is most inappropriate to seek the opinion of a committee consisting of the operator, the foreman, the plant manager, etc. to offer wise comments regarding the cause of vibration at the site of the disturbance. Serious injury to personnel can result from this sort of deliberation by technical personnel at a disaster site. Instead, one person who has the proper judgment and authority should come and shut the equipment down. Consideration of the problem may then proceed once the imminent danger has been thwarted. Potentially dangerous failures call for meticulous and regular monitoring of equipment for such warning signs as reduced wall thickness, subcritical cracks caused by corrosion, or untoward vibrations.

Failure investigations range from the simple to the complex in scope. Some may take minutes, and others months of effort. The experience of the investigator and the nature of the failure play a big part in the extent of investigation necessary. The experienced person may diagnose at a glance, from a sample, or from an accurate description of the problem. The neophyte may conduct a full-scale investigation heading in the wrong direction and never find the answer. Full information on the background is important to the proper analysis of material problems. How long the piece lasted has to be compared with how long it should have lasted. If the two correspond and are reasonable, replacement is more or less routine. The question of whether or not there is a better alternative can then be tackled on a nonemergency basis. As mentioned in Chapter 10, periodic replacement of some part at, say, two-year intervals may turn out to be the most economical strategy. Certainly, there is little point in giving further thought to a nuisance failure which calls for replacement at reasonable intervals.

A further phase of failure analysis is the collection and investigation of evidence. An important first step is the selection of representative samples illustrating the problem. It is worth mentioning that samples that have been burned or battered in removal, pickled or modified in a preliminary inspection, or do not illustrate the problem can hardly be called "representative."

Consider an example. There is a pump held down by four bolts, one of which fails by fatigue. This overloads the remaining three, which fail by overload. Correct analysis of the failure is only possible if the initially failed bolt is sent to the laboratory for analysis. It is vital that the item, which was the key to the whole process, comes under scrutiny. Examination of one failed bolt picked at random is not likely to tell the story.

In many cases, failure of small parts in a machine or instrument necessitates shutting down the equipment for repair. Replacement "in kind" often will put the unit back in operation. In this type of failure, the complete failed part can be submitted to the laboratory for study.

Complete failure of large units, or localized corrosion failure within large parts or units, raises questions as to sampling procedures because it is often impractical to send large items to the laboratory. For instance, it would not be practical to send a 5,000 gallon reactor to the failure analysis laboratory for study of a crack near one of its seam welds. A decision is needed on whether to cut out a sample for laboratory study.

The first question which must be answered affirmatively prior to removal of the sample is, "Is it necessary to remove a sample for study?" There are many new instruments and techniques available which make a wide range of field studies possible. The final decision to remove the sample for study should result from one or more of the following reasons: intuitively and/or obviously required; backup for proof, reports, future use, etc.; extenuating circumstances and other underlying causes; litigation; technical or economical justification; preventive maintenance; and safety and accident investigation.

One problem encountered many times is that vital evidence often has been destroyed before the engineer has a chance to examine the failure; corrosion products have been scraped or washed away; fracture surfaces have been picked at or rubbed together.

In many cases, once the engineer has become knowledgeable in the field, determining the cause of failure can be carried out quickly, sometimes with only a cursory glance. This also can be dangerous. For example, an austenitic stainless steel part is cracked and the cause seems obvious — chloride stress cracking from the water side. However, just to be on the safe side, one takes some microsections and finds that the cracks did not originate on the water side, but on the process side, and they are intergranular instead of transgranular. Thus, what looked like a simple problem has now become much more complex.

Some techniques used in failure analysis are discussed in the following sections.

Visual Examination. A keen and experienced observer can gather much information concerning a failure from a careful visual examination. Dimensional changes reflect swelling or thinning. The pattern, extent, or nature of corrosion or cracking is often an important clue to the cause of the trouble (consequently, the examination may be hindered by a sample that is too small). Discoloration or rusting on stainless may signal iron contamination. Heavy tube deposits could be either a cause or effect of overheating. The visual examination will indicate the direction for further work. The investigation should be planned at this stage. Care must be used so that evidence is not altered or destroyed inadvertently. Provision should be made to preserve some of the original sample to provide material for a fresh start if a blind alley is encountered. Sketches and photographs prepared at this time are helpful for later reference in interpreting results.

Microscopic Examination. A wide range of techniques is available for metallurgical examination of corroded parts. The starting point is to take a macrophotograph of the item, normally with a scale included, to give an automatic record of the magnification. Stereophotography techniques also can be helpful as they permit later precision measurements to be taken, should these turn out to be necessary. A standard textbook on photogrammetry should be consulted for details. Examination at higher power normally follows the macroexamination. The optical microscope has been the instrument of choice for this examination, but requires considerable specimen preparation. The scanning electron microscope (SEM), with its much greater depth of field, is now the preferred instrument. It can use samples that require little preparation. The transmission electron microscope (TEM) has a higher magnification range than the scanner, but requires meticulous preparation of replicas. Now the STEM has been introduced and can function both as a transmission or scanning microscope.

Figure 17.03 shows the optical and electron optical arrangements in the light microscope, the TEM, and the SEM. For many applications to failure analysis, SEM is the most versatile.

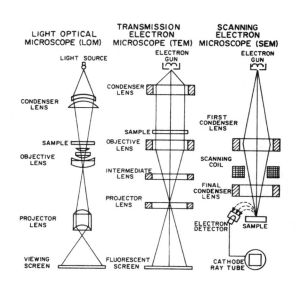

Figure 17.03 Comparison of microscope types.

296

Chemical Analysis. Information on corroding agents is usually obtained by analysis of corrosion deposits, scales, and residues on metal surfaces or fracture faces. For example, the silver nitrate test may be performed on residues clinging to a pitted stainless surface to confirm the presence of chloride ion, a common cause of pitting. Wet chemical methods are often supplemented by x-ray techniques for identification of constituents which, in turn, may identify corrodents.

Mechanical Tests. Fatigue, tensile, or creep rupture tests may be used to determine if strength characteristics were suitable for the service conditions. Hardness tests may be used to check whether correct or uniform heat treatment was applied, or if hardening occurred from overheating, carburization, or phase changes in service. Impact tests indicate brittle tendencies, and so on. But, in many cases, it will be possible only to prepare samples for testing that are smaller than normal ASTM sizes. Results of the tests, e.g., using the Houndsfield Tensometer, will be indicative rather than conclusive.

Fractography. A brief introduction to the science of fractography may be valuable since the fracture topography identifies the mode of failure for the sample under study. It can also relate the observed separation to the type of corrosion. Information concerning various features of fracture surface markings aids in three ways. First, the crack origin can be located, and evidence indicating the cause of failure may be observed. Second, the fracture surface demonstrates a visible record of the stages of crack growth. Third, the distinct fracture zones which are present, as well as their respective sizes, qualitatively indicate the quality of the material as it relates to the application, and they furnish a check on the actual loading conditions in service.

People concerned with investigating corroded parts of machinery or equipment have been handicapped for many years by the limited ability to observe and interpret the topography of fracture and corrosion surfaces. It has long been known that a fracture surface shows the nature of the separation: A fibrous surface structure indicates ductile failure, and a shining crystalline surface indicates brittle failure. It must be remembered, however, that most fractures are heterogenous in appearance and nature. The ductility of a metal has been assessed in this manner since the early days of the development of metallurgy as a science. Although this method would distinguish between ductile or brittle failures (but here again, one must be careful of assumptions), much of the essential information was unobtainable for the lack of sufficient resolution of detail. Standard optical microscopes have been employed to study fracture surfaces, but due to the irregularity of the surface, together with the limited depth of focus, results often were discouraging. No important gains were made in this vital part of failure analysis until the SEM became available with its combination of high resolving power and great depth of focus.

Macro- and microfractography is the science of studying fracture surfaces to obtain information with regard to the mechanics of separation. In this chapter, electron fractography will be emphasized and macroexamination and work with optical microscopes will not be elaborated on further.

The Fracture Process

The fracture process for metals needs to be broken down into two parts. One of these will relate to essentially ductile failures while the other relates to essentially brittle failures. The former case is simpler in concept. Engineering materials in this class only fail due to the action of external factors. Often, corrosion in almost any form reduces the ability of a structure to carry a load. Relation (1) describes the uncorroded condition:

$$S_c < P/A \qquad (1)$$

Where S_c is the critical stress, P is the load, and A is the cross section area.

If S_c exceeds P/A, failure occurs. In cases where corrosion is involved, this could result from reduction of the area available for carrying the load by corrosion. In other cases, the value of S_c could be reduced; e.g., by excessive heat. Where there is brittle failure, on the other hand, a new set of criteria apply. In order to correlate the fractographs to the actual occurrence, it is necessary to have a grounding in the mechanistic aspects of fracture. Fracture mechanics is a subject in its own right that is beyond the scope of this text, but a few of its ideas are needed at this stage. It attempts to provide a quantitative measure of the resistance to unstable crack propagation independent of the size and shape of the crack, the geometry of the cracked part, and the manner in which external and residual loads are applied.

Fracture mechanics implies that an unstable fracture occurs when K, a stress intensity factor describing the elastic stress at the crack tip, reaches a critical value K_c, known as the fracture toughness at a particular value of K. The quantitative factor, K_c, that results from linear elastic fracture mechanics, is a characteristic of the material as are its tensile and yield strengths. As a crack or flaw grows, the energy expended is controlled by the material hardness and geometry, which, in turn, control the degree of localized plastic deformation at the tip of the crack.

This means that during plastic deformation of stronger alloys the tip of the crack becomes more localized, resulting in a reduction of the energy expended. This causes a reduction in the K_c and in the flaw size that can be tolerated. Griffith's original work was mainly done on glass.[2] For brittle materials, he gave the key equation of fracture mechanics as:

$$\sigma = \sqrt{\frac{2E\gamma}{\pi a}}$$

Where: σ = fracture stress
a = ½crack length
γ = surface energy

For metals, the formula needs to be changed somewhat. The value of G_c for steels is typically at least 1,000 γ, showing that much larger cracks can be tolerated.

$$\sigma = \sqrt{\frac{EG_c}{\pi a}}$$

G_c = surface energy absorbed in plastic deformation per unit area of crack extension, or "critical strain energy release rate." Fracture mechanics uses this basic formula or its equivalent expressed as K_c, the "fracture toughness."

$$\sigma = \frac{K_c}{\sqrt{\pi a}}$$

where $K_c^2 = EG_c$

One must remember that K_c and G_c will reduce to small values as the thickness of the plate increases.

This points out the condition of instability which depends on crack size and energy absorption.

Fracture in polymeric materials also involves some unusual features. Polymers often will undergo substantial creep, as can be quantified in the Larson-Miller treatment, prior to embrittlement. In this respect, they are similar to metals in the secondary and tertiary stages of creep, which would usually involve a relatively high temperature.

Designing to Avoid Brittle Fracture

The factors which lead to an increased risk of brittle fracture need to be identified so they can be avoided. Metallurgical factors would include coarse grain size, lack of proper annealing, and presence of interstitial impurities. The design must take into account environmental factors that might lead to brittle behavior as well as considering the design per se.

Environmental effects th-at could lead to brittleness include low service temperature; exposure to hydrogen, including particularly corrosion product hydrogen; and exposure to liquid metals. Design factors that could have bad effects include tensile stresses, particularly if enhanced by notches, or welding imperfections, including cracks. Anything that could restrict ductility, multiaxial stresses and three dimensional continuity should be avoided, including thickness and welding geometry. A high rate of stress application and an increasing rate of stress application both increase the risk of brittle behavior. On the positive side, riveted or bolted seams can act as crack arrestors.

Fracture Morphology

The morphology of the fractured surface often gives clues which enable the fracture process to be identified. At this stage, the features which help to characterize the various modes of fracture need to be considered. Ductile failures proceed by way of microvoid formation followed by coalescence of these microvoids under the influence of stress. Figure 17.04 shows a schematic diagram of the three most commonly encountered modes of failure: tension, shear, and tensile

300

tear. In each case, there is microvoid coalescence prior to the final failure. This gives rise to equiaxed dimples in tension, and elongated dimples in the other two cases. However, note that the elongated dimples are oriented contrary to each other on the mating fracture faces for shear. For tensile tear, however, the elongated dimples are oriented in the same direction on each fracture face.

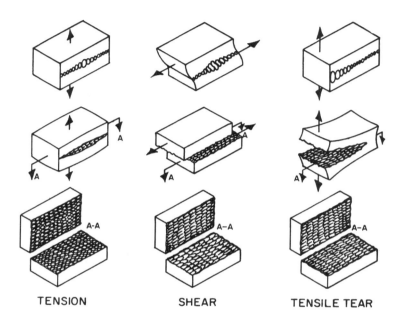

TENSION   SHEAR   TENSILE TEAR

Figure 17.04 Schematic of failure modes.

Figure 17.05 shows a tensile test bar that was plastically deformed then cross sectioned. Growth and coalescence of the voids is clearly visible; dimple formation is the result of the coalescence. Since the load is perpendicular to the viewing surface, the voids will merely coalesce and separate, and the eventual fracture surface will show equiaxed dimples.

Figures 17.06 and 17.07 show TEM recordings of the eventual fracture faces in a tensile test bar, showing cup (tension-overload) and cone (shear) failure areas. Note equiaxed dimples in the former and elongated dimples in the latter.

Figure 17.05
Cross section of plasti-
cally deformed tensile
tensile test bar showing
microvoid coalescence.

Figure 17.06
TEM of tensile test
bar failure face
(cup) showing
equiaxed dimples.

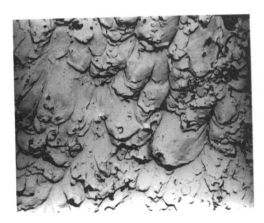

Figure 17.07
TEM of tensile test bar
failure face (cone)
showing elongated
dimples.

302

On the other hand, brittle fractures do not show dimples. Cleavage or transgranular failures are particularly featureless and have an icy appearance (Figure 17.08). Fatigue failures are, in fact, a type of cleavage fracture in which the crack front progresses in stages with each cycle of load. Figure 17.09 shows a fatigue failure as exposed by the fracture surface of a failed titanium valve. The main feature of the striations in failure of this type is that each striation represents a cycle of the load and the fracture progresses normally to the applied stress.

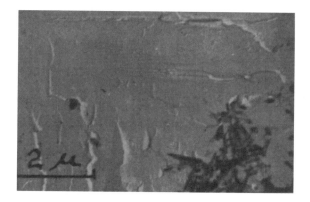

Figure 17.08 *TEM of transgranular fracture showing ice-like fracture face when fractured at -50°C.*

Figure 17.09 *TEM of fatigue fracture surface of failed titanium valve.*

In most types of fracture, the general plane of fracture is perpendicular to the maximum principal tensile stress. These types include cleavage and other brittle fractures, ductile fractures (also called microvoid coalescence and dimpled rupture), fractures under plane strain conditions (in thick sections), fatigue fractures (at least in the intermediate stages), and stress corrosion cracks.

Other types of fractures propagate along planes of maximum shear stress. These types include ductile fractures under plane stress (that is, in thin sections or near free surfaces), shear fractures, and the intermediate stages in some torsional fatigue fractures.

It is also possible to glean information from the crack itself. A fast running crack in a sheet or plate will branch frequently as it propagates, but it will almost never join another crack to continue as a single crack. Second, if a running crack joins a preexisting fracture, it will usually meet it at approximately a 90° angle, not at a shallow angle. Third, it is almost impossible for an intersecting crack to cross and propagate beyond a preexisting fracture. These considerations lead to the following useful guidelines concerning crack origins (Figure 17.10): (1) The direction of the crack origin is always opposite to that of the crack branching; and (2) if crack B meets crack A at about a 90° angle, then B occurred later and the origin should not be sought in it, but in crack A. This is known as the T junction method of crack origin location.

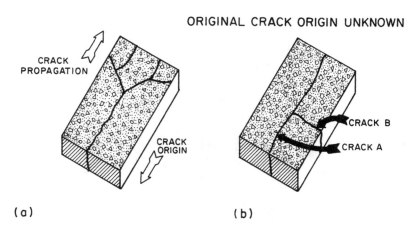

(a)   (b)

Figure 17.10   *Information conveyed by crack configuration: (a) branching cracks; and (b) T junction cracks.*

The initial section to fracture transfers its original load to adjoining sections, and in all probability it overstresses them. In ductile material, these overstressed sections will show considerable deformation so another means of tracing the origin is to look for the zone of least deformation.

Now let us consider the difference between intergranular and transgranular fracture paths. Transgranular crack propagation through the grains of the metal leaves a relatively flat and featureless fracture face, as shown in Figure 17.08. This is typical high speed and/or low temperature cleavage fracture.

On the other hand, intergranular fracture shows distinct grain boundary surfaces resulting in a "rock candy" structure. An example is shown in Figure 17.11. Fractures of this type expose some inherent or developed grain boundary weakness. Such weakness may develop from the presence of extensive grain boundary precipitates, such as FeS inclusions in steel, or from a reaction between the grain boundaries and the environment, as in SCC of high strength steels or of hard drawn brasses. On occasion, there will be some minor amount of a divided fracture, along with the predominantly intercrystalline failure.

Figure 17.11 TEM *of intergranular (rock candy) structure.*

An interesting case of intergranular corrosion is shown in Figure 17.12. In this case, a Monel 400 heat exchanger was being fabricated, and the tubes were filled with a low melting alloy during the bending operation. After welding, however, cracking was detected presumably because the low melting alloy had been incompletely removed.

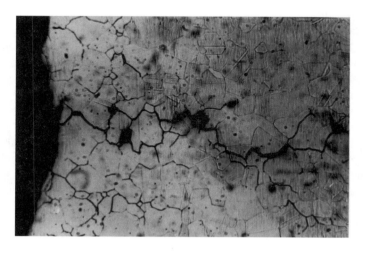

Figure 17.12   *Intergranular corrosion of Monel 400 by liquid metal.*

Failure of polymeric materials is a potentially important field where there is much work to be done. Many polymers or polymer combinations are very resistant to a wide range of chemical reagents. But stress, by itself and especially in combination with a vapor that can cause the polymer to swell, can be destructive. The combination resembles stress corrosion cracking. UV light or oxygen or a combination of the two also can cause continuing polymerization and eventual embrittlement.

This presentation of the interpretation of fracture analysis is necessarily oversimplified. One must bear in mind, however, that fractures are heterogeneous, and dimple, intergranular, and cleavage rupture could all be observed on one fracture face. Thus, the fracture surface must be examined on a statistical basis and a predominance established. For example, this multiface fracture would occur even on a sample tensile test specimen. The familiar tensile cup-cone fracture represents a dual fracture mode; the usual 45° angle cone failed by shear while the bottom of the cup failed by tensile overload.

Since the surfaces are to be examined at high magnification, care must be taken to preserve fracture faces. Handling fracture faces with fingers, rubbing, mating fracture faces, or picking at the fracture with a sharp instrument can cause serious damage or produce artifacts. Rough treatment or further corrosion will obscure or destroy vital information. Laboratory-prepared samples usually are in excellent condition, whereas service fractures often are in poor condition.

By observation of the latter, often only the most general conclusions can be made regarding the mode of failure. In many cases, these failure analysis techniques may be sufficient to pinpoint the cause; if not, a literature search, consultation, or even hunches may have to be used.

The final phase of failure analysis is the interpretation of the evidence to determine the cause of failure and recommend remedial measures. Most failures are explainable on the basis of concrete evidence, rather than such things as minor composition variations, hazy intangibles, or new hypotheses of materials behavior.

The responsible investigator cannot reach a certain conclusion on the basis of uncertain evidence or information. Full background information greatly aids the investigators in arriving at firm conclusions that otherwise are "hedged" against a complete background history and representative samples, and service failures can consistently be analyzed successfully.

Corrective Strategies

If human error has led to corrosion or other failures, steps must be taken to prevent recurrences. Education of personnel is an important option. The need for correct labelling of all materials in stores and a firm ban on material substitution without authorization are two examples. Time should be taken to inform technical staff of the errors that led to past failures.

In many cases, the effective solution is to limit the range of materials that may be brought to a site. For example, a chemical plant may insist that since type 304L stainless is vital in some operations no type 304 stainless will be purchased or stocked. Another example is that a marine or naval store may stock only arsenic-inhibited brasses or bronzes so that any yellow metal will be reliable for seawater use.

Once an inappropriate failure has been identified, three kinds of action are required. First, there has to be a stopgap action to restore the function of the affected item. Second, there has to be an interaction with the design office to identify necessary changes in material, design, and manufacture, or to prescribe process limitations. Third, there has to be predictive action so future problems can be identified and anticipated prior to a repetition of total failure. Maintenance of adequate records is essential.

This brief chapter is intended merely to serve as an introduction to the challenging subject of failure analysis. The interested reader is directed to the *ASM Metals Handbook*, 8th Edition, Vols. 9 and 10 (1975). This handbook covers the subject in considerable detail. One more item is of great importance — the engineer who is studying the failure must see the physical evidence promptly to establish legal liability. Clues that were initially present at the site may soon be lost, and detail on fracture surfaces tends to get blurred after storage for months or years in the dank vaults of provincial courthouses.

References

1. M.E. Shank, "Brittle Failure of Steel Structures – A Brief History," *Metal Progress* 61, 9(1954): p. 83.
2. A.A. Griffith, *Phil. Trans. Roy. Soc.* 221A, (1920), 163. Tetelman, K. McEvely in *Fracture*, V. 6 (New York, NY: Academic Press, 1969).

Recommended Reading

1. D.C. Drucker, ibid V.1.
2. G.E. Inglis, *Trans. Inst. Naval Architects*, 55 (1913): p. 219.
3. E. Wessel, *Short Course in Fracture Mechanics* (Bethlehem, PA: Lehigh University, 1970).
4. P.C. Paris, G.C. Sih, "Fracture Toughness and its Applications," ASTM STP 381 (Philadelphia, PA: ASTM, 1965).
5. W.S. Pellini, *Criteria for Fracture Control Plans* (Washington, DC: Naval Res. Lab., 1972).
6. E.P. Polushkin, *Defects and Failure of Metals* (New York, NY: Elsevier, 1956).
7. H. Thielsch, *Defects and Failures in Pressure Vessels* (New York, NY: Reinhold, 1965).

8. R.D. Barer, B.F. Peters, *Why Metals Fail* (New York, NY: Gordon and Breach, 1970).
9. D. Broek, "Failure Analysis and Fracture Mechanics," *Metals Handbook,* 9th ed., Vol. 3 (Metals Park, OH: ASM, 1986), p. 47.
10. H.L. Ewalds, R.J.H. Wanhill, *Fracture Mechanics* (London, UK: Arnold, 1984).
11. H. Van Droffelaar, R.S. Charlton, *Canadian Chemical Processing* 12 (1967), 1 (1968).
12. G.E. Inglis, *Trans. Inst. Naval Architects* 55 (1913): p. 219.

18

Use of the Computer in the Practice of Corrosion

The Corrosion Data Survey furnishes an excellent example of a collection of data, originally in book form, now available on a floppy disc that can be accessed by any compatible personal computer.[1] One advantage of this method of data presentation is that it becomes possible to reproduce the actual tables of data from each original reference rather than compress the data onto a small graph. In many cases, footnotes contribute to the overall usefulness of the data. In a book, the furnishing of such detail would have caused both the size and cost to escalate.

The next stage of complexity is to combine a large computerized data bank with a program that allows particular calculations to proceed from that data to prepare selections of derived data, charts, etc. The most obvious application to corrosion would be the preparation of Pourbaix diagrams from basic thermodynamic data. The FACT program discussed in chapter 2 is one example. Such programs allow the extrapolation of the calculations to 200 to 250°C (392 to 482°F), and allow the determination of Pourbaix diagrams for alloy systems and for reaction with multicomponent solutions or solutions containing particular contaminants. This allows the calculation of data beyond the range in which actual experiments have been performed. The usefulness of this data depends upon the adequacy of the calculations and extrapolations.

Mathematical modelling is the next step. Unfortunately, there are many areas of corrosion where suitable rigorous models do not exist. But in those cases where there is a model, the technique is useful. Models are in place for: crevice corrosion, active and passive behavior of stainless steel, and the distribution of attack under cathodic protection or galvanic attack.[2]

The usefulness of the mathematical model is determined by its ability to make accurate predictions. In practice this means that the model will be restricted to a rather narrow range of applicability. And it will, in the corrosion field, be restricted to those few areas in which the whole corrosion story can be told by a particular equation or set of equations.

A number of such models have been developed in recent years, covering active-passive behavior of stainless steel,[3-5] crevice corrosion[6] and the distribution of attack from galvanic corrosion along with the residual attack under cathodic protection.[7] Models of this nature are both powerful and critical of the theories on which they are based. It is common for them to expose the need for much more experimentation than would originally have been predicted. But, once this has been done, it is usually possible to refine the theory and fine tune the model.

So far, the use of computers has been restricted to more or less familiar paths, making use of the virtually limitless capacity to store data, and the ability to perform calculations at very high speed. But, there is a further goal. Why not create some sort of a working model of the way in which human thought processes work, and use the computer as an aid in the decision-making process? In the first place, it could clarify the bases of decisions, and in the second place, it could simulate the human brain and actually indicate the decision to be made.

Such systems are termed "expert systems" and have the objective of allowing the computer to perform more like human beings, at least in limited ways. Those readers who want to understand the process more fully will have to consult a specialized text. Turban's text is probably the most helpful contemporary publication.[8]

Decision Tree Method

The decision tree approach can be regarded as an intermediate stage between an information bank and a true expert system. In this approach the information and advice are contained on discrete "pages" linked in a decision tree arrangement. This is multidimensional, and the pages are linked in such a way that they guide the user toward the solution of a problem. The user chooses which path to follow through the tree structure. This approach can handle more complex situations than can be handled by documents.

This approach has many advantages. An effective tree can be constructed with less effort than required for the alternatives, and it is easy to incorporate optional explanations and background, thus taking on some of the features of an expert system. But, despite this, it is not a true expert system.

One weakness is that, if a wrong choice is made at a node, it may lead the user in an inappropriate direction. The tree structure is more useful when the user is starting with a moderate background than with none at all.

Expert Systems

The computer strategies that have been outlined so far are applicable to very specific cases and can lead to an answer only if the system falls within these narrow constraints. The search for a more generally applicable tool has led to the development of the so-called expert system. This attempts to duplicate the modus operandi of a corrosion expert by distilling the expert's reasoning processes into a set of rules which can be applied by the computer.

Correctness and applicability are both required of these rules. Any shortcomings in the rules will negate the usefulness of the expert system. But, it is not necessary for the rules to be 100% certain. The concept of "fuzzy logic" allows for a statement qualified by a particular degree of certainty. And, answers based on this kind of input will, following the prescribed rules, assign a certainty factor or rank to the derived information. Along with this can be a list of limitations and pitfalls relevant to the particular situation.

The expert system can thus supply a good deal of useful information to a lay person in corrosion. This information could well be a short list of potentially suitable materials for an item of a chemical plant, for example. These would all be ranked and supplied with a list of particular dos and don'ts. This would furnish a rational basis for material selection or for a short list of materials to undergo specific testing. The advantage of the expert system would be that all materials in its data bank would have been evaluated, and their potential shortcomings would have been exposed. This would allow an efficient test program to be drawn up, assuming that the total cost picture would justify the testing. If testing were to be foregone, there would be data to help provide a decision on the proper interval for continuing in-service monitoring of the equipment.

In this particular example, the expert system could only begin to be useful if the designer recognized the need for advice and knew of its availability. The output might still lead the designer to a human expert for a final answer.

The human expert could probably get to the answer more quickly by themselves, at least initially, because of the ability to sort out what was important and concentrate on that. However, the use of the expert system as a teaching tool should not be underestimated. After a number of uses of the expert system, some of it would rub off on the designer and help make the process more efficient. But an expert system would always be helpful for a beginning designer or for a designer moving into new territory.

Interestingly, it has been found by investigators at the NACE-NIST Corrosion Data Center at Gaithersburg, Md. that the name "expert system" has a connotation for some potential users that it is intended for experts and not for those who need information.[9] They prefer to go out to the public with a title such as "Materials Selection Advisor Systems."

Expert Systems and Artificial Intelligence

There are three main variants of expert systems. They can be based primarily on rules, facts, and examples. Those that are based on rules are, potentially, the most versatile and might eventually have the widest applicability. We need to find out more about how these rule based systems are constructed, and how they work.

There are two main elements that we should be aware of. In the development environment the expert system builder introduces expert knowledge into the expert system environment. Once this has been done, there is the consultation environment in which the non expert extracts expert knowledge and advice.

According to Turban, the expert system should comprise the following components: knowledge acquisition, knowledge base, inference engine, work place, reasoning capability improvement, user interface, explanation facility, and knowledge refining system.[8] The inference engine is, in effect, the brain of the expert system. Its major elements are a rule interpreter, a scheduler (which estimates the effects of different rules), and a consistency enforcer. The knowledge refining program is not yet available in commercial expert systems, but is a current research target. At the moment, most improvement in expert systems comes about as a result of interaction between the end user and the developer of the system, often on a more or less ad hoc

314

basis.

Building an expert system from scratch is a time-consuming and costly operation. It is more practical to start with a "shell," which is an expert system that has been stripped of its expert knowledge. What is left is an inference engine and a rule set manager. The inference engine can reason with rule sets that are built with the manager. The nature of the particular shell that is selected will, of course, have a profound effect on the expert system that is eventually developed. The strengths and weaknesses of particular shells in particular fields need to be carefully considered.

Rule-based systems employ "If-Then" statements. The "If" part of the statement must determine whether the rule is true or applicable by examining sets of conditions. The "Then" response is the set of actions that follows if the rule is true. Other rules also may be scanned as part of the consistency enforcing process. More advanced systems also have a further open alternative, "Else." This can take care of, for example, sensor malfunction causing an inconsistent set of input data.

The sets of rules can be combined in two ways — forward chaining and backward chaining. The choice is set by the particular shell that was selected in the first place. The forward chaining mode starts with a particular premise and finds the solution by examining all relevant rules and information. A backward chaining system, on the other hand, poses a hypothetical solution to the problem, and then goes through the rules to confirm that the solution is valid and logical. Backward chaining becomes more appropriate as the system becomes increasingly more complex.

The Expert System in Practice

A family of expert systems are currently under development for materials selection in the chemical process industry at the NACE-NIST Corrosion Data Center.[9] An expert system, developed to assist engineers with corrosion problems has recently been published.[10] An interesting feature is that this Canadian system is bilingual and can be used in either English or French. Extension of this sort of program to other languages would be more or less routine.

A paper by Loushin describes an application of an expert system within an oil refinery.[11] There had been a serious array of corrosion problems in the crude unit. The crude unit overhead system appeared to be the principal source of trouble. Excessive chloride concentrations in the overhead accumulator water appeared to trigger excessive pH excursions. The desalter efficiency stayed too low because of equipment reliability problems and because of larger-than-designed variations in crude oil feedstocks. Attempts to correct the pH with additions of caustic were frustrated by fouling and coking problems.

The initial attempts to control the problems were certainly not wrong, but were based on an over simplistic view of the total set of problems. It transpired that there were 88 factors in the corrosion problems of the crude unit. It was found possible to simplify the approach to the problem by determining the effect of each of these on six different areas of activity. They are:

1. Process system modifications;
2. Engineering technology;
3. Tank farm operating practices;
4. Desalter operating practices;
5. Crude unit operating practices; and
6. Operating practice guidelines and recommendations.

The original conditions were that the chloride content of the crude unit overhead accumulator water, targeted at 20 ppm, was between 100 and 400 most of the time with one excursion above 1,000 and another below 20 in a one-year period. The target range of 5.7 to 6.2 pH was only achieved for half of the total time, being lower the rest of the time, and the corrosion rate indicated by resistance probes also was over the intended 5 mpy half the time.

The primary operational parameter selected was the pH of the overhead accumulator water, partly because of the ease and speed with which it could be measured. A rule-based expert system with forward chaining was selected and put into place. The control system was modified from a basic reset control, recognizing the potential disturbances that could result from over compensation. The degree of response was modified so that a severe problem would be met with a higher specific corrective action and a minor problem would elicit a lower specific correction. In this way it was hoped to approach the ideal of proportional control reasonably closely.

The use of an expert system to control a process has some advantages over a less sophisticated control procedure. One of these is that if a data item is missing for any reason, a strategy can be formulated to take care of the omission. The simplest of these is to insert the unchanged data from the previous reading of that variable. Also, if there are apparent inconsistencies in a number of inputs, the probable causes can be determined and displayed.

The effect of the control system has been extremely good. The chloride content of the crude unit overhead accumulator water has decreased by a factor of 4 in both the maximum and long term average readings. There was an increased production of 200,000 barrels in the first year, along with an increased ability to tolerate a wide range of feedstocks so that feedstock control ceased to be a concern. There was an initial gain in value-added production of 40% in the first year with indications that 75% would be achieved in the second.

Another expert system in the corrosion field has been reported by Hines and Basden.[12] The AUSCOR system relates to the corrosion of 28 alloys, including the common ferritic and austenitic stainless steels as well as some of the more recently developed ferritic, austenitic or duplex stainlesses as well as higher nickel alloys up to Hastelloy C276 [UNS N10276]. It will accommodate a wide range of liquid corrodents—acids, alkalis, waters, and brines — at temperatures up to 300°C (572°F). It predicts the probability that the alloy will be passive, active or transpassive. It also predicts probabilities that there will be localized corrosion (pitting, under deposit corrosion, or crevice corrosion) or that stress corrosion cracking will occur.

The conclusions are displayed at various levels of detail, including the sensitivity of the main conclusions to changes in the environmental conditions. The user can elect to make successive changes in the environmental factors and make an appropriate number of such loops to gain a better understanding of the behavior to be expected of the alloy of interest.

Another general characteristic of expert systems is evident in this example. While a great number of polarization curves were available and could be used to define conditions at both anode and cathode, there had been no need to combine the data into suitable normalized form. Figure 18.01 shows such a plot for the pitting potential and its response to a normalized halide concentration.

The normalized halide concentration allows for any combination of bromides and iodides; their concentrations need to be converted into an effective chloride concentration. When this was done the 250 or so measurements representing the whole range of alloys studied fell within a scatter band around two straight lines when the ratio of the

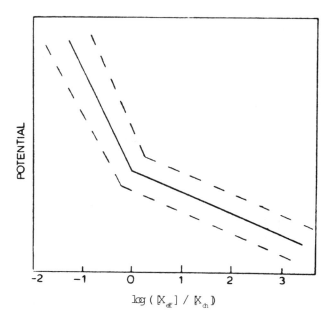

POTENTIAL

$\log ([X_{eff}] / [X_{ch}])$

Figure 18.01   *Normalized relation between pitting potential and halide concentration: 95% of some 250 values for a variety of alloys lie between broken lines, which represent notional confidence limits; [X_{eff}] = effective halide concentration: [X_{ch}] = characteristic halide concentration.*

effective halide concentration to the characteristic halide concentration was unity. Similar results were found for both repassivation and crevice potentials, but they intersected at lower halide concentrations.

This procedure identifies a characteristic effective halide concentration. The author of the paper offers no theoretical justification for this. The process, which was followed in the first place to facilitate computer calculations, may be opening a window on some potentially useful new theory. But it seems clear that the exercise of developing a new expert system will force its instigator into either constructing new theory or performing new experiments in a way that has been suggested by how the expert system itself is developing. Perhaps, in this sense at least, we will see expert systems as an emergent and significant experimental tool.

318

References

1. N.E. Hamner, ed., *NACE Corrosion Data Survey* (Houston, TX: NACE, 1974).
2. J.G. Hines, "Corrosion Information and Computers," *Brit. Corros. J.* 21, 2(1986): p. 81.
3. C. Edeleanu, J.G. Hines, Proc. 8th Int. Cong. on Metallic Corrosion, held September 1981 (Mainz, Germany: DECHEMA, V.2 1899).
4. C. Edeleanu, *Brit. Corros. J.* 18, 1(1983): p. 6.
5. J.G. Hines, *Brit. Corros. J.* 18, 1(1983): p. 10.
6. J.W. Oldfield, *Brit. Corros. J.* 13, 1(1978): p. 13.
7. D.J. Astley, J.N. Rowlands, *Brit. Corros. J.* 20, 2(1985): p. 90.
8. E. Turban, *Decision Support and Expert Systems* (New York, NY: MacMillan, 1988).
9. C.P Sturrock, W.I. Pollock, *Materials Protection* 28, 11(1989): p. 58.
10. J.J. Lamoureux, J.J. Hechler, CORROSION/89, paper no. 593. Houston, TX: NACE, 1989.
11. L.L. Loushin, *Materials Performance* 27, 6(1988): p. 77.
12. J.G. Hines, A. Basden, *Brit. Corros. J.* 21, 3(1986): p. 151.

Index

Auto ignition, 246
Automobiles. *See also* Tires
  cathodic protection of, 110
  chromium plating, 134-135
  cooling system, 61
  corrosion cost, 160, 161
  corrosion testing, 168
  design details, 146-147
  painting of, 132-133

B

Bacterial corrosion, 99-101
Bearings, fretting of, 92
Benzoates, 60
Biocides, 99
Biological attack. *See* Microbiological corrosion
Blast furnace stove, explosion of, 162
Boilers. *See also* Nuclear reactors
  caustic embrittlement of, 90, 117
  code. *See* ASME Code
  explosions, 117
  leaks in, 119-120
  magnetite formation, 48
  nuclear, 119, 120
  oil-fired, superheater tubes in, 79
  pitting of, 57
  scaling in, 251
  water control, 30, 53
  water treatment, 117-120
Breakaway oxides, 74-78
Bridges, 162-164
Brittle coating test method, 189
Bumpers, coating of, 135
Butler-Volmer equation, 7, 8-10, 12, 175

C

CANDU nuclear reactor, 78-79
Capital cost factor, 152
Carbon, effect on stainless steels, 264, 265, 267, 268, 281
Carbon steels, 39, 43-44, 154, 157-158, 220-222
Carburization, of austenitic stainless steel, 280
Cast irons
  gray, 43, 219-220
  high-silicon, 220
  malleable, 220
  nickel, 220
  nodular, 220
  white, 219
Cathodes, impressed current, 63-64
Cathodic current, 6
Cathodic protection. *See also* Anodic protection
  and bacterial corrosion, 101
  of boats and ships, 24, 98, 105-106
  and corrosion fatigue, 84
  cost of, 108
  and electrostatics, 112-114
  of pipelines, 106-110
  principles of, 106
  of reinforcing steel, 110-111, 163-164
  system design, 111-112
  of underground structures, 107-110
Cathodic reactions, 5-6, 67-68
Caustic embrittlement, 86, 90
Cavitation corrosion, 97-98
Cavitation erosion, 97-98, 252
Cementite, 39
Certification, of NDE operators,

worksheets, 153-156
Cracks. *See* Fracture
Crack configuration, 304
Creep, of plastics, 231-233
Crevice corrosion, 33, 281
Cubic equation, 52
Crystals, 37-39, 42

D

Daniell cell, 1, 3, 23
Decision tree method, 312-313
Dehumidification, 121-122
Deicing salts, 49, 50, 102, 111,
  162-164, 168
Delta ferrite, in austenitic stain
  less steels, 280
Deposit corrosion, 33
Depreciation, 152
Design
  of cathodic protection
    systems, 111-112
  considerations, 247-252
  for corrosion control, 141-
    148
Design safety, 87, 90-91, 209
Detecting corrosion, 179-193
Dezincification, 43, 223
Differential aeration cells, 108
Differential expansion, 244
Differential stress, in austenitic
  stainless steels, 280
Differential velocities, 252
Diffusion, 39
Disasters, corrosion-related, 162.
  See also Failures
Dissimilar metals, joining of, 142,
  143, 145, 146
Drainage (as design detail), 142,
  143, 144
Dry fatigue, 84
Ductility, of steels, 221

E

Economics of corrosion, 149-164,
  255. *See also* Costs
Eddy-current testing, 186-187
Efficiency of operation, and
  material selection, 253-254
EIS. *See* Electrical impedance
  spectroscopy
Electrical impedance spectroscopy,
  176
Electrochemical tests, 174-178
Electrochemistry
  of corrosion cells, 23-36
  general background, 1-22
Electrode potential, 1
Electrode processes, 6-8
Electrodeposited coatings, 134-136
Electrodeposition, of paint, 130
Electrodes, reference. *See* Refer-
  ence electrodes
Electromotive force, 12
Electromotive series, 1, 2, 27, 270
Electron holes, 70
Electrostatics, and cathodic
  protection, 112-114
End-face attack, 44, 147, 281
Energy consumption, 160
Energy conversion, 68
Entry into confined space, 210-212
Environmental effects, 254-255
Equilibrium processes, 6-11
Erosion, 95-98, 252
Eutectics in oxide, 79
Evans diagrams, 24
Exchange current, 6, 7, 8, 13-15
Expansion joints, 244
Expert systems, 312, 313-318
Explosion bonding, 137

Hot air welding, of plastic pipe, 233
Hot dipping, 134
Hot water systems, 25-26, 61, 116-117
Housekeeping, 208
Huey test, 86, 169, 172-173
Humidity control, 121-122
Hydrazine, 60, 119
Hydrogen damage, 93-95, 109
Hydrogen overpotential, 13-15
Hydrostatic testing, 190

I

IBI. *See* Interval between incidents
IHI. *See* Individual hazard index
Impingement, 252
Inclusions, 39
Incoloy, heat exchanger, 156, 157-158
Individual hazard index, 203-205
Industrial atmospheres, 50, 166-167
Inflation, 150
Information management, 191
Inhibition and inhibitors, 53, 54, 57-62, 84, 114, 234, 250
Inorganic coatings, 137-139
Inspection, 147-148, 179-182. *See also* Nondestructive evaluation
Inspection nozzles, 147-148
Inspectors, 180-181
Insulation, of plumbing systems, 25-26
Interest rate, 150-151, 159
Interface, wetted. *See* Wetted interface
Intergranular corrosion, 86-87

of austenitic stainless steel, 273-279
of Monel 400 by liquid metal, 306
Interval between incidents, 203, 216
In place metallography, 188
Inverse logarithmic equation, 52
Iron
cast. *See* Cast irons
oxides, 72, 79
Pourbaix diagram, 29-30
Isotopes, 183, 184

J-L

Joining, of plastics, 233
Kevlar, 236
Knifeline attack, 276-277, 278,
Laboratory safety, 206-209
Laboratory tests, 172-174
Lacquers, 130
Langelier Index, 114
Larson-Miller parameter, and plastics, 232
Lattice parameter, 47
Lead and lead alloys, 226-227
Leak detection, 185, 190
Legault-Preban treatment, 51, 167
Limiting current density, 12-13
Linear polarization, 10, 113, 174-175
Liquid metal attack, in austenitic stainless steels, 281
Liquid metal corrosion, 80-81
Liquid oxides, 79-80
Liquid penetrant testing, 187-188
Liquid spills, 245-246

O

Oil well inhibitors, 62
Organic coatings, 128-137
Overpotential, 8, 11. *See also*
    Hydrogen overpotential
Overvoltage, 8, 10
Oxidation
    of alloys, 72-73
    and high-temperature corro-
        sion, 67-82
    of metals, 69-71
    of polymeric materials, 234-
        235
Oxides. *See also* Films
    breakaway, 74-78
    classes of, 70
    liquid, 79-80
    volatile, 79
Oxygen, solubility in water, 115
Oxygen concentration cells, 5-6,
    33

P

Packaging, 121
Paints and painting
    adhesion, 125-127
    application, 130
    automobiles, 132-133
    failure, 125
    maintenance contracts, 132
    pigments, 128, 130, 131
    primers, 127-128, 131, 133
    selection, 131
    surface preparation, 125-128
    and weathering steels, 51
Parabolic equation, 52, 72
Passivity, 54-57, 63-64
Patination, 49-50
Pearlite, 39, 41, 44

Penetrants. *See* Liquid penetrant
    testing
Permeation, and material select-
    ion, 253
Phase diagrams, 39, 41
    aluminum-copper, 40
    iron carbide, 40
    of iron alloys, 264
PHI. *See* Process hazard index
Photoelastic test methods, 189
Pickling restrainers (inhibitors),
    58, 62
Pigments, 128, 130, 131
Pipe to soil potential, 108
Pipelines
    cathodic protection of, 106,
        107-110
    erosion of, 95
    and oxygen concentration
        cells, 33
Pitting, 33-35, 42, 165
    and corrosion testing, 171
    in stainless steels, 57, 99, 281
    and stress corrosion cracking,
        86-87
Plant inspection, 179-182, 209-
    210
Plastics. *See also* Fiberglass
reinforced plastics; Polymers
    joining of, 233
    mechanical properties, 229-
        233
    types of, 228
Plasticizers, 128, 130, 235
Poison pads, 281
    Polarization, 8-12. *See also*
        Linear polarization; Resis-
        tance polarization
        diagrams, 23-24
Polymers. *See also* Plastics
    deterioration of, 54, 102-103,
        234-237

failure of, 306
Pourbaix diagrams
  computer-generated, 31-32,
  311
  higher-temperature, 31-32
  for various metals, 27-31
  for water, 20
  for zinc in water, 21-22
Precious metals, 73, 227
Precipitation hardening, 41, 241
Pressure, 244-246
Pressure tubes, in nuclear reactors,
  78-79
Pressure vessels
  ASME Code, 195-197, 248
  corrosion allowance, 248-249
  fiber-reinforced plastic, 103,
  237
  quality assurance, 197-200
Primers, 127-128, 131, 133
Process hazard index, 203-205, 216
Process industries, materials
  selection for, 167-168
Process risk calculation, 216
Propellers, erosion of, 98
Protection. *See* Anodic protection;
Cathodic protection
Protective coatings
  anodizing, 138-139
  breakaway oxides, 74-78
  chemical conversion, 139
  films, 47-48
  inorganic, 137-139
  metallic, 133-137
  organic, 128-130
  paints. *See* Paints and painting
Purchase specifications, 201-202
Pure metals, 42
Purity of process stream, 254

Q-R

Quality assurance requirements,
  197-199
Radiography, 182-184
Railroad axles, fretting in, 93,
  146
Rain. *See also* Acid rain
  and atmospheric corrosion,
  49
Real dollars, 150
Real interest rate, 150
Rebar. *See also* Reinforcing
  steel
  cathodic protection of, 110-
  111
Redox potentials, 1, 2
Reference electrodes, 4
Refractory metals, 79, 227
Regulations and specifications,
  195-202
Reinforced plastics. *See* Fiber-
  glass reinforced plastics
Reinforcing bar. *See* Rebar
Reinforcing steel. *See also*
  Rebar
  cathodic protection of, 110-
  111
  road salt, effect of, 162-164
Relaxation, of plastics, 231-233
Residual oils, 79-80
Resistance polarization, 12, 174-
  175
Road salt. *See* Deicing salts
Rope, polyolefin, 102-103
Rubbers, 227-228, 234
Rural atmospheres, 50
Rust, and weathering steels, 50-
  51
Rust paints, 126-127